D1243531

MODERN HYDROLOGY

HARPER'S GEOSCIENCE SERIES

CAREY CRONEIS, *Editor*

MODERN
HYDROLOGY

RAPHAEL G. KAZMANN

LOUISIANA STATE UNIVERSITY
AND
AGRICULTURAL AND MECHANICAL COLLEGE

HARPER & ROW, PUBLISHERS

NEW YORK

Modern Hydrology/Copyright © 1965 by Raphael G. Kazmann.
Printed in the United States of America. All rights reserved. No
part of this book may be used or reproduced in any manner
whatsoever without written permission except in the case of brief
quotations embodied in critical articles and reviews. For information address Harper & Row, Publishers, Incorporated, 49 East
33rd Street, New York, N.Y. 10016.

Library of Congress Catalog Card Number: 65-11137

JOINT UNIVERSITY
LIBRARIES
NASHVILLE. TENN.

Geology

GB
661
.K37 Science

500689

DEDICATED TO THE MEMORY OF

OSCAR EDWARD MEINZER

(November 28, 1876–June 14, 1948)

THE FATHER OF MODERN GEOHYDROLOGY

CONTENTS

EDITOR'S INTRODUCTION

Modern Hydrology by Raphael G. Kazmann is, as the title suggests, an up-to-date reference work written in a lucid textbook style on a subject of transcending importance to man. Lawyers, legislators, farmers, and industrial, urban, state, and regional planners, as well as concerned citizens, have long needed an authoritative but readable reference source on this vital subject. Equally pressing has been the need for a teachable textbook in a too long neglected category of the geosciences, which is of great practical interest and growing scientific significance. In *Modern Hydrology* the author has been able substantially to fulfill both public and academic needs.

From primitive societies to their most sophisticated and highly industrialized offspring, a basic requisite, not merely for man's advancement but for his survival, has been and still is an adequate supply of fresh water. The ready availability of such a resource has conditioned the development of cultures throughout man's long recorded history. Today, as in the past, it is involved in decisions regarding war and peace. In short, water has always influenced the very course of civilization.

Until recently, unfortunately, most universities have paid little or no attention to the important subject of hydrology. Formalized courses are rare and talented hydrologists are not commonly members of university faculties. As has been rather characteristic of man in dealing with all vital resources—physical, organic, or human—he begins to study the problems involved in their development, utilization, and conservation only when they become so pressing that the absolute necessity for their solution becomes readily apparent to the entire body politic. That necessity is apparent now. For example, the National Science Foundation is supporting for the summer of 1965 an initial Summer Institute on Water Resources. This Institute has been especially designed for the training of college teachers of engineering and earth sciences in modern hydrology.

That the problems surrounding the general field of hydrology are indeed serious may be judged from the fact that our nation is currently using about 350×10^9 gallons of water per day. More important, the level of consumption is growing almost exponentially. This means that in any area where a shortage of potable water engenders economic and social, as well as industrial, problems today, such problems will soon become virtually insoluble without significant direct action in the very near future.

One answer which is commonly given to the problem of how to obtain the necessary fresh water for the development of marginal agricultural areas, or adequate supplies of industrial water for great commercial and industrial complexes, is the desalination of sea water. Such a process is particularly attractive to peoples seeking to develop relatively arid areas which lie reasonably close to the oceans or the seas. Philip H. Abelson and others have pointed out that in very large-scale projects in which nuclear reactors can be used, it is perhaps possible to produce fresh water at a cost of about 22¢ per thousand gallons at plants located at sea level. Of course, distribution of any fresh water thus obtained would involve very large additional costs. Because of the expenses involved in desalination, however accomplished, many areas of the world have new water-development plans based on precipitation and storage. Many of these are imaginative in concept and spectacular in size and cost, but there seems little doubt that some of them eventually will be put into operation if only because of the sheer necessity of obtaining the water for exploding populations which are progressively industrializing.

One of the most imaginative of such projects is that being sponsored by the North American Water and Power Alliance, sometimes called the NAWAPA plan, as outlined by the Ralph M. Parsons Engineering Company. This is a grandiose approach to the utilization of part of the North American Continent's natural water supply. It has been estimated that in the northwestern part of North America some 800×10^9 cubic meters of water flow to the sea annually. It is believed that the potential use of this supply, properly trapped and distributed, would solve some of the continent's water problems for as long as a century. Although the cost of this twenty-year project—involving the damming of the water in a great 500-mile-long lake in the Rocky Mountain Trench, with all the manifold engineering operations required to do so—is estimated at not less than 100 billion dollars, the proposal is presently being studied by a Senate subcommittee under the chairmanship of Senator Moss of Utah. It must be readily apparent from this example alone that the time was overripe for the publication of *Modern Hydrology*.

The Kazmann volume is presented in seven chapters, two of which—those on surface water and ground water—are virtual treatises in their own right. The "Introduction" is concerned with definitions, a discussion of the hydrologic cycle, and the historical development of the general subject. The latter is itself a fascinating and rewarding treatment of the progress of man and his various civilizations plotted against his ability to cope with the problem of water supplies.

Chapter 2, "Precipitation," evidences the logical type of organization which characterizes the other sections of the volume. Measurements are discussed first, the applicability of the facts obtained through measurements is then soberly considered before such data are subjected to a complete analysis. The status of plans and procedures for weather modification, and the state of that "art"—which today is as much discussed in public forums as in legislative halls—is given full treatment prior to an analysis of the new problems in hydrology which the modern world seems constantly to spawn. Through all of the development of the subjects in this, and later sections of the book, the social and humanistic—as well as the political and industrial—aspects of hydrology are given full consideration.

Chapter 3, "Evaporation" puts the importance of this subject in proper perspective. Chapters 4 and 5, "Surface Water" and "Ground Water," mentioned earlier, are modern in approach, but they have a sort of classical simplicity which should make them particularly helpful both to teachers and to students. Chapters 6 and 7, "Water Resources Development" and "Summation and Outlook," should prove no less interesting to members of the academic world, but all those persons concerned directly with providing the public with an adequate supply of fresh water should find them of outstanding value. On the other hand, the excellent set of questions which the author has prepared especially for the use of teachers and students may also prove of considerable interest to the growing number of nonacademicians who are professionally, politically, or even socially interested in one of the many ramifications of modern hydrology.

Fortunately, Raphael Gabriel Kazmann, the author of *Modern Hydrology*, has been able to bring to its preparation an unusually broad background of academic and professional experience. Mr. Kazmann is a native of Brooklyn, New York, who took his engineering degree at Carnegie Institute of Technology, and then went on for graduate work at Pennsylvania State University, where he became an assistant in the Department of Civil Engineering. During the early Forties he advanced from the rank of junior hydrological engineer to associate hydrological engineer with the United States Geological Survey, and from 1946 to 1950 he was the engineer in charge of investigations and research for the Ranney Method Water Supplies, Inc. Mr. Kazmann became a private consulting engineer in 1951, with a widely ranging practice in ground water geology and hydrology. He was concerned with such problems as river infiltration as a source of ground-water supply and the induced filtration of river water to wells. He also studied the role of aquifers in water supply and the problems involved in their recharging. Additionally, he was concerned with the dewatering of various mines and spent considerable time in devising means for developing adequate water supplies for rice irrigation.

In September, 1962, Mr. Kazmann became associate professor of civil engineering at Louisiana State University, where he was charged with the responsibility of planning and developing a complete academic program leading to the M.S. and Ph.D. in the field of hydrology. Mr. Kazmann accepted this scientific and academic responsibility with enthusiasm. The results to date not only demonstrate his own competence, but the growing awareness of both universities and students of the important opportunities to be found in the broad field of hydrology, which has been too long neglected by the general public as well as by scientists and engineers.

CAREY CRONEIS

Rice University
February, 1965

PREFACE

There have been many fine books written on the general subject of hydrology and on its numerous subspecialities. Many of these are cited as references in this text; they contain much useful information and the conclusions expressed are the result of clear thinking based on careful observation. Why then has the writer thought it necessary to undertake still another book on the same general topic? What specifically can the present book say that is not already elegantly and lucidly expressed in the extant literature?

This book is an attempt to bring into a single focus the methodology and science of hydrology and the practical applications that have resulted. It is written for the specialist in one phase or another of hydrology who is interested in learning how his work relates to the broad, general field that he is working in. Scientists, engineers, and advanced students in fields other than hydrology who are interested in water and who are confronted with an overabundance of information and an absence of unifying principles may find this volume useful as a guide. The mathematical treatment has been deliberately subordinated to the use of diagrams and, the writer hopes, lucid exposition. Optimistically perhaps, a man with a college education who dislikes advanced mathematics but who can distinguish uphill from downhill on a contour map will readily be able to understand the fundamental problems in the field of hydrology and water development and the answers that have been presented. In short, this is a book written to simplify and to elucidate the technical problems associated with the occurrence of water and its development.

This book also contains the results of an attempt to form valid judgments, based on certain definite standards of behavior, concerning hydrologic projects. For, as will be seen, the study of hydrology and the application of hydrologic principles are directly and immediately affected by feedbacks and side effects *not only from previously completed projects but also from presently contemplated projects.* Consequently the rate of introduction of these complicating factors will be dependent on the philosophy behind their construction. This in turn must be evaluated by standards of human behavior not included in the so-called "physical" sciences.

It is this interdependence between hydrology and the construction and operation of hydrologic structures that makes it so difficult to discern the issues and alternates of water-resource development projects. It is here that a

desire to improve the human condition through the control of water, combined with a knowledge of hydraulics and machine-age technology, often
leads to hydrologic disaster. We should constantly remind ourselves that the
power of falling water is much greater than is normally recognized, and that
technique and good intentions, while necessary, are insufficient to assure
success. It's not what you hope, what you think, what you believe, what you
say, or what you intend—it's what you do that counts. For the forces associated with hydrology, and in particular the one we describe as the law of
gravity, operate with complete indifference to man's thoughts and feelings,
reacting only to his actions. And it is in predicting the time, form, and magnitude of these reactions and their effect on the human condition, that hydrology, the discipline, may make its contribution.

The analyses and evaluations presented in the following pages constitute,
possibly, a first approximation or a trial balance of the hydrologic ledger as
it benefits man. The book could easily have been expanded by more detailed
examination of specific case histories, yet the writer has kept the number of
examples to a reasonable minimum and has tried to present all important
facts in each of the representative instances. If any errors of fact have crept
in despite the author's strenuous efforts to avoid them, and despite the
excellent and patient criticisms and suggestions made by the author's long-
time friends and professional associates, the present writer accepts full
responsibility.

Many persons have assisted in the preparation of this book. Some have
suggested additional references, others have furnished copies of publications
and other reference material not readily available. Some of the writer's
friends and associates have been kind enough to read and formally criticize
certain portions of the manuscript. The writer is most grateful for such
assistance and, where feasible, has acknowledged this in the body of the
text. However, special acknowledgment should be made of the helpfulness of
the following: Dr. Phillip E. LaMoreaux, State Geologist of Alabama;
Doyle B. Knowles, Chief Engineer of the Alabama Water Resources Division;
Dr. George B. Maxey, of the Desert Research Institute of the University of
Nevada; William C. Ackermann, Head of the Illinois State Water Survey
Division; Floyd A. Huff and Glen E. Stout, hydrologists of the Illinois
State Water Survey Division; and George J. Vencill, Hydraulic Engineer of
the Union Electric Company of St. Louis. Their comments have enabled the
writer to improve the phraseology and to substantially reduce the number of
ambiguities and discrepancies.

Finally the efforts of my wife, Caroline Beem Kazmann, in patiently
typing and retyping the seemingly endless revisions and corrections, is noted
with appreciation and affection.

R. G. K.

Baton Rouge, Louisiana
February, 1965

MODERN
HYDROLOGY

I

Introduction

DEFINITION OF HYDROLOGY

Hydrology may be defined as the discipline dealing with the properties, occurrence, distribution, and movement of water on and beneath the surface of the land.

Meinzer defined it as the science concerned with the occurrence of water in the earth, its physical and chemical reactions with the rest of the earth, and its relation to life on earth (*13*, 1). Some twenty years later, in June, 1962, the Federal Council of Science and Technology for Scientific Hydrology said:

Hydrology is the science that treats of the waters of the earth, their occurrence, circulation, and distribution, their chemical and physical properties, and their reaction with their environment including their relation to living things. The domain of hydrology embraces the full life history of water on the earth (*8*).

None of these definitions is completely satisfactory, primarily because each is overinclusive. To limit the scope of this volume to manageable proportions, certain aspects of the occurrence and movement of water have been arbitrarily eliminated from consideration. For example, atmospheric moisture in its vapor form is excluded. Meteorology, a sister science, deals principally with water as vapor; meteorology's interest terminates in the study of the occurrence and distribution of precipitation on the surface of the earth.

The American Geophysical Union (AGU) sponsors both a Section of Hydrology and a Section of Meteorology. Of course, certain activities in meteorology—for example, weather modification—are of direct interest to the hydrologist, since the results will affect his thinking and outlook. Moreover, developments in meteorology that may enable the meteorologist to assign extreme values to the occurrence and distribution of precipitation

1

affect plans based on hydrology. Thus, hydrology overlaps meteorology to some extent.

Another example: The hydrologist is not directly concerned with the oceans. But oceanography, also recognized by the AGU as a separate field of study, and hydrology overlap. Large inland lakes, for example, resemble certain seas; fresh and salt water are in contact in tidal estuaries, river deltas, and the boundary zones of aquifers that discharge into the sea. The hydrologist is interested in the oceanographer's data, theories, and conjectures.

The complexity of hydrology is not even suggested by the neat mathematical models that can be prepared to simulate one or another of the components of hydrologic phenomena. The final arbiter of any difference of opinion regarding hydrologic theory is the observed fact or, where possible, the well-planned, carefully executed experiment. Many facts are not adequately explained by any accepted theoretical framework—and this should be interpreted as an indication that new, more comprehensive theories await formulation. For a phenomenon to be completely *hydrologic* it must occur only as the result of the interplay of certain natural factors and recur only as the consequence of similar natural circumstances.

Hydrology is sometimes confused with hydraulics, for all hydrologic data are expressed as measurements of quantities that involve water. And the nature of the difference between hydraulics and hydrology is not adequately brought out by stating that, while all hydrologic measurements are hydraulic, all hydraulic measurements are not hydrologic. A clearer understanding may be provided by the following examples:

On the most elementary level the construction of a cistern is the province of the contractor. But the capacity of the cistern must be determined by simultaneously considering hydrology (precipitation), available catchment area, and probable water demand—and this is hydrologic engineering.

The flow characteristics of a culvert for any specified discharge rates are expressed by a hydraulic formula, but determining the size of culvert needed for extreme conditions depends on a hydrologic study which establishes the rate of culvert discharge appropriate to a given location.

Determination of the shape, crest, and flow characteristics of a dam spillway for any given condition of discharge at a specific site is a hydraulic problem. But the design magnitude of the flow must first be specified as the result of study of the hydrology of the upstream basin in view of channel capacities, probable rainfall and runoff, probable time of occurrence, and so forth.

The design of a turbine to produce hydropower is an application of the science of hydraulics. The size and probable utilization factor of the turbines for use in connection with an impoundment are determined by the quantity and availability of water—a hydrologic matter.

The diameter of a well, the size of screen openings, and the design of the pump are matters of hydraulics. The long-term yield of the well and the appropriate pump setting are matters to be decided on the basis of hydrology. This, of course, is more important if a great number of wells are needed in a large area and a high offtake rate is required for a very long time. In such a case the overall relationship between replenishment, the capability of the water-bearing formation to act as a pipe line, and the desired rate of well-water production must be worked out, and this is a hydrologic matter.

For all of its unfinished business, hydrology has proved to be most useful to mankind. Although it is almost trite to say that there is nothing certain in life but change, we are always interested in the probable direction of change. As hydrology has developed, it has improved in its ability to predict the direction of change in the occurrence and distribution of water and the possible and probable extremes to be reached after any interval of time.

THE HYDROLOGIC CYCLE

This book is organized in accord with the endless movement of water from the atmosphere to the land and back to the sea: This well-described process has been termed the "hydrologic cycle". The cycle is powered by solar and planetary forces: The sun provides the energy for the evaporation of sea water; the earth's gravitational field and coriolus force are important controls on the movement of winds; and the gravitational fields of at least the sun and moon directly affect the balance of forces at any time (2, 3). In addition, there are the more subtle changes caused by the electromagnetic field of the earth as it reacts to solar flares or sunspot activity, the incidence of cosmic debris (the meteorite showers), and the varying intensities of streams of high-energy particles encountered as the earth moves through space. Hydrologists are aware of these influences upon the hydrologic cycle, and an occasional attempt has been made to correlate the occurrence of precipitation with the earth's passage through a debris shower, or the hydrographs of rivers with the sunspot numbers. However, these are considered to be on the fringes of the mainstream of hydrology, and their effects on the availability of water for mankind's purposes remain to be discovered.

The hydrologic cycle is illustrated schematically in Fig. 1.1. Although other diagrams, equally good, have been published elsewhere, this one is especially useful because it shows, to some extent, the methods and points of measurement, including the rain gage, evaporation station, observation well, and the quality of water, sedimentation, and stream-gaging station.

Within the hydrologic cycle there are shorter cycles that by-pass parts of it. For example, the precipitation that reaches the vegetation may evaporate from it directly, thus short-circuiting the cycle. Or water may reach the ground and be held in the soil by capillary and molecular forces until it evaporates. This water would not be included in surface- or ground-water discharge. It is a matter of record that of the 30-in. average depth of water that falls annually on the United States, 21 or 22 in. are vaporized and only 8 or 9 in. appear as clearly defined liquid water either on or below the surface of the ground. One must hasten to point, however, that the water that is not found in the runoff phase of the cycle goes to sustain plant life, including the crops planted and harvested by man.

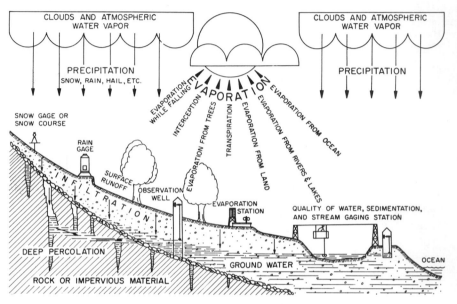

Fig. 1.1. The hydrologic cycle. (After Hydrology Handbook, 1949, *Am. Soc. Civ. Eng. Manual of Eng. Practice*, no. 28, p. 2.)

The geochemical cycle, which is less widely known, also operates as part of the gross hydrologic cycle. It can be outlined as follows:

1. Water evaporating from the ocean carries off with it a small but significant quantity of dissolved mineral matter such as common salt.
2. Compounds of nitrogen and molecules of oxygen and carbon dioxide are all dissolved in the water precipitated during storms.
3. Carbon dioxide in the soil, the product of organic decomposition, is also dissolved as the water percolates through the upper layers of soil.
4. The dilute carbonic acid enables the water to react chemically with mineral fragments, liberating bicarbonates and carbonates which may also go into solution.
5. Any other soluble minerals or salts are dissolved by the incoming water.
6. Many reactions may take place in the water once it enters the geologic matrix—for instance, the less soluble compounds may precipitate as solubility limits are reached, or bacteria may reduce sulphates in solution.

7. Finally, the water either returns to the atmosphere by evaporation (leaving behind mineral matter in the soil) or the water returns to the sea as ground-water discharge or stream flow, carrying its mineral burden with it.

There are a number of possible chemical reactions at each step of the way—some are reversible if the chemical or physical environment changes. Davis and his colleagues have summarized the geochemical cycle in an illustration (Fig. 1.2) that merits study (6).

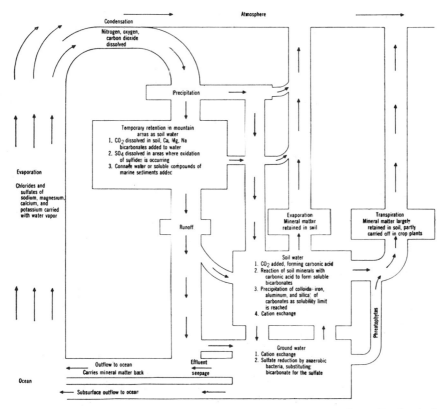

Fig. 1.2. Geochemical cycle of surface and ground waters. (From G. H. Davis *et al.*, 1959, *Ground Water Conditions and Storage Capacity in the San Joaquin Valley, California, Water Supply Paper 1469,* U.S. Geol. Surv.)

HISTORICAL DEVELOPMENT OF HYDROLOGY

Before the Industrial Revolution

The successful application of force to the environment that we term engineering is the forerunner of science. Only after sufficient trials have been made, and enough successes registered, is it possible to distill the scientific principles underlying the practice. These principles, in turn, guide us to new engineering applications. Science is, in a sense, a progression from the complex to the simple—for example, from a complex mass of apparently unrelated data to the statement of laws linking datum to datum. And it is no accident that mathematics, sometimes called the handmaiden of science, is also the oldest experimental science. It grew from the earliest and least complicated fields of engineering: the setting of boundaries to land, the division of time into units, and the practice of commerce and trade. As, one by one, the engineering arts have given birth to sciences, the order of their evolution has depended on the complexity of the phenomenon involved: the more complicated the phenomenon, the later has the engineering art evolved to a logical science.

It should not be surprising, therefore, that hydrology as science did not begin to develop until the seventeenth century. Its forerunner, hydrologic engineering—for example, maintenance of water supply, channel improvement, construction of levees for defense against floods, and canals for crop irrigation—had, by that time, been practiced for at least 5000 years.

It is instructive to review the prescientific history of hydrologic and hydraulic engineering. Projects built by our remote ancestors possess a remarkable air of modernity, and their achievements have been equaled only during the past 100 years. The principal difference between our projects and theirs is to be found in our increased ability to move the earth and in our recent advances in the field of communications. Drower discusses water supply and irrigation in the era preceding 500 B.C. (7) and the writer is indebted to him for much of the material in the following paragraphs.

The earliest civilizations in the arid valleys of the Nile and the Tigris-Euphrates rivers were dependent upon irrigation. Indeed, only as man became more proficient at irrigating could he attain higher levels of civilization. Undoubtedly, the first attempts in this direction occurred in predynastic Egypt (before the Old Kingdom, circa 3400 B.C.). The so-called Pharaonic system of basin irrigation traces back at least to Menes, the legendary first Pharaoh who captured the waters of the Nile and harnessed the floods.

Basin irrigation consisted of dividing the flood plain into a checkerboard of dike-enclosed areas ranging in size from about 1000 to 40,000 acres. During floods, the basins were filled by the overflowing waters of the Nile. This water was held on the land by closing the openings in the dikes. After the land had been thoroughly saturated, the standing water was drained to lower basins, or to the river, so that planting could take place. Each year the flood waters deposited a thin layer of organic silt that enriched the soil and raised its elevation. Calculations, based on an almost unbroken series of records for the 1300 years since the Arab conquest, show that silt deposited in the Nile

Valley has raised the elevation of the land by approximately 8 ft. By extrapolating, we can conclude that in Pharaonic times the flood plain may have been some 20 ft lower than its present level.

The early Egyptians were immediately confronted by a problem in hydrology: the determination of probable flood height and, hence, the acreage that would be flooded in any reach of river. Moreover, up to a point, the higher the flood the greater was the quantity of land that could be brought under cultivation. Above that point, the flooding would be too severe: The banks of the dikes would be overtopped, washouts would occur, and the area that could be irrigated would be lessened. Thus, too high or too low a stage would mean famine. On the other hand, an extra-high stage at one place might signify an acceptable flood at another. Thus, the failure of irrigation works at one point might not mean disaster if arrangements could be made downstream for the cultivation of additional, higher land. Hence, the Egyptians were forced to devise a system for measuring and recording the height of the Nile at many points to enable comparison of the daily river rise with records of previous years. Guided by this information, they could forecast the high-water mark at any downstream point with some accuracy.

By the time of the Twelfth Dynasty (circa 2000 B.C.), data were being recorded as far upstream as the Second Cataract, near the present Egyptian-Sudanese border—the readings, engraved on rock, have been discovered. Information from so far upstream could be sent posthaste to the Pharaoh, and preparations for the high water could be made in advance of its arrival. A modern parallel is to be found in the operations of the Tennessee Valley Authority, which maintains river gages in the upper reaches of the Tennessee Valley. The data obtained from these instruments are transmitted to the computing center so that predictions and downstream preparations can be made. In their flood forecasts, however, the Egyptians enjoyed an advantage: The Nile is far more regular and predictable than the Tennessee River.

In the Valley of the Tigris-Euphrates, a similar development occurred in pre-Sumerian times. There is evidence that long before 3000 B.C., marshland in the lowlands of the Persian Gulf and along the lower Euphrates had been reclaimed. These people had learned to drain and irrigate land by means of canals, the traces of which, according to Sarton, can still be seen from airplanes (16). In some respects these irrigation and drainage projects are more worthy of admiration than those of Egypt. For one thing, the hydrology of the twin rivers is far more complex and far less predictable that that of the Nile. Moreover, the waters of the Tigris-Euphrates system carry approximately five times the concentration of sediment carried by the Nile. Consequently, canals and water distributaries soon become choked with silt, the boundary landmarks are buried, and maintenance or reconstruction of the channels is needed. The twin rivers carry water more highly mineralized than that of the Nile, necessitating overirrigation and subdrainage to counter-act excessive concentrations of salt in the soil.

Floods in Mesopotamia were an annual and almost unpredictable hazard. As long as the occurrence of floods on the two rivers was out of phase, things were under control. But when floods on both rivers peaked simultaneously, they covered the land with devastating effects. Fear of flood was ever present with the Sumerians and their successors, the Babylonians. The story of Noah derives from the Sumerian legend of the greatest of all floods. A system of enclosing Mesopotamian towns and cities with high substantial earthen levees, or walls, was established at an early date. These served to protect their builders against floods, as well as against human invaders. It is note-worthy that the Persians, who came from the highlands to the north, did not build walled cities until after they had conquered Babylon.

The conquest of Mesopotamia by Hammurabi (circa 1760 B.C.) led to strong centralized control of water. Several of the laws in this Code dealt with irrigation: Each man had to keep his own part of the dike and ditch system in repair, and if he did not he had to recompense the neighboring farmers whose land suffered through flooding. Royal letters to local governors show that each district was responsible for the upkeep of its own canals. In one letter, the king complained that a canal bed had been imperfectly cleared and that boats could not enter the city of Erech. The governor was directed to rectify matters in 3 days using the men at his disposal. Evidently, although no records have survived, the state of the art of hydrologic engineering was at a high level. Today, nearly 4000 years later, Hammurabi's influence on the development of the water resources of arid lands is still somewhat in evidence.

The sophistication of the early Mesopotamians in the field of irrigation is shown by a map of an area near Nippur. The photograph of the original property-record (baked clay) and the probable translation are shown in Fig. 1.3. This tablet was probably a part of the official Nippur equivalent to the record of the present-day county tax assessor. Most of the privately owned property is labeled with the dwelling or "headquarters" of the owner.

The hydraulics of the irrigation and drainage system is not well defined by this property map. Presumably, during a period of high water in the river, the water, was allowed to enter Hamri's canal from which it was distributed to channels variously called, canal or irrigation. The "streams" may have been drainage ditches for use during low-river stages to get the water out of the cultivated areas. The earthen embankments used could not have been very high (although they were probably overgrown with weeds and canes), and the fields must have been fairly small—possibly much less than 10 acres per individually irrigated field. Over a long period, the land would have slowly filled due to the deposition of silt and the canals would have had to be raised higher and higher. This in turn would have reduced the irrigable area inas-much as, in the absence of pumps, the natural height of the river would have had to provide the motive power to force the water over the land. There is no reason to suppose that river stages tended to be progressively higher.

The unnamed parcels might have been in the process of changing hands, or in litigation, so the tax collector or record keeper may have been in doubt as to exact ownership. Possibly the tablet was marked "provisional—check court records next year".

The engineering and legal sophistication indicated by the tablet is fully comparable to that of the present day when allowances have been made for technological progress. Similar maps can be found in any County Assessor's office, and a lawyer skilled in property transfers would find himself at home in the "courthouse record" shown in Fig. 1.3. One wonders, however, what system of indexing was used, whether any attempt was made to produce a map to scale, and how the scribes were trained to produce such good drawings on tablets of soft clay. The hydrologic-engineering capabilities of the Mesopotamians were evidently of a high order. Nor were the military applications of hydrologic engineering unknown. There is a well-authenticated story that the first move made by the Persian, Cyrus the Great, in his attack on Babylon was to divert the Euphrates River from the channel that took it through the city. He then utilized the river bed as a roadway for troops, entered Babylon unopposed, and captured it with only minor fighting. Certainly only skilled engineers and an efficient earth-moving organization could have diverted the river rapidly enough to take the Babylonians by surprise. The hydrology of the river must have been studied carefully and the date of attack carefully selected to minimize the work and to reduce the hazard of high river flows.

Thus, the study of water in its natural state, as epitomized by a flood-warning network and by computation of the necessary height of flood walls around cities, is not new. Equally ancient are the systematic irrigation and drainage of lands, establishment of a system of water rights and obligations, and the purposeful maintenance of navigation in alluvial streams. But the general level of technology necessary for a culture to distill scientific principles from millenia of successful hydrologic engineering was not available. Consequently a science of hydrology, as opposed to a rule-of-thumb practice of hydrologic engineering, did not develop. We may not be greatly in error if we conclude that prior to the destruction of the irrigation works in Mesopotamia by the Mongols, a system of irrigation agriculture had been in continuous operation there for more than 4000 years. This, a truly remarkable achievement, provides a yardstick against which to measure the lives of current water-development projects.

By any objective standard, the Egyptians and the successive inhabitants of Mesopotamia possessed an excellent working knowledge of hydraulics and of hydrologic principles. Whether this knowledge was transmitted orally, in writing, or, as is likely, by a combination of these methods is not

Fig. 1.3. Map of the fields and irrigation canals near Nippur, Mesopotamia, *c.* 1300 B.C. The main irrigation canal encloses the central field in a parabola. The elongated rectangular fields on the right may have been included to "key-in" this tablet with other tablets that depicted an adjacent area, and the field-shapes may be distorted. (Photo courtesy of the

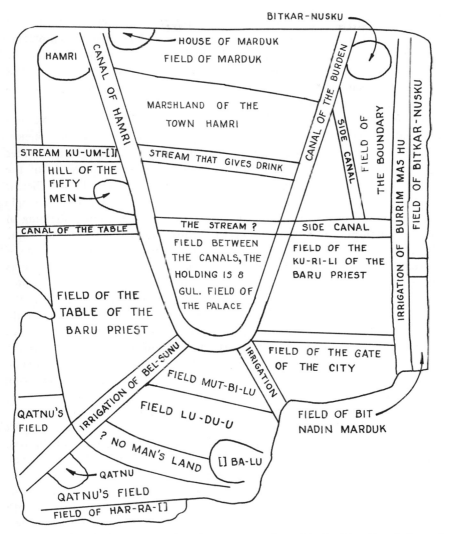

University of Pennsylvania Museum that possesses the original tablet. Translation of cuneiform, shown in outline map, from M. S. Drower, 1954, Water Supply, Irrigation and Agriculture, Chap. XIX, *A History of Technology*, Oxford Univ. Press, New York, v. 1, p. 549. Reprinted with permission from *Endeavour* review, London.)

clear, but it is certain that they developed complicated and enduring systems for the control and use of water. Even now, in the twentieth century, it remains to be demonstrated whether our understanding and application of hydrologic principles, as applied to arid-zone conditions, is in any way superior to theirs. In passing, we should note that parallel, independent developments seem to have started in the valley of the Yellow River in China at about the same early date, and have continued to the present time. We know far less of the achievements of the Chinese because little or no documentation is available to Western scholars.

In the humid regions of Europe, the area in which modern Western civilization gestated and developed, major hydraulic works—and hence, hydrologic knowledge—were not needed. The city was the principal water consumer, but the quantity required was relatively small in terms of the readily available supply. Irrigation was not needed since rainfall was sufficient for crop production. At the start of the Christian era, the largest single city system was probably that which supplied Rome. We know something of this system from the writings of Julius Frontinus, water commissioner of Rome from 97 to 103 A.D. He was responsible for the operation and maintenance of the eight aqueducts that supplied Rome at that time. Five were fed by springs or artesian wells, the others from streams. There was no provision for water storage beyond that provided by individuals in their homes. Apparently the Romans had not acquired hydrologic knowledge. They took what they could get, and, because of the multiplicity and variety of sources, the flow tended to be more uniform and less subject to extreme variations than if a single source had been used. Nor had they mastered even elementary hydraulics as we can deduce from Frontinus' attempts to balance input with offtake by measuring the cross sections of water in the intake conduits and comparing these dimensions with those of pipes and channels delivering water to consumers. He concluded (and was probably right) that water was being stolen, but part of the discrepancy may have reflected his lack of understanding of the role that velocity plays in fixing the quantity of water flowing during a given period of time through a given cross-sectional area (15).

The beginnings of the science of hydrology, as contrasted to the arts of hydraulic and hydrologic engineering, had to await the end of the fifteenth century and the beginning of the sixteenth century. According to Meinzer, Leonardo da Vinci (1452–1519) and Bernard Palissy (1509–1589) independently arrived at an understanding of the hydrologic cycle (13, pp. 12, 14). Their grasp of the circulation of water from the sea to the atmosphere, to the land and back to the sea seems to have been more of a manifestation of genius than the outcome of analyzing and meditating upon the meaning of quantitative measurements, since there were few, if any, of these. Hydrology was not established on a quantitative basis until the seventeenth century when the works of Pierre Perrault (1608–1680), Edmé Mariotte (1620–1684), and the English astronomer Edmund Halley (1656–1742) Fellow of the Royal Society of London were published.

Perrault measured rainfall during a three-year period and roughly estimated the drainage basin of the Seine River above a point in Burgundy as well as the runoff at that point. By computing the precipitation to be six times the quantity discharged by the river, he demonstrated that rainfall is adequate in volume to account for the river and spring discharge. Perrault also conducted experiments on the natural evaporation of water and other liquids and established the approximate limits of capillarity in sands.

Mariotte used floats to determine the velocity of water in the Seine River at what he considered to be its mean stage. He also demonstrated that the source of ground water in an area could be precipitation upon the overlying land surface. For this purpose he utilized the seepage into the cellar of his Paris Observatory, which he compared with the depth of rainfall in the vicinity.

Halley investigated the evaporation of salt solutions possessing the concentration of sea water, concluding that evaporation from the Mediterranean was ample to balance the quantity of water entering through the rivers that drain into it. He also studied the effect of altitude on the rate of precipitation.

Herschel, the famous hydraulic engineer, who translated Frontinus' books on the water supply of Rome, had this to say concerning the early development of hydraulic science:

To appreciate Frontinus' position with regard to a proper knowledge of the velocity of efflux and generally of the velocity of running water, it is instructive to follow the development of the art from his time until we arrive at the formula $V = \sqrt{2gh}$ now known to every beginner in hydraulic science, and the very foundation stone of that science as it is known at the present day. This formula and the numerical values it gives to velocities of efflux were not discovered until about the year 1738, when Daniel Bernoulli and John Bernoulli, his father, each published a different mathematical demonstration of this law.

Castelli (1577–1644), a Benedictine monk, the pupil of Galileo, first showed the quantity of efflux in a given time depended by law on, or was a function of, the depth of water in a bowl—that is, was a function of the head. It was his pupil Toricelli (1608–1647), the inventor of the barometer, the grandson, in a professional sense, of Galileo, who first proved, in 1644, or only two years after Galileo's death, that the velocities of efflux are as the square roots of the head .... Huygens (1629—1695), the inventor of pendulum clocks, first found the numerical value of the acceleration of gravity, commonly represented by the letter "g", in 1673. Sixty-five more years had to elapse until the genius of the two Bernoullis, father and son, in 1738, finally laid the foundation of modern, determinate hydraulics ... (10).

Others contributed to the development of hydrologic engineering and hydrology in the eighteenth century. Noteworthy were Bernard Forest Belidor (1697–1761), who suggested the siphon theory for ebbing and flowing springs, and Jean d'Alembert (1717–1776), who helped to create the mathematical foundations for hydraulic theory. Less than 25 years after the work of the Bernoullis, Paul Frisi published his *Treatise on Rivers and Torrents* which included quantitative data on stream flow and corrected some hydrologic misconceptions while proposing equally erroneous theories.

Frisi was a good engineer who had little confidence in the application of mathematical theories to problems of hydrodynamics. Allowing for the fact that statistics and the mathematics of probability were only to become understood and useful half a century after he wrote, his attitude was reasonable and his words bear repeating even now:

One single reflection is sufficient to show that all hydraulic problems are beyond the reach of geometry and calculus. The difficulty of all problems is increased in proportion to the number of conditions (variables) . . . . Thus mechanical problems become so much more complicated as the number of bodies whose motions are sought and which act in any way on each other is augmented . . . . In a fluid mass which moves in a tube or in a canal the number of bodies acting together is infinite; whence it follows that to determine the motion of each body is a problem depending on an infinity of equations, which it is, of course, beyond all the powers of algebra to reach (9).

At this writing the statement that it is impossible to solve hydraulic problems solely on the basis of mathematics can be considered to be true, but only in the same sense that the trisection of an angle is impossible: If you limit yourself to the use of a straightedge and compass, an angle cannot be trisected. However, we can trisect an angle to any desired degree of accuracy by using additional instruments, such as a protractor. Similarly, we can compute the gross movement of water in a stream by multiplying its velocity by its cross sectional area. In practice, we can measure instantaneous velocities at a number of points and the cross sectional area of the water stream; then, by suitable, computational devices we can determine the *total* flow (but not the path and velocity of movement of single molecules of water) to any desired degree of accuracy. To determine the movement of single molecules, radioactive tracers might possibly be used and, with suitable instrumentation, the movement platted—not computed. For Frisi was saying, in effect, that under conditions of turbulent flow one cannot compute, a priori, the path and velocity of a water molecule. And our rejoinder must be that we have no need to accomplish this; that the gross, mass movements of water molecules are our principal concern and that we can compute these and determine them in the field. Then, by applying arbitary coefficients, we can bring theoretical computations into accord with the observations—and, by so doing, prove that Frisi knew what he was talking about.

During and after the Industrial Revolution

As we have noted, principles of ground-water movement and knowledge of the interrelationship between ground and surface water were developed very slowly before the nineteenth century. There were several reasons for this. For one thing, the construction of a well consisted primarily of the

construction of a shaft, like a mine shaft, a slow, expensive, laborious under-taking. Even if there were a sufficient quantity of water in the well, getting it out was a problem: Power sources were expensive and pumps were large and inefficient, and could more economically be used for other purposes. Besides, it was not until the cholera epidemics of 1849 and 1853 that John Snow established statistically the correlation between cholera incidence and water source (5).

Efforts to dewater mines stimulated the construction of pumps and the first prime movers (wind mills, steam engines, and so forth). But the very fact that water was treated as a common enemy, to be pumped out of the ground and into a disposal ditch, tended to divert attention away from hydrology, for a man either could or could not install enough pumps in a mine and keep it dewatered; water source was not important. Moreover ore bodies are found under extremely complex, nonhomogeneous, geologic conditions and the water usually appears to be coming from cracks or fissures. No man could compute from what direction water came, even if the fissures were traced into the orebody and back into the surrounding country rock. Thus, while miners were the first ground-water engineers, the principles of ground-water move-ment were not discovered until men sought to use water rather than to get rid of it.

As technology progressed during the Industrial Revolution, wells of smaller and smaller diameter were drilled, usually by the cable-tool method. Drillers often encountered confined aquifers containing water under pressure; such wells were called "artesian" after the flowing well drilled in Artois, France, in 1126. If a man were lucky, he could drill a well of small diameter yet obtain a large flow of water without having to invest in a pump. On the other hand, the expense of drilling these deep holes with the available rope and using hollowed-out tree trunks as casing—combined with the ready availability of surface water for private and municipal uses—made the drilling of artesian wells somewhat prohibitive. Wells were either large in diameter and shallow in order to reach a convenient aquifer, in which case the water was not under pressure, or they were of relatively small diameter (24 in., more or less), deep, expensive, and a financial gamble, with only a possibility of finding an artesian aquifer. There was only a limited market for well water, and this primarily for medicinal purposes.

Despite the scientific endeavors of Henri Darcy, who published in 1856, and other early geologists and hydrogeologists, the use of ground water in large quantities (except from springs) was unusual throughout most of the nineteenth century. It was not until the local population increased to the point that the surface waters of an area had become extremely polluted by human, animal, or industrial wastes that ground-water development (and the con-struction of water filtration plants) took place. Water-borne epidemics were a common occurrence in the centers of population prior to and throughout the nineteenth century. Such diseases as dysentery, cholera, and typhoid were daily health problems in every large city. However, in the past 50 years the incidence of these diseases has decreased, because of water treatment and disinfection, to the point that epidemiological studies of these diseases no longer yield any information as to the sanitary quality of private or public water supplies.

Undoubtedly, the need to produce water free from pathogenic organisms was *the* motivation for drilling wells and the development of ground-water supplies. This need also impelled the construction of the first slow-sand filter in the United States (for the town of Poughkeepsie, New York, in 1872). Thus, in the 1880s, artesian wells began to be drilled throughout the United States wherever favorable hydrogeological conditions were found. To increase output, deep pits sometimes were excavated and wells were drilled from the pit bottoms. This method provided enclosures large enough to accommo-date the pumps which were used to force the water directly into the mains, and increased the drawdown of the artesian head, which also furthered the output.

The problem of pumping water from deep, small-diameter wells remained unsolved, however, until the 1880s. The airlift method of pumping was one of those employed: A stream of compressed air was forced into a tube that ended deep in the well. The air mixed with the well water and formed a mixture of lesser density than the original column of water. Thus, the mixture was forced to the surface by the pressure of the surrounding aquifer water. In the Frasch process, an adaptation of this system is still used to pump liquid sulphur from certain wells.

In the latter part of the 1890s, centrifugal pumps, small enough to go into a 30-in. hole, were developed. Such pumps were rotated by means of shafts driven from the land surface by prime movers—usually steam or, later, electric power. The hole diameter required for pump installation decreased and the efficiency of pumping equipment improved rapidly after the beginning of the twentieth century. At present submersible pump-motor combinations that will operate at depths of up to 1000 ft and go into a 4-in. casing are available commercially.

The rapidity of the development of the ground-water resources of the United States is remarkable. For example, the first deep well in Chicago, drilled in 1864, flowed with a pressure of 25 lb per sq in. Hundreds of wells were drilled in the Chicago area during the succeeding 30 years, many from the bottoms of deep pits. By 1890, the wells were providing 10 million gal a day, and water levels had declined to the elevation of the land surface. At this point, the air-lift pump was introduced, but before it could become firmly established, it was replaced by the more efficient turbine. By 1915, the water level in Chicago area was 150 ft or more below the land surface, and a supply of 45 million gal a day was being withdrawn from the underlying aquifers.

By 1958, water levels in Chicago had been lowered an additional 350–400 ft and the offtake had risen to some 75 million gal a day (*17*).

Developments elsewhere paralleled the Chicago experience—and many surpassed it in the rates of offtake. With the increasing exploitation of ground water, it soon became apparent that a systematic study should be undertaken to evaluate its magnitude and to facilitate its discovery and utilization. Noteworthy in this connection was T. C. Chamberlin's pioneering study (1873–1879) of artesian conditions in Wisconsin. His well-known paper, "The requisite and qualifying conditions of artesian flow," was published in 1885 by the U.S. Geological Survey.

Many capable men devoted time and energy to the study of geohydrology and hydrogeology, among them the geologists N. H. Darton, F. Leverett, and W. H. Norton, who were followed by W. C. Mendenhall, A. C. Veatch, and O. E. Meinzer. The work on the hydraulic, quantitative aspects of hydro-geology, undertaken by Allen Hazen, F. H. King, and Charles S. Slichter, has been continued by their eminent present-day successor, C. V. Theis. In Europe, there were Adolph and Günther Thiem, K. Keilhack, E. Prinz, E. Martel, A. Herzberg, W. Badon-Ghyben, J. Pennink, P. Forcheimer, and many others.

This introduction, however, is not primarily a history of hydrology. In truth, the history of hydrology is one small facet of the general historical development of engineering and science that has taken place since 1850. Measurement and analytical techniques and construction methods in hy-drology have both reflected and influenced progress in other scientific and engineering disciplines. For example, widespread drilling of deep wells had to await mass-produced steel casing, which became available only after the intro-duction of the Bessemer process in 1855 and the open-hearth process in 1860. The water wells of Chicago in 1864 (and the Drake oil well of 1859) marked the beginning of a new era simply because the supporting technology—and an effective demand for the products of drilling—were in existence. Prior to that time deep wells, mostly drilled for salt, were few in number and deser-vedly famous. Brantly provides an excellent account of the history of well drilling and well completions (*4*).

The measurement of surface water and the study of its occurrence under natural conditions received great impetus from the needs of canal construction and water supply in the early decades of the nineteenth century. However, neither in Europe nor in the United States was there any need during the nineteenth century for water control, conservation, and distribution projects on the vast scale of those in ancient Mesopotamia or Egypt. It was not until 1879 that the U.S. Geological Survey was established. In 1881, Major John W. Powell, a man intensely interested in the water resources and irrigation possibilities of the West, became its director. Through the effort of Powell and others who shared his concern, the first federal appropriation for stream gaging was obtained in 1887 and the field work was started in 1888. Probably in 1871, T. G. Ellis constructed the first truly rugged current meter for the Army Engineers; this propeller-type instrument was later adopted for use by the Geological Survey in its stream-gaging program.

Despite the paucity of data and lack of extensive experience in arid-zone hydrology, the Bureau of Reclamation, established in 1903, completed construction of its first really large project, Elephant Butte Dam, on the Rio Grande in 1916. This is probably the first major application of machine-age technology to water control in a nonhumid environment; some of the British achievements in India may have been of comparable scope. Because of its seniority we will return to Elephant Butte Dam and its associated reservoir and delta and examine the lessons this project may hold for us.

After the establishment of the Bureau of Reclamation, which was followed by a flurry of dam building, construction of water impoundments, and the establishment of the first irrigation projects in desert lands, there was a slowdown. Projects to bring water to 3 million acres had been authorized by the federal government between 1903 and 1910, but during the next 20 years only an additional 1 million acres were authorized for reclamation by means of impounded water.

Mead published some notes on hydrology in 1904 (11). A book by Meyer followed in 1917 (14), and another by Mead in 1919 (12). Then, until the appearance of Meinzer's volume on hydrology in 1942 (13), a team effort sponsored by the National Research Council, no general text dealing with hydrology appeared. However, there were many books that dealt with hydraulics, water supply, ground water, irrigation, drainage, floods, and so forth. During the 23-year hiatus between Mead's *Hydrology* and the volume edited by Meinzer (who also contributed to it), there was considerable progress in collecting and analyzing data and then utilizing the results for the planning of water-development and water-control projects.

Since World War II there has been a great increase in observational data concerning stream stages and discharge, surface-water mineralization and temperature, precipitation and evaporation rates, the occurrence of water-bearing formations and the water levels in the wells that tap them, and the subcycles within the hydrologic cycle. A considerable backlog of facts has been built up and an impressive number of projects involving hydrology have been constructed. However, too little effort has been devoted to distilling scientific principles from the experience. Hydrologists have not evolved a clear-cut science of hydrology, nor have they come to any consensus on how to evaluate water-development projects from the standpoint of hydrology. Moreover, no procedure has been proposed for the evaluation or even systematic analysis, of the side effects of hydrologic projects. The prevalence of trees still obscures the forest. Ackermann, who served (1961–1964) as president of the AGU Section of Hydrology and has long been chief of the

Illinois State Water Survey Division, recently expressed his thoughts on the present status of hydrology:

What is the state of our science . . . . Is the science like the multiplication table that doesn't take a mathematician to understand? Or is our science like an early arithmetic that hasn't yet progressed to algebra, geometry, calculus, and beyond?

Perhaps there are many ways of judging the state of development of our science, but I will cite just two sources to indicate that ours is still a primitive science. For the first I would cite the 1960 publication *Design of Small Dams* by the U.S. Bureau of Reclamation. I have every reason to believe that this comprehensive book is up-to-date and employs the latest available scientific and engineering methods. In a section on "Estimating Runoff from Rainfall" starting on page 32, here are a few quotations:

"However, the infiltration rate approach is applied on an empirical basis to obtain a practical solution to the problem of determining the amounts of runoff, recognizing that the values used are of the nature of 'index' values rather than 'true' values. Natural events are studied and the difference between rainfall and runoff determined. Since this difference includes all the losses described above, it is usually called a retention loss or retention rate. Such retention rates derived from available records may be adjusted to ungaged watersheds by analogy of soil type and cover.

"Two methods may be used to determine rainfall excess: by assuming a constant average retention rate throughout the storm period, and by assuming a retention rate varying with time.

"Because the use of a varying retention rate requires a complicated method of computation, and because present knowledge of the exact shape of the infiltration curve is rather limited, it is often preferable to assume an average retention rate (sometimes referred to as infiltration index) with an estimate of initial loss being made if antecedent conditions are relatively dry."

Mind you, I am not quoting this to be critical of the Bureau of Reclamation—I believe this is the best we can do.

Let me cite another example. Back in my own State, Illinois, our agency recently completed an exhaustive study of rainfall intensity, frequency, and duration. This has been welcomed by a number of agencies who will use it in the formula $Q = CIA$, for estimating peak discharges. This is an ancient method, and we are still guessing at the values of C (I).

NOTES

1. Ackermann, W. C., March, 1961, Needed—three wise men, *Trans. Am. Geophys. Union*, v. 42, no. 1, pp. 5–8.
2. Adderley, E. E., Mar. 1, 1963, The influence of the moon on atmosphere, *J. Geophys. Res.*, v. 68, no. 5, pp. 1405–1408.
3. Bowen, E. G., Mar. 1, 1963, A lunar effect on the incoming meteor rate, *J. Geophys. Res.*, v. 68, no. 5, pp. 1401–1404.
4. Brantly, J. E., 1961, in *History of Petroleum Industry*, American Petroleum Institute, ch. 5.
5. Bruce, F. E., 1958, Water supply, in *History of Technology*, v. 5, ch. 23, Cambridge, Oxford Univ. Press.

6. Davis, G. H. *et al.*, 1959, Ground-water conditions and storage capacity in the San Joaquin Valley, California, *U.S. Geol. Surv. Water Supply Paper 1469*, p. 168.

7. Drower, M. S., 1954, Water supply, irrigation, and agriculture, in *History of Technology*, v. 1, ch. 5, Cambridge, Oxford Univ. Press, pp. 520–557.

8. Federal Council of Science and Technology for Scientific Hydrology, December, 1962, *Trans. Am. Geophys. Union*, v. 43, no. 4., p. 493.

9. Frisi, P., 1762, *Treatise on Rivers and Torrents*, J. Garstin (trans.), 1860, London, John Weale, p. 57.

10. Herschel, C. (trans.), 1899, *The Two Books on the Water Supply of the City of Rome, by Sextus Julius Frontinus*, Boston, Dana Estes and Co., pp. 216–219.

11. Mead, D. W., 1904, *Notes on Hydrology*, Chicago, S. Smith & Co.

12. Mead, D. W., 1919, *Hydrology*, New York, McGraw-Hill.

13. Meinzer, O. E. (ed.), 1942, *Hydrology*, Physics of the Earth Series, New York, McGraw-Hill (reprinted Dover Publications, New York, 1949) pp. 1, 12, 14.

14. Meyer, A. F., 1917, *The Elements of Hydrology*, New York, Wiley.

15. Rouse, H. and Ince, S., 1957, *History of Hydraulics*, Iowa Inst. of Hyd. Res., pp. 23–32.

16. Sarton, G., 1952, *A History of Science: Ancient science through the golden age of Greece*, Cambridge, Harvard Univ. Press, p. 59.

17. Suter, M. *et al.*, 1959, *Summary Report and Preliminary Report on the Ground-Water Resources of the Chicago Region, Illinois*, Urbana, Illinois State Water Survey and Illinois Geological Survey Cooperative Reports 1 and 1-S.

2

Precipitation

Precipitation represents the outcome of natural circumstances and may be considered the "cleanest," or least "dirty," class of data used by hydrologists. A variety of statistical methods and analyses may confidently be applied and few, if any, arbitrary corrections are needed. Admittedly, now and then a tall building or a squat blast furnace constructed near an established rain gage will necessitate abandoning the station. Apart from such gross disturbances, however, the data collected at any point are statistically valid. That is, we believe that the data constitute an acceptable sample of a long sequence of natural events and can be reliably analyzed by statistical methods. Unfortunately the data cannot be used directly in civil engineering projects except to compute the filling of cisterns. The same quantity and rate of precipitation will produce quite different results in different places depending upon topography, geology, man-made surfaces, season of year, and antecedent conditions.

Nor is a study of meteorology of great practical value to the engineer in predicting the probability, magnitude, and extent of rainfall—except when adequate records are lacking and he has no other guide. When crucial information is not available, serious consideration should be given delaying design until adequate records are accumulated. Undertaking projects without such records results either in underdesign, which needlessly damages investments dependent upon their success, or extravagant and wasteful overdesign, which imposes needless burdens on the beneficiaries. Nor does the availability of studies that specify the maximum rainfall meteorologically possible in certain areas seriously modify this viewpoint—the occurrence of drought and the recurrence of useful rain are not yet reliably predictable.

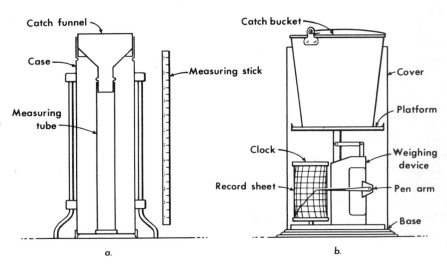

Fig. 2.1. Rain gage types; (a) standard 8-in. nonrecording; (b) weighing-recording.

METHODS OF MEASUREMENT

The rain gage is the basic measuring device used in studies of precipitation. The standard weather-bureau rain gage exposes a circular area, 8 in. in diameter, for the interception of precipitation. There are two principal designs (see Fig. 2.1): *manual*, in which total precipitation for the preceding period, usually 24 hr, is determined by direct measurement of water caught by the gage, and *weighing-recording*, which makes a record (see Fig. 2.2) of accumulative precipitation as it falls. The accuracy of the weighing-recording gage is satisfactory and the chart is readily analyzed for the time distribution of precipitation.

APPLICABILITY OF DATA

Although the "sampling area" represented by the rain gage may seem excessively small when compared with the area represented by the station, experiments disclose no significant differences between the catches of gages of smaller and larger diameters (6). The quantity collected probably coincides pretty well with the precipitation in the immediate area, if the area is geographically quite small and of uniform topography. So whether you use a 1-in. tube or a gage the size of a swimming pool to collect rainfall, you can expect just about the same results that would be obtained by use of a standard gage. If the gage is out in the open, away from trees, and in a representative area, the data will be reliable and comparable.

Rain-gage records are subject to the statistical error of sampling one point of a nonhomogeneous field. The error increases with the variance of the field. For example, the rainfall observed for any given day may not be applicable to a very large area: Small summer downpours that leave most of an area untouched would distort a short-period record. However, as the record period increases, the record at a given gage is believed, within certain limits, to become representative of an increasingly larger area.

We still do not know for how many years precipitation must be recorded in order to apply the observations to large areas with confidence. Figure 2.3, which shows the average annual precipitation at Urbana for the 10-year period 1949–1958, is very thought provoking. In this level, 10-sq mile area, 12 rain gages installed in accordance with Weather-Bureau standards were operated with results that varied as much as 15 percent between the minimum and maximum over a 10-year period. Obviously our knowledge of the actual microstructure of long-term rainfall distribution would benefit from extensive study and experiment. There is even greater variability in the case of larger areas and shorter records. No one has computed how long it would take for the short-term record to approach the long-term record with a difference of less than 10 percent, but there is every indication that even a 25- or 50-year

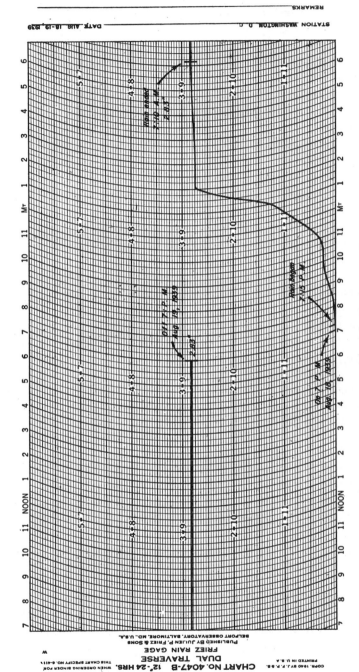

Fig. 2.2. Typical chart from weighing-recording rain gage. (By permission of Friez Inst. Div. Bendix Aviation Corp., Baltimore, Md.)

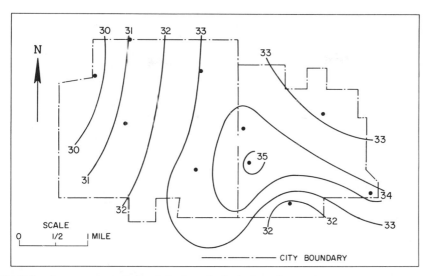

Fig. 2.3. Average annual precipitation (inches) for Champaign-Urbana, 1949–1958. (After G. E. Stout, March 1960, Natural variability of storm, seasonal, and annual precipitation, *Proc. Am. Soc. Civ. Eng., J. Irr. and Drainage Div.*, v. 86, no. IR-1, pt. 1, pp. 127–138.)

period would be none too long if the findings are to be considered representative of a large area.

The effect of rainfall variability on the observed rainfall over a large area for a 1-year period is illustrated by Figs. 2.4 and 2.5. Figure 2.4 was drawn from the U.S. Weather Bureau network in the area; Fig. 2.5, from this same network supplemented by data from additional stations in the area operated by the Illinois Water Survey Division. The effect of increasing the number of rain gages is very apparent and is somewhat disconcerting.

Stout has discussed the effect of increasing the density of the rain-gage network on our understanding of the distribution of precipitation (*13*). His observations of rainfall distribution were made during the course of a lengthy study of natural precipitation intended to establish a basis for evaluating the results of weather-modification experiments in the area. A little later Stout and Huff summarized the results of extensive studies of severe rainstorms in Illinois in the following manner:

A study of the distribution of heavy rainstorms over an urban area of 10 sq miles showed that a point-rainfall record is a satisfactory index of the frequency distribution of areal mean rainfall, although a point observation records only approximately 50% of the excessive storm quantities in the area. Also, it was found that the majority of the excessive quantities for storm periods of from 30 min to 24 hr occur in the same storms.

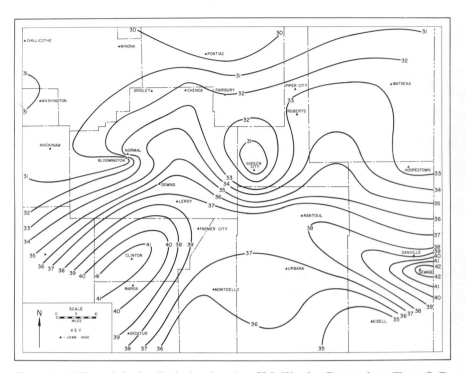

Fig. 2.4. 1958 precipitation (inches) as based on U.S. Weather Bureau data. (From G. E. Stout, March 1960, Natural variability of storm, seasonal, and annual precipitation, *Proc. Am. Soc. Civ. Eng., J. Irr. and Drainage Div.*, v. 86, no. IR-1, pt. 1, pp. 127–138.)

Field surveys of major flood producing storms since 1948 have demonstrated the need for such investigations to evaluate accurately the time and space distribution of rainfall in these storms, particularly with respect to maximum rainfall at the storm center. The field surveys have shown that 24-hour storms with quantities exceeding 10 in. are not rare occurrences in Illinois, although these storm centers are seldom detected by the hydroclimatic network in the state (*14*).

The data from single stations equipped with recording gages are used in studies of storm-sewer capacity and ditch and culvert design and for planning the protection of property of high value from excessive flows. Storms in which the rainfall rate is exceedingly high are usually of short duration and are limited in extent to only a few square miles. Data of this nature were first analyzed by Yarnell in 1935 (*16*). More recently Hershfield has extended and revised Yarnell's work (*5*). The information has been summarized in charts that show the rainfall intensities for various rainfall durations to be expected at a single point for return periods of up to 100 years. Figure 2.6 shows the 25- and 50-year maximum rainfalls to be expected during 6 and

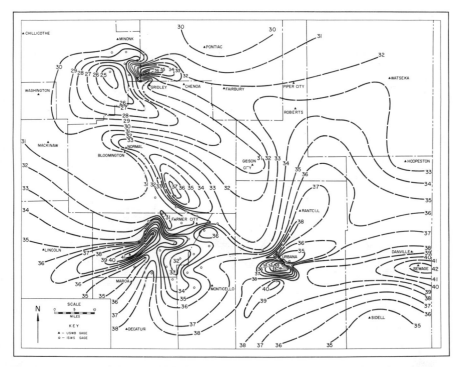

Fig. 2.5. 1958 precipitation (inches) as based on U.S. Weather Bureau and Illinois State Water Survey data. (From G. E. Stout, March 1960, Natural variability of storm, seasonal, and annual precipitation, *Proc. Am. Soc. Civ. Eng., J. Irr. and Drainage Div.*, v. 86, no. IR-1, pt. 1, pp. 127–138.)

12 hr of precipitation. Where the importance of the design warrants, time should be taken to check the critical data, first in the annual reports and year books of the Weather Bureau and, more completely, from the manuscript records on file in the Weather Bureau and other depositories.

DATA ANALYSIS

Precipitation

Where records from networks of stations are available, maps have been prepared from the records showing contours of equal precipitation (isohyets) for given storms by seasons, by years, for average years, and for extreme years. Figure 2.7 is an isohyetal map of the United States showing annual precipitation. Such a map might be considered to be primarily climatologic rather than hydrologic inasmuch as only the broadest generalizations could be made from it and no structure would be designed on the basis of this

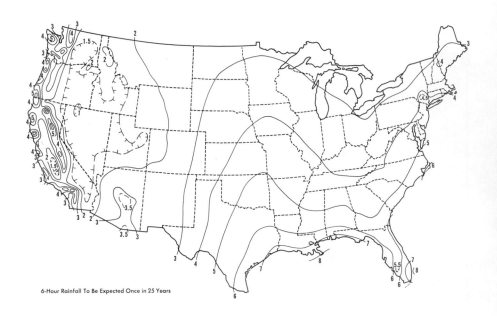

6-Hour Rainfall To Be Expected Once in 25 Years

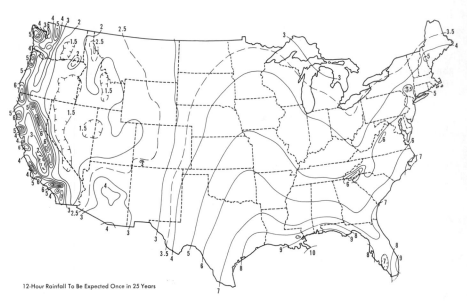

12-Hour Rainfall To Be Expected Once in 25 Years

Fig. 2.6. Rainfall (inches) for 6 and 12 hours duration to be expected once in 25 and 50 years. (After D. M. Hershfield, 1961, *Rainfall Atlas of the United States*, U.S. Dept.

28

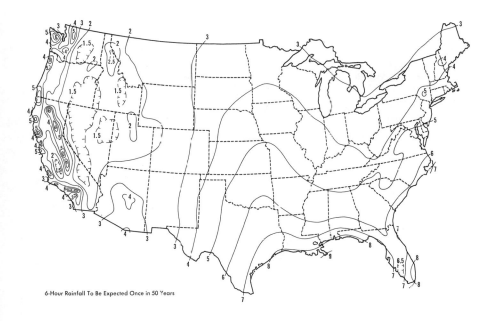

6-Hour Rainfall To Be Expected Once in 50 Years

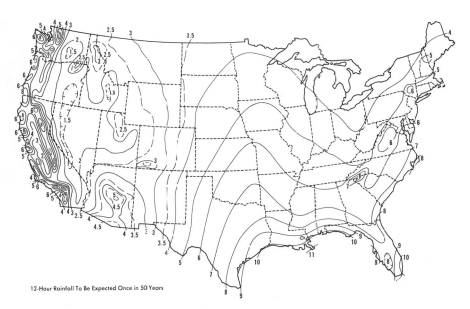

12-Hour Rainfall To Be Expected Once in 50 Years

of Commerce, Weather Bureau, *Technical Paper* 40, Washington, D.C., Government Printing Office.)

29

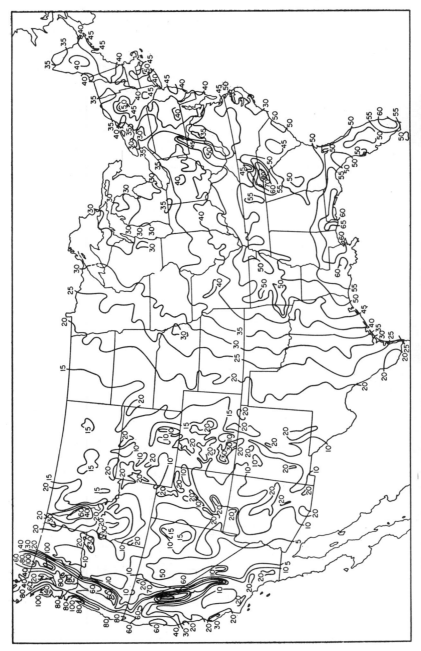

Fig. 2.7. Average annual precipitation (inches) in the United States for the period 1899–1938. (From Interior and Insular Affairs Committee, House of Representatives, 1952, *The Physical and Economic Foundations of Natural Resources*, v. II: *The Physical Basis of Water Supply and Its Principal Uses*, Washington, D.C., Government Printing Office, p. 17.)

information. More useful for design purposes is an isohyetal map, such as that of an intense storm in New England (Fig. 2.8), prepared from a study of many rain-gage records. Also of value are detailed records such as those collected on storms in Illinois, the interpretation of which has been improved by analysis of radar data (7).

How are these data useful? In addition to applications mentioned previously, this information can affect the spillway design of farm and municipal reservoirs, the width, depth, and slope of drainage ditches, the size and capacity of pumps for internal drainage of areas protected from high water by levees, the size and number of bridge openings, and the size of culvert needed. It can also serve as a basis for computing possible ground-water replenishment. As the storms studied cover greater areas and longer periods, the design of larger and more extensive structures is involved. From culverts we go to channel improvements and levees; from spillways of farm ponds we progress to large flood-control dams and their associated reservoirs and appurtenances.

Control of water, the public nuisance and common enemy, is greatly influenced by the data available on the frequency, magnitude, and duration of precipitation. In fact, curves have been prepared (Fig. 2.9) to show the depth-area duration of particularly severe storms, thus summarizing in convenient form all applicable rainfall data for design purposes. Again, as structures become more complex and expensive, it becomes worthwhile to study the frequency, depth, and distribution of precipitation more intensively. In this connection, high-speed digital computers are proving more and more useful in analyzing the probabilities of extreme rainfalls and potential benefits to be derived from construction. In some instances, where rainfall records are short, synthetic rainfall records, based on the observed probability of meteorological events, have been prepared to improve the basis of design. Synthetic hydrology is of great interest but must be used with caution.

The *Hydrology Handbook* of the American Society of Civil Engineers has this to say about maximum rainfall intensities and an analogous statement can be made about all generalized formulas dealing with precipitation phenomena:

The equation most frequently used to represent this (intensity-duration-frequency) relationship is hyperbolic, and takes the general form

$$i = \frac{KT^x}{a + t^n}$$

in which i is the average rainfall intensity in inches per hour, T is the frequency in years with which the intensity is reached or exceeded, t is the duration of rainfall in minutes, and K, a, x and n are coefficients, constants, and exponents varying with geographic location (1).

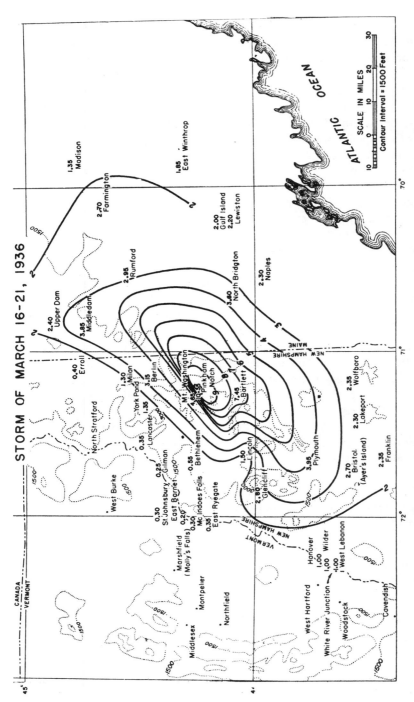

Fig. 2.8. Isohyetal map prepared from records obtained during a two-day period of a prolonged storm in northern New England. The heavy contour lines show the two-day depth of rainfall in inches; the dotted contours relate to the topography of the land surface. (From *Hydrology* by Oscar Meinzer. Published by Dover Publications, Inc., New York 14, N.Y. and reprinted through permission of the publisher.)

We have here three variables, all of which may be determined by measurements over a period of years, and four constants that are, essentially, variable and not really subject to prediction or a priori determination.

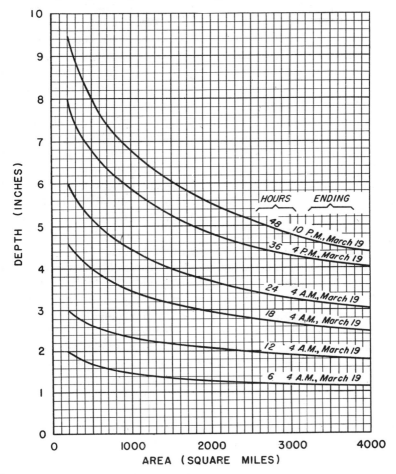

Fig. 2.9. Maximum area-depth curves for storm of March 16–21, 1936, in northern New England. (From *Hydrology* by Oscar Meinzer. Published by Dover Publications, Inc., New York 14, N.Y. and reprinted through permission of the publisher.)

The *Handbook* then goes on to advise against the use of such formulas if important structures are to be designed:

The computation of intensity-duration-frequency values for a particular locality, using a generalized formula, may lead to erroneous results unless a check is made to ensure its applicability. . . . As the data in most cases are now more extensive than when the older published formulas were developed, it is usually worthwhile to bring the . . . relationship up-to-date in a newly derived equation.

Any discussion of precipitation cannot be considered complete without some reference to new technical developments and their associated problems. One of the more interesting developments is a method of approximating the distribution of precipitation by means of radar observations. This work was pioneered by the Illinois State Water Survey; their results have been reported in the organization's *Report of Investigation* series. Radar is presently used to delineate the areal extent, relative intensity, and movement of storms. This information can be correlated with records from a dense network of rain gages within a storm zone and with meteorological data on air-mass movements (particularly the interfaces, or fronts); thus, an estimate of rainfall volume within the storm can be obtained that is more accurate than that provided by either the rain gages or the radar alone. Although the ultimate importance of radar in this connection cannot be evaluated at present, it is reasonable to expect that our knowledge of the time and space distribution of rainfall will be improved by its use and, therefore, will result in more reliable probability estimates of rainfall extremes for hydrologic applications. The U.S. Weather Bureau has established a WSR-57 radar network for this purpose. Associated with this work are studies to determine the size of raindrops and the most suitable wavelength to use in radar studies.

But water is not always the common enemy. Invariably men have found it to be not merely useful, but completely irreplaceable. The many uses of water, from a cool tub in a man's home on a hot day to the cooling of the condensers of a steam-electric generating plant; from turning the overshot wheel to turning the hydroelectric turbines; from the watering of a flower garden to the irrigation of millions of acres of crops; from a simple drink of water to a major city's water supply—all of these and more serve to delineate the uses of fresh water, the giver of life, the grandchild of rain.

Droughts

From the standpoint of water use—and particularly its second most important direct use, the production of food—the critical question is the frequency and duration of periods during which no rainfall occurs. Food must be produced each year, and even a humid area that is subject to infrequent but prolonged periods of rainlessness will not long support human life. Mindling studied the occurrence and duration of dry periods, using a total of 1 in. of precipitation as the criterion for the end of a drought (*11*). Inasmuch as the only direct use of rainfall is the support of vegetal life, it turns out that in this area the rainfall records that have been most important are most important for the negative information they have yielded. The records have been carefully studied to determine rainless periods and the duration and frequency of such periods, as well as the duration and frequency of periods of less than 0.25 in. per day have fallen, or 0.5 in. per day, or other small quantity, the criterion being the amount needed to prevent the death or serious impairment of crops. Huff and Changnon have published an elaborate study of drought-frequency in Illinois, which centers attention on the frequency and duration of periods of dry weather (*7a*). They found no evidence that droughts occur in cycles, or at predictable intervals.

Not surprisingly, drought data have proved of very great significance and have been increasingly used to determine the need for supplemental irrigation in "humid" areas and the need for large reservoirs to supply water to concentrations of people and industry during dry periods. Again, from a theoretical standpoint, the data are statistically good, and the longer the period of record, the more probable it is that the events recorded will repeat themselves. Maps can be prepared to show the frequency of any selected drought condition, plans can be made to maintain crop production, and reservoirs can be designed large enough to furnish minimum quantities of water during certain selected, critical dry periods.

Thus, of all branches of engineering it is in agricultural engineering that raw data on rainfall occurrence can be used most directly in planning. All other branches utilize rainfall data indirectly, concerning themselves with what remains of the water after it has been intercepted by vegetation and soil. And the handbooks are full of empirical formulas that enable men to convert rainfall data into directly useful flow quantities, although the general applicability of such formulas outside the area wherein they have been derived is, as we have seen, open to question.

Snow and Ice

Still another form of precipitation is important in engineering hydrology: the solid form of water, for snow and ice are also collected by rain gages. In this connection, because the water must first change from the solid to the liquid state before it runs off the land surface and becomes available for use, direct utilization of the data for design purposes is not feasible. As the snow changes physical state, there is a good possibility that it may sublimate rather than turn into liquid water. And before it changes its state, it may be blown by the wind into large accumulations or drifts in locations far removed from the point where it fell. None of this is indicated by the quantity accumulated in a gage. Moreover the gage is somewhat less reliable when used for measuring the catch of snow than it is for rain. Snow may be blown out before it melts and is recorded as precipitation (gages have been devised to surmount this problem and have been elevated to reduce ground effects, but stratagems are only partially successful).

When measurement of snowfall in the solid state is attempted we find that the same water content may result in different depths of snow, depending upon its structure. It has also been observed that snow tends to pack as it accumulates and that some of the water reenters the atmosphere directly through ablation. All in all it has been found far more satisfactory to measure snow on the ground after it has fallen and to collect cores of the snow pack and measure their water content rather than to rely on the accumulation of snow in a rain gage as an index of liquid water content. Church, a meteorologist who devoted his life to the study of water in its many solid-state forms, discussed the subject adequately, and at length, from a practical standpoint. The position is approximately this: the direct observation of the quantity of solid-state precipitation is unreliable for all practical purposes (*10*). However, snow depth on the ground, if measured and sampled about 10 days after a storm, has been found satisfactory as an approximate measure of the effective precipitation as it will be expressed in the form of runoff. This type of measurement, made at frequent intervals over very elaborately organized *snow courses* (a snow course is a line, possibly 50 yds long, along which fixed points are sampled and depths determined each year in a standardized fashion) is the accepted practical method of measuring solid-state precipitation and has proved most useful in serving as the basis for the prediction of runoff, floods, possible growth of ice field, and so forth.

WEATHER MODIFICATION

More significant to the student of hydrology has been the persistent attempt to modify rainfall distribution by cloud seeding. This effort seems to have started seriously immediately after World War II, when General Electric's famed Langmuir undertook studies of the role of nuclei in the creation of droplets and soon thereafter announced the possibility of modifying clouds by artificial means. Researchers have pursued three major objectives: to increase rainfall, to decrease rainfall, and to determine its potentialities as a weapon in military operations. Effective weather control would also enable us to prevent the build-up of damaging hailstorms and dangerous electrical storms. Even hurricanes might be eliminated or their harmful potential reduced.

The military potentialities of the control of rainfall are almost self-evident but they are not hydrologically significant and will only be enumerated. From a tactical viewpoint, the possibility of an attack or retreat under the cover of a seemingly natural but really prearranged rain or fog is attractive. Creating muddy conditions for the enemy and preventing rain in your own area, especially where paved roads are lacking, is another possibility. An artificial cloudburst when an enemy is fording a creek would be an effective weapon in the hands of an imaginative commander. And if, by stretching the imagination a little, we concede that we will learn how to produce fog, sleet, and hail, the research on rain-making methods is worthwhile, even though it is geared to military applications. On a strategic level the production of rainfall during harvest time or the prevention of rain during the early part of the growing season would have great influence on an enemy's production and even greater effect on his morale. A heavy, unexpected snowfall would tend to snarl traffic over wide areas and decrease productivity—the strategic possibilities are numberless.

It is when we examine the record of civilian rain making and evaluate its potential impact on hydrology, either as a science or as an engineering discipline, that we find reason to be concerned. For purposes of this discussion it is not really relevant whether nucleation is caused by ground-based generators of silver iodide or the seeding of clouds with dry ice or water particles (to mention some of the most common nuclei).

Krick described the efforts of his firm to alleviate the Dallas water shortage of 1952 in the following rather optimistic words:

The skilled commercial cloud seeder is qualified by training and experience to undertake the large-scale operations that make cloud seeding economically worthwhile. He is rarely concerned with the single cloud operation favored by the pure experimentalist, although commercial field techniques and operational procedures are, of course, based on a series of researches into cloud physics and precipitation mechanisms.

The qualified commercial operator recognizes that the effect of cloud seeding must be cumulative to be of economic value. Therefore, he attempts to build up in his target area, by continuous operations on all suitable cloud formations, a total effect that may be discerned over a long period as an increase in precipitation with respect to rainfall in surrounding, unseeded areas. He operates on moving cloud masses, associated with migratory storm systems, in such a way that the seeded segment of the cloud system lies continuously over his target area.

The operational period of the commercial cloud seeder is a function of the total number and the duration of storms susceptible to cloud seeding. Hundreds of operational hours may be required before a significant (relative) increase in the precipitation recorded in a target area will satisfy the requirements for a true evaluation. (It may be remembered that the question of evaluation occupied a prominent place in an earlier paper on the theory and practice of cloud seeding) (8).

The Dallas operation is an example of the large-scale type mentioned in the previous section. Undertaken as the result of a critical water shortage in the city, it serves to demonstrate what cloud seeding can achieve, not only for the purpose for which it was initially instituted—raising the level of water in Lake Dallas—but also for the agriculture of the surrounding area (9).

Orville, chairman of the Advisory Committee on Weather Control (established by Congress in 1953) was also optimistic about the efficacy of cloud seeding:

The advisory committee has established, with a satisfactory degree of probability, that cloud-seeding operations on the windward slopes of the Pacific Coast States during the cooler and moist winter and spring months have produced significant overall increase in precipitation from the storms seeded over the which would have been expected without cloud seeding.

At this time the advisory committee's studies do not enable it to apply these conclusions either to the results of artificial precipitation increasing in other portions of the Nation or to the possibilities of hail and lightning suppression (12).

Braham and Battan of the Cloud Physics Laboratory at the University of Chicago summarized the results of their experiments in cloud seeding as follows:

Through a long and very careful series of field experiments, it has been shown that the formation of precipitation can be induced in relatively small cumulus clouds, in which it would not form naturally, through the use of water spray released inside the clouds.

Experiments involving the treatment of supercooled cumulus clouds with dry ice released into the cloud at levels where the temperatures were favorable for ice crystal growth did not result in demonstrable seeding-effects—either positive or negative. It was shown that it is unlikely that dry ice seeding will result in spectacular development of cumulus clouds or spectacular increases in the amount of precipitation from them, or both. The reason for this is thought to be that the lifetime of an average cumulus cloud is about equal to the time required for introduced ice crystals to grow into precipitation particles. This does not mean that seeding with ice-forming materials cannot have positive effects. Successful rain initiation conceivably can result from: (1) the initiation of precipitation in marginally small clouds which would not have lasted long enough to rain naturally; (2) the growth of small (non-precipitation) ice crystals in one cloud and the transfer of these particles to a second cloud as the first cloud dissipates; or (3) resupplying clouds with ice nuclei after the natural ones have been consumed in the precipitation processes. Only further basic research can solve these problems (3).

In August, 1959, a conference on weather modification was held in Denver, Colorado, and 14 papers presented at the conference were later published by the American Society of Civil Engineers (2). One table printed in this journal summarized 14 instances of cloud seeding in the tropics (2, p. 62) between 1947 and 1958. Another table (2, p. 66) listed 17 commercial-seeding projects that used silver iodide as the "trigger" and showed the duration of the attempts and the probable percentage of increase in precipitation.

The general tenor of the papers is that the science of weather modification is no longer completely experimental or without practical application, that the results are statistically valid, and, in general, beneficial in that an increase in rainfall was experienced over that which might otherwise have occurred. The participants in the conference were confident that all difficulties in operating and evaluating projects would be overcome and that the natural precipitation could, and would be increased as the need for additional water became apparent.

Court, a Department of Agriculture Meteorologist summarized matters this way:

What then is the present status of cloud-seeding evaluations: Has any progress been shown in the dozen years since the first experiments, or in the years since the 1952 conference in Denver? Certainly methods are improving, and evaluations are becoming more reliable. In fact, the quality of evaluations is increasing much faster than the fault-finding of the statisticians. At the present rate, it will soon meet all these objections—and even those that will be raised in the future.

Eventually evaluation must be in economic terms, so that the customer can ascertain exactly whether he is receiving a fair return for his expense. Such evaluation requires work by economists and others to develop a method of predicting yield (crop, electric, etc.) from all factors, including weather. Until such estimates are possible, meteorologists will continue to evaluate the meteorological effects of cloud-seeding—but they must consider all meteorological effects, not just the one that is desired, and list them all beforehand.

Comparability of all data must be assured, and transformations handled properly. Other difficulties with current evaluations, not cited herein, can also be overcome. Then the efficacy of cloud seeding will finally be subject to rigorous and unassailable evaluation (2, p. 126).

Field work is continuing and the results of careful (and costly) experiments in cloud seeding have been described by Malkus and Simpson:

We believe that the series of control calculations establishes, beyond reasonable doubt, the causal relationship between seeding and the explosive cloud growth which followed. . . . This experiment has barely scratched the surface; its repetition, with a number of improvements, is mandatory. . . . We must learn more of the natural freezing behavior of tropical oceanic clouds. . . . The important conclusion is that . . . a real atmospheric phenomenon is at last subject to a relatively controlled and theoretically modeled experiment. . . . Here meteorology is taking the first small steps toward becoming an experimental science, which it must become if man is ever to exert real control on his atmosphere (9a).

In a field so-swiftly changing, the last word cannot be written today. Research workers for the Rand Corporation under a National Science Foundation grant recently published a review on weather-control research (4). In essence, they found that cause and effect, as they determine the phenomena of meteorology, are imperfectly understood. That, for instance, meteorologists have only a rudimentary and fragmentary knowledge not only of how energy fluctuates among the various scales of atmospheric motion but also of how these scaled phenomena are interrelated. They point out that man may long have been modifying weather inadvertently by polluting the atmosphere with smokes and gases and, more recently, by means of rocket exhausts. The direction and magnitude of these inadvertent modifications, where such exist, have not been satisfactorily analyzed. They call for a broad attack on the problems of atmospheric phenomena, ranging from theoretical and small-scale studies of convection phenomena through studies of the growth of cloud particles (which finally results in precipitation). These would cover the gamut of possibilities and would also include research on inadvertent climatic modification, the development of laboratory models of large-scale weather modification, and the accomplishment of actual large-scale cloud-seeding experiments. There is, evidently, much to be learned about the phenomena whose interactions result in weather, before effective weather modification will become possible. The scientists most directly involved in weather modification, however, have stated and restated their belief in ultimate success.

NEW PROBLEMS OF HYDROLOGY

As matters stand it is still not certain whether or not cloud seeding is a practical engineering tool. There are indications that it may finally become one, but this has not yet been conclusively demonstrated. The problem that may confront the engineering profession, is expressed by Taylor, a lawyer well versed in the legal and engineering aspects of developing water supplies:

> Artificial rainfall has already been produced with some success, but it has also raised involved legal problems. The major question is who owns the clouds. Ultimately, it may be necessary to regulate rain, making rules of nationwide application and by international treaty. Now is the time for water lawyers to measure the scope of such regulations and pave the way for a workable plan of administration (15).

This quotation does no more than hint at some of the problems posed by rain making. Rain is both friend and foe: as between the farmer whose crops are too dry, the resort owner who hates rain, the city that needs more water in its reservoir, and the roadbuilder working on a tight schedule, where lies the equity? And whose is the responsibility when the tropical rainstorm that fills a city's reservoirs engenders a flood that overflows the lowlands, the streets, and the basements? "A workable plan of administration" would appear to be far off.

But even though the legal situation is confusing and chaotic, there are strong indications that the real damage to society will be found elsewhere, in the field of hydrology. For the whole science of hydrology is based on the assumption that every observed hydrologic event is meaningful: that it could happen again, given the same set of meteorological circumstances. In other words, if, over a five-year period, continuous rainfalls totaling 1 in. or more occur X times a year, it is probable within certain computable confidence limits, that such rainfalls will occur in the future in the same frequency. And the longer the period of record, the more closely can we compute the probability, and the more reliable are our economic analyses. This holds true for all branches of hydrology.

But if the occurrence of rainfall is to be determined by some ever-changing administrative regulations, which authorize tampering with clouds, rather than by natural meteorological events, we will find that hydrology has been completely politicalized. Thus, depending on the state of the art, the quantity of rainfall falling at any point will depend on the relative political influence of individuals, corporations, municipalities, governmental bodies, and international obligations. This influence, of course, will change as time passes—first one will exert more power, than another. At any specified time, however, the situation of the water supply of a town located away from the seacoast will be completely unpredictable inasmuch as anyone needing rain, and situated closer to the coast, may have first chance at the clouds, depending on the relative political strengths. Moreover, even a town on the coast may not be permitted to influence rainfall because of laws or regulations.

We may anticipate such questions as this: How large a reservoir must a city own to supply K gallons of water a day during the longest probable drought period? On what basis is this design drought to be selected? It will be noted that rainfall records will be useless for this purpose, since any given set of meteorological circumstances is subject to political modifications, should it recur.

The farmer or agriculturalist who depends on rain during the growing season may not receive it if the cities and industries nearer the seacoast need rain (even if they only want a cheap way to wash the streets or cool off the city). The converse, of course, may be true during "wet" years—the cities may inhibit, dissipate, or divert the rain clouds and the water may then be dumped on the farms, which may already be suffering from surplus of moisture.

Moreover, the possibility of accident is a real one: no human endeavors are ever perfectly conducted. What happens when an unexpected rain is dumped into a full flood-control reservoir by accident? Spillway designs are predicated on the basic hydrologic assumption that observed meteorological events are repeatable. If the spillway is small, under the assumption that the rainfall will be controlled, and a large storm gets away, overtopping spillway and dam alike, what then? The logical answer to this problem, as far as it concerns spillway design, is to assume that the largest storm ever recorded will come when the reservoir is full, and build on that basis. Then one immediately runs into trouble: recorded where and when? Before the control of rain was practiced or after? And, as rain-making (or rain-inhibiting) technology progresses, the possibilities will change and the situation will closely approach chaos as far as design data are concerned. Rainfall records will be historical records rather than statistically repeatable, independent, hydrologic observations.

The situation with regard to flood control, channel improvement, water supply, sewage disposal, and all other forms of hydraulic and hydrologic engineering will then become one of increasing uncertainty. Factors of safety, already large, will inevitably be increased (and the increases will prove, in many instances, to be inadequate), and the cost of construction will mount. The economic evaluations that must precede construction will be totally unreliable inasmuch as they must be based primarily on a political assessment and only secondarily on observed facts and current (or probable) costs and benefits. This, of course, will lead to wasteful construction of uncertain utility and will not be beneficial to society.

The sum total appears to be this: The price of weather control will come high, and it is far from certain that the benefits to society will exceed its cost. Although control of the occurrence of rain seems to be a problem for future generations, there are today a number of extremely competent and respected meteorologists who believe it to be possible. Should current experiments in weather control succeed, much thought will be required to overcome the chaotic conditions that will be produced in the field of hydrology and the fields of engineering based on hydrologic data.

NOTES

1. Am. Soc. Civ. Eng., 1949, Hydrology handbook, *Manual of Engineering Practice*, no. 28, p. 18.
2. Am. Soc. Civ. Eng., March, 1960, *J. of the Irrigation and Drainage Div.*, v. 86, no. IR-1, pp. 62, 66, 126.
3. Braham, R. R., Jr., and Battan, L. J., February, 1958, Effects of seeding cumulus clouds, *J. Am. Water Works Assoc.*, v. 50, no. 2, pp. 191–192.
4. Greenfield, S. M. *et al.*, December, 1962, A rationale for weather-control research, *Trans. Am. Geophys. Union*, v. 43, no. 4, pp. 469–487.
5. Hershfield, D. M., 1961, Rainfall atlas of the United States, *U.S. Dept. of Com., Weather Bureau, Tech. Paper 40.*
6. Huff, F. A., August, 1955, Comparison between standard and small-orifice rain gages, *Trans. Am. Geophys. Union*, v. 36, no. 4, pp. 689–694.
7. Huff, F. A. *et al.*, 1958, Hydrometeorological analysis of severe rainstorms in Illinois, Urbana, Illinois State Water Survey, Rept. of Inv. 35.
7a. Huff, F. A., and Changnon, Jr., S. A., 1963, *Drought Climatology of Illinois*, Urbana, Illinois State Water Survey, Bull. 50.
8. Krick, I. P., November, 1952, Increasing water resources through weather modification, *J. Am. Water Works Assoc.*, v. 44, no. 11, p. 1009.
9. Krick, I. P., November, 1953, Cloud-seeding operations at Dallas, *J. Am. Water Works Assoc.*, v. 45, no. 11, p. 1144.
9a. Malkus, J. S., and Simpson, R. H., August, 1964, Modification experiments on tropical cumulus clouds, *Science*, v. 145, no. 3632, pp. 541–548.
10. Meinzer, O. E. *et al.*, 1942, *Hydrology*, Physics of the Earth Series, New York, McGraw-Hill, ch. IV, pp. 83–148. (Reprinted Dover Publications, New York, 1949.)
11. Mindling, G. W., 1944, Weather headlines in Ohio, *Ohio Eng. Sta. Bull. 120.*
12. Orville, H. T., 1957, *Western Water News*, v. 9, no. 12, p. 7.
13. Stout, G. E., March, 1960, Natural variability of storm, seasonal, and annual precipitation, Am. Soc. Civ. Eng., *J. Irr. and Drainage Div.*, v. 86, no. IR-1 pt. 1, pp. 127–138.
14. Stout G. E., and Huff, F. A., July, 1962, Studies of severe rainstorms in Illinois, Am. Soc. Civ. Eng., *J. of Hydraulics Div.*, v. 88, no. HY-4, pt. 1, p. 145.
15. Taylor, E. F., July, 1959, Progress in the development of municipal supplies, *J. Am. Water Works Assoc.*, v. 51, no. 7, p. 841.
16. Yarnell, D. L., 1935, Rainfall intensity-frequency data, *U.S. Dept. of Agri., Misc. Pub. 204.*

3

Evaporation

Evaporation may be defined as the process by which a liquid or solid is changed to a gas. The direct transformation of a solid to a gas is sometimes termed sublimation, or ablation. As used in this chapter, the term *evaporation* applies to both of these transformations and also includes the concept *transpiration* which implies that plant life has used the water just before it was vaporized.

The process of evaporation has been carefully studied in the laboratory, yet, as applied to conditions encountered in nature, quantitative methods of evaluating its rate or the total amount over a long period of time are neither precise nor completely reliable. The reason for this is not hard to find: Many factors affect evaporation itself and the measurement of evaporation. Researchers studying the process under natural conditions have attempted to correlate evaporation with solar radiation, air and water temperature, humidity, vapor pressure, wind movement, altitude, and water quality. Each of these factors has its own effect on evaporation rate and some of them are, in addition, independently interrelated. For the water substance to experience a change of state, energy must be added to it or removed from it. Ultimately, the source of all energy for evaporation is current or recent solar radiation impinging on water, the soil-water complex, and the plant-life-water complex. Man-released energy is excluded from this analysis, since, compared to solar energy, its relative importance in the hydrologic cycle is close to zero. In most cases of evaporation only a portion of the water acted upon is changed in state. The remainder and its environment are changed in temperature, with the original volume of water undergoing a reduction in mass.

As solar energy is absorbed by water and its environment, the temperature of the complex is raised, heat is conducted downward, away from the exposed surface, upward into the air, and a portion of the water is evaporated. Many independent and semiindependent influences modify the speed and magnitude of response to the gain or loss of energy. To complicate matters further, the substance involved, water, is a two-phase physical system and the entire process devolves about the system in its most unstable aspect. The system in its entirety is hardly amenable to exact mathematical prediction, even though the equations governing the components of its action and response are well known. It is no wonder that the engineering literature over the past 30 years has been filled with reports of studies, experiments, theories, and semiempirical formulas which, while possibly clarifying our understanding of the physical process, have not resulted in appreciably more accurate or more reliable design data.

METHODS OF MEASUREMENT

For a long time, and continuing through the present, most serious studies of evaporation in nature have used the evaporation pan as an analog. This work has all been based on the theory that there may be some determinable relationship between the rates of evaporation from the small water surface of an evaporation pan and from a large water surface in the same locality that has been subjected to the same natural influences. Of the several pans available, the most widely used is the Class A Land Pan. For many years this has been employed by the U.S. Weather Bureau in its weather stations. Continuous records of observations have been accumulated in all parts of the country. The observation of evaporation requires the greatest attention to minute details: Films of dust, oil from sprays, the oily secretions of inquisitive insects alighting on the water, birds bathing in the pans, and screen covers placed over the pan to keep out the birds can cause systematic error in observation.

The Class A pan is 4 ft in diameter and 10 in. deep; water is maintained between 2 and 3 in. from the top. It is set on timbers so that the bottom of the pan is 6 in. above the ground. Earth is banked within 1 in. of the top of the timbers, thus leaving some air circulation under the pan.

In analog-prototype studies, evaporation of water from the pan is converted to evaporation of water from a large, exposed water surface such as a lake or reservoir. This type of study necessitates field measurement of all inflow of moisture from the atmosphere in the form of rain or snow, runoff from the land surface, ground-water contributions from the surrounding soil, and outflow, both natural and man-made, to all of these media. The difference between measured liquid inflow and measured liquid outflow is attributed to evaporation. Considering the limited accuracy of hydraulic measurements in the field, it is not difficult to comprehend why, even with the same model-prototype system, no exact relationship has been established. In such evaporation measurements, all observational errors show up as evaporation, or lack of it; the inherent error is probably not less than about 20 percent for large bodies of water. Further compounding the difficulties in model-prototype correlation is the cyclical variability of annual evaporation: The annual seasonal change has one influence on the exposed evaporation pan and another on the nearby lake at the same time. It is surprising that there is any reasonably ascertainable, approximate relationship at all.

The observed annual pan evaporation, when multiplied by a coefficient of between 0.70 and 0.80, will yield a reasonable first approximation of the evaporation from the nearby lake. A tremendous amount of instrumentation and a long period of observation would be required to obtain a more accurate coefficient for a given locality. Except for particular projects, for example, evaluating the efficacy of evaporation-reducing chemicals, such studies are seldom worthwhile—the accuracy of other factors involved in a water-development project: Rainfall, surface runoff, bank storage, or ground-water flow, are rarely known precisely.

Other pans are also used as analogs. One of these is the sunken, screened pan which is a standard pan in which the water is shaded by a $\frac{1}{4}$-in. mesh galvanized wire screen. The screen is believed to reduce the water loss from the pan to approximately that from a large water area—the coefficient is about 1.0. The Bureau of Plant Industry (U.S. Department of Agriculture) uses a pan that is 60 in. in diameter and 36 in. deep and is set 33 in. into the ground. This has an average evaporation coefficient of 0.95—not a particularly significant difference from that given by the screened pan even though the factor varies (as does that of other pans) throughout the year, being smaller in the spring and larger in the fall. Still others used include a floating pan (which experiences trouble from splashes caused by wave action), the Colorado sunken pan, and sundry special pans designed by individual investigators. With commendable—although possibly misguided—energy, each of a large number of investigators has devised his own analog of the natural prototype to overcome some real or fancied difficulty with the analogs in general use.

Researchers have investigated the relationship between evaporation, as measured by the change in water volume in the evaporation pan in the light of air temperature, wind velocity, vapor pressure, water temperature, and solar radiation. Factors affecting the direct observation of evaporation include the effects of air eddies caused by the rim of the pan, the color of the pan, and the salinity of the surface layer of water in the pan. Evaporation from natural bodies of water is reduced roughly in proportion to the salinity. For example evaporation from the ocean, which contains about 3 percent of salts in solution, is believed to be about 3 percent less than that to be expected from an equivalent body of fresh water. This is due to the change in vapor pressure of the mineralized solution as compared to fresh water. To avoid a possible source of error, water in the evaporation pan should be changed periodically before minerals found in tap water have a chance to become overly concentrated.

The Meyer Formula

Where pan evaporation data are lacking, but other meterological information has been obtained, one of the more widely used formulas for computing the monthly evaporation from a free water surface is the Meyer formula:

$$E = C(V_w - V_a)(1 + W/10).$$

E = Evaporation measured in inches depth.
V_w = Maximum vapor pressure, in inches mercury, corresponding to the mean temperature of the surface water of the given lake or reservoir. Temperature measurements are to be made about 1 foot below the water surface.
V_a = Actual vapor pressure, in inches mercury, in the atmosphere about 25 feet above the water surface or above the surface of the surrounding land area.
W = Wind velocity, in miles per hour, measured about 25 feet above the surface of the water or above the surrounding cleared land, or the tops of trees or buildings.
C = An empirical constant dependent upon time, and upon the size and character of the water body, and having the following values:

  $C = 15$ for monthly evaporation from fully exposed pans, small puddles of water, and intercepted rainfall on the surface of soil and vegetation while moisture is available.
  $C = 11$ for monthly evaporation from small lakes and reservoirs when the actual vapor pressure in the air is determined from the mean of the daily maximum and minimum temperatures and the mean of the morning and evening relative humidity measured about 25 feet above the surface of the water or the ground.
  $C = 10$ for monthly evaporation from small lakes and reservoirs when the actual vapor pressure in the air is the mean of the morning and evening or of more frequent, equally spaced, determinations of actual vapor pressure measured about 25 feet above the surface of the water or the ground (11).

The formula yields widely varying quantities for the computed evaporation depending on the wind velocity. It would seem that if arrangements are made to measure all of these meteorological elements, then surely an evaporation pan could be installed at the same time and then operated.

WIND AND OTHER INFLUENCES

The effect of wind on evaporation rate has been studied for many years and reported in many technical papers. As water vapor is 60 percent as dense as the dry gases of the atmosphere, it continually tends to rise of its own accord. There is good reason to believe, however, that atmospheric turbulence is a principal mechanism of vapor transfer in the atmosphere above land and water surfaces.

In 1961, Homan stated that as the velocity of wind increases above approximately 2 mph, all other factors being the same, the rate of evaporation can be expected to be a constant (6). Homan referred to research carried out in 1954 by Yamaoka (15). Working in a wind-tunnel laboratory, Yamaoka studied transpiration of plants exposed to constant temperature and relative humidity, with radiation intensity and wind velocity as the controlled variables. He reported that for any given radiation intensity, transpiration remained practically constant for all wind velocities above approximately 2 mph; a definite relationship between radiation intensity and the evaporation by plants was also noted. However under an "oasis" condition, with a hot, dry wind contributing significant quantities of energy to a small water area or vegetation-sustaining land area, the evaporation rate would be significantly increased by a high wind velocity.

The individual who must estimate the evaporation will find the series of maps prepared by Meyer invaluable. Figure 3.1 shows the mean annual evaporation to be expected from shallow lakes and reservoirs. Figure 3.2 shows the average difference between annual precipitation and annual evaporation. Figure 3.3 shows the difference between mean summer precipitation and mean summer evaporation and is probably a fairly good guide to the need for supplemental water to insure the proper growth of plants during the summer.

Penman's conclusion is that "The transpiration of a short green cover cannot exceed the evaporation from an open water surface exposed to the same weather (12). This statement has gained general acceptance among researchers, thus widening the interpretations and utility of Meyer's work.

Engler's careful study of the duty of water in the irrigation of rice in Arkansas over the 12-year period, 1928–1940, showed an average water use of about 33 in. during the growing season (May–September) (3). This compares well with Fig. 3.4 which indicates a mean (April–October) evaporation of about 40 in.

In the irrigation of rice, fields are flooded and maintained in a flooded condition during a growing season of about 120 days. During this time the fields may be allowed to dry once or twice to control disease, but flooding is resumed to kill weeds. Water loss is due almost entirely to evaporation inasmuch as an impervious hardpan underlies the topsoil. On many farms, wells are operated continuously during the growing period to make up for evaporative loss. The rate of evaporation from a field is about equal to the pumping rate: One hundred acres of rice requires the operation of a well producing about 700 gal a min 24 hr a day throughout the season in order to compensate for evaporation—a dramatic visual demonstration of the

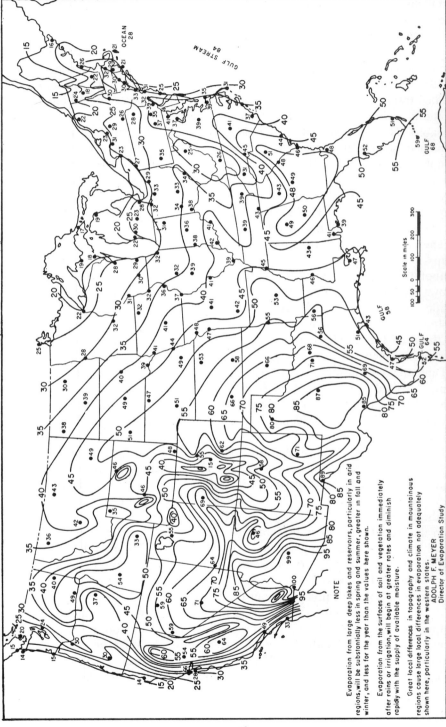

Fig. 3.1. Mean annual evaporation (inches) from shallow lakes and reservoirs. (From A. F. Meyer, June, 1942, *Evaporation from Lakes and Reservoirs*, St. Paul, Minn., Minnesota Resources Commission, p. 55.)

NOTE

Evaporation from large deep lakes and reservoirs, particularly in arid regions, will be substantially less in spring and summer, greater in fall and winter, and less for the year than the values here shown.

Evaporation from the surfaces of soil and vegetation immediately after rains or irrigation, will begin at greater rates and diminish rapidly with the supply of available moisture.

Great local differences in topography and climate in mountainous regions cause large local differences in evaporation not adequately shown here, particularly in the western states.

ADOLPH F. MEYER,
Director of Evaporation Study

Scale in miles
100 50 0 100 200 300

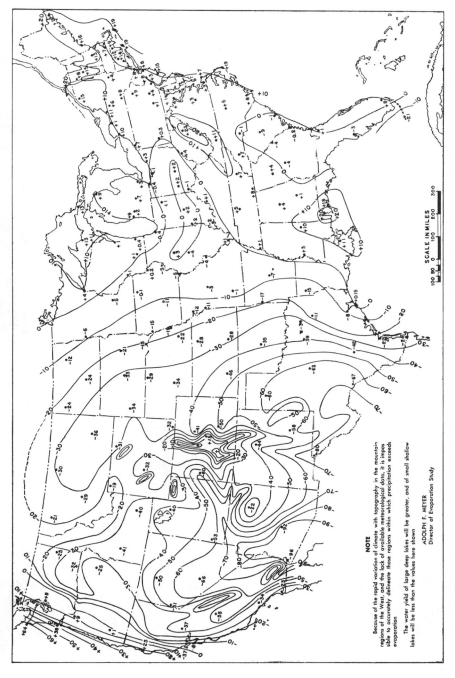

Fig. 3.2. Mean annual precipitation less mean annual evaporation (inches). (From A. F. Meyer, June, 1942, *Evaporation from Lakes and Reservoirs*, St. Paul, Minn., Minnesota Resources Commission, p. 58.)

49

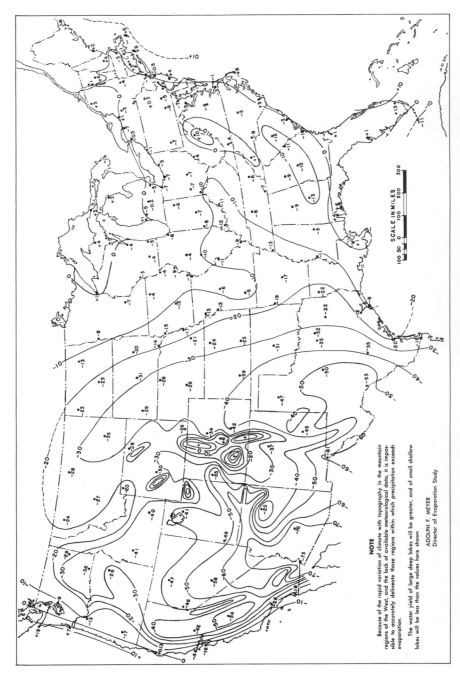

Fig. 3.3. Mean summer precipitation less mean summer evaporation (inches). (From A. F. Meyer, June 1942, *Evaporation from Lakes and Reservoirs*, St. Paul, Minn., Minnesota Resources Commission, p. 58.)

50

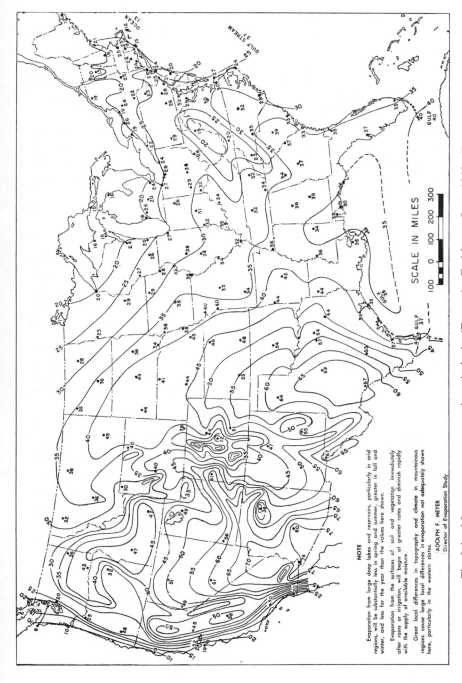

Fig. 3.4. Mean summer evaporation (inches). (From A. F. Meyer, June 1942, *Evaporation from Lakes and Reservoirs*, St. Paul, Minn., Minnesota Resources Commission, p. 55.)

NOTE

Evaporation from large deep lakes and reservoirs, particularly in arid regions, will be substantially less in spring and summer, greater in fall and winter, and less for the year than the values here shown.

Evaporation from the surfaces of soil and vegetation immediately after rains or irrigation, will begin at greater rates and diminish rapidly with the supply of available moisture.

Great local differences in topography and climate in mountainous regions cause large local differences in evaporation not adequately shown here, particularly in the western states.

ADOLPH F. MEYER
Director of Evaporation Study

SCALE IN MILES

100   0   100   200   300

51

evaporation rate. It should be emphasized, however, that all of these maps and studies refer to averages obtained over a number of years of observation and that conditions during any particular year may differ significantly from the average.

We have already pointed out that the measurement of evaporation from a free water surface is not a simple, certain process. The measurement of evaporation or evapotranspiration from the land surface adds the complication of water availability to the foregoing difficulties. For there can be no evaporation from land when there is no water to evaporate. And there is an infinity of different possible conditions of soil saturation between a swamp condition and a desert condition. This complicates matters, especially when the rate of evaporation from the land surface at any time must be determined in advance.

WHY DETERMINE THE EVAPORATION RATE?

The theoretical and experimental studies of evaporation over the past 50 years have been purposeful. They have been designed to yield a useful estimate of the natural evaporation from land and water without measuring it directly, since this is generally impracticable. In 1949, the American Society of Civil Engineers stated it this way:

The practicing engineer is frequently called upon to estimate evaporation from lakes and reservoirs in a particular locality. Seldom are observational data, whether they are records of observed evaporation from pans or complete meteorological data for computing evaporation by means of empirical formulas, available for the given locality (*1*).

Hickman reported the reason for his experiments in this way: "The evaporation experiments reported in this paper were conducted at Duluth, Kewaunee, Detroit, and Buffalo for the purpose of providing a basis for estimating the evaporation from the water surfaces of the Great Lakes (*5*)." Blaney, in 1956, reported on a study of the effect of altitude on evaporation and found that attempts to correlate evaporation rate with altitude usually lead to the conclusion that other factors were more important (*2*). He noted: "The efficient design and later operation of a water supply project is dependent on an awareness of the quantity of water that is lost through evaporation (*2*)."

Looking objectively at all of these studies, one feels that the real, although unstated, reason for conducting them was simply intellectual curiosity. For it is apparent that the evaporation from an area will be balanced to some degree by precipitation in the area. And we have seen that rainfall is not uniform, so even if the evaporation were known exactly, the net difference over any specific period would not be known precisely. The shorter the period, the more unlikely it would be that the estimates were accurate.

Class A pan evaporation, as observed over many years by the Weather Bureau, appears to be a reasonably sound basis for estimating evaporation—for purposes of water supply, use of the raw data will yield water-loss figures in excess of the actual anticipated water loss by about 40 percent and thus allow for the unusually dry year. In this matter employing a coefficient of 0.8 instead of 0.7 is probably safe for all practical purposes. And where pan measurements are not available, the maps prepared by Meyer or, more recently, by Kohler (7) can be used.

In recent years, however, the question of evaporation has appeared in a new form: How much water can be saved by controlling evaporation, or by reducing it? Reference is made, of course, to the use of monomolecular layers of cetyl alcohol (hexadecanol) or similar substances to inhibit evaporation from a free water surface. Another version of this new look at the importance of evaporation and the need for quantitative evaluation is epitomized by Leopold's report that, as far as the Colorado River Basin is concerned, the average annual volume of water to be obtained from the river by the construction of reservoirs has reached its limit (9). To paraphrase his statement: In the Colorado River Basin total reservoir capacity in excess of about 40 million acre-ft (the total storage available when Glen Canyon Dam is in operation) would result in no additional useful flow if the increased evaporation loss is subtracted from annual regulation. Presumably, similar figures could be developed for other western river basins—the validity of the figures being dependent on a reliable figure for the evaporation from lakes or reservoirs. We will encounter the subject of ultimate useful reservoir capacity again and examine it from another viewpoint.

Evaporation data have widespread applicability for beneficial use despite their variability and the computational difficulties. For there is considerable leeway in the required limits of accuracy, and this leeway would exist even though the evaporation were a constant month after month and year after year. For example, in designing a reservoir to store water for the irrigation or supplemental irrigation of crops, the water requirement must be balanced against the cost of producing the water. Plants can survive a wide variety of climatic conditions, and above a certain minimum the crop yields are not entirely dependent on the quantity of available water. Thus the computations of benefits and costs are only approximate, at best.

The computations are far less certain for supplemental irrigation in humid regions than for total irrigation in semiarid regions, as the water requirement in a humid area is merely the difference between rainfall and total potential evaporation. This in turn depends upon the availability of water to the plant. From a practical standpoint, the farmer determines the need for irrigation by examining the condition of the plants and, sometimes, testing the soil. For example while 33 in. of water are required for the irrigation of rice in the Grand Prairie of Arkansas, an average water supply of about 21 in. has been found satisfactory for so-called dry crops. This would reduce the supplemental water required from 22 in. for rice during the irrigation season to about 10 in. for dry crops. During certain drought years, when the rainfall during the growing period has been as little as 4 in., the supplemental water requirement for dry crops might have to be increased to 17 in. During very wet years, as little as 6 in. of supplemental water might be ample. By comparison, in planning the California Central Valley Project, the Bureau of Reclamation estimated an average annual use of 30 in. of water in the valley and 24 in. in the foothills, and this is the average that must be furnished by the projects under consideration—the maximums and minimums have not been separately determined inasmuch as total irrigation is deemed necessary (14). The calculation of demand has been based, however, on the assumption that certain crops will be grown. Any important change in agricultural practices might result in a completely different set of water demands.

SUPPRESSION OF EVAPORATION

We noted previously that waxy films on the water surface caused by insects or sprays are a source of error in measurements of water loss from evaporation pans. This phenomenon has been the subject of intensive study since 1954 (interest had lagged for 20 years after pioneer laboratory work of Langmuir (8) and Hedestrand (4) during the twenties and thirties).

The materials that act as evaporation suppressors are among a broad class of polar compounds—substances whose molecules have at one end a great affinity for water. When these substances are in contact with water, each molecule tends to align itself with one end in the water and the other end projecting from the surface of the water. Ideally this would form a film one molecule thick on the water surface—a monolayer. In any case, a thin layer of certain high-boiling-point, saturated, straight-chain alcohols on the water surface suppresses evaporation by preventing the escape of water molecules into the atmosphere. At its thinnest, the film is less than a micro-inch thick. It is invisible and exhibits none of the interference patterns of color associated with thick, multilayered, oil films. Its presence on the surface of the water is characterized by the absence of tiny wavelets, since these have been suppressed by the film.

A glance at Fig. 3.4 will suffice to indicate the potential value of reducing evaporation from reservoirs. For example, in West Texas, the mean summer evaporation approximates 5 ft of water. Thus, a 600-acre surface reservoir with an average water depth of 10 ft could be expected to lose half of its water non-beneficially during the growing season. A 20 percent decrease in evaporation would not only increase the water supply by 20 percent (and thus the irrigated acreage), but it would also decrease the mineralization of the water by 17 percent, since the water evaporated is distilled, mineral-free water. The economic value of evaporation reduction, especially as regards municipal and industrial water, might be very high. With respect to large reservoirs in the West, where the estimated evaporation loss is in the order of 8 ft a year, very attractive economic benefits might result were it possible to develop a practical method to reduce evaporation.

The first problem is to measure the reduction of evaporation caused by establishing a monomolecular layer of oil or wax on a water surface. Under laboratory conditions, or even in evaporation pans, or stock tanks, this is not a difficult task. And the first overoptimistic reports of field experiments indicated reductions in evaporation of as much as 40 percent over 30-day periods. The substance most frequently used was hexadecanol, otherwise known as cetyl alcohol, which is actually a sort of wax. Another substance that has been found efficacious is octodecanol (steryl alcohol), also harmless and cleared for use in large-scale experiments by the U.S. Public Health Service. Recently these two substances have been used in mixtures containing 50 percent of each.

There appear to be many practical difficulties to overcome in the course of achieving an increase in useful water by means of evaporation control—aside from the difficulty in proving that the expected reduction in evaporation has occurred. For example, high winds and the associated wave action break the film or deposit it on the shore, eliminating it from the water surface. Moreover, bacteria seem to thrive on it, necessitating the addition of bactericides. Some reports indicate that where pellets have been used to supply the monolayer, birds have eaten the pellets. There is also the problem of establishing and maintaining the film over large areas in an economic fashion.

The suppression of evaporation from large reservoirs also runs into the problem of conflict of interest—for example, the use of the reservoirs for recreation. It has yet to be shown that water skiing, swimming, boating, and fishing are compatible with the maintenance of monolayers—especially since it appears that the layers must be initiated and maintained from a large number of points—optimistically as few as one per acre—over the entire water surface. Such mundane achievements as economically anchoring the film-dispensers have not yet been satisfactorily accomplished.

By 1962, systematic and comparative studies had been extended to water areas the size of small swimming pools (75 × 100 ft) so that methods of film application could be studied and the suppression of evaporation could be directly determined (6a, 10). The effectiveness of the methods as applied to larger areas was not completely certain due to the basic difficulty in determining the rate of evaporation with adequate reliability and precision: When you're looking for a 25 percent reduction in evaporation over a short period and your methods of measurement, over short periods, are about plus or minus 20 percent in error, there are some understandable difficulties in proving anything.

An extremely interesting variation in the study of the reduction of evaporation was reported by Roberts who applied the monolayer technique to the problem of transpiration by plants (*13*). In carefully controlled laboratory experiments, in which suppressants were added to water and plant food, he noted reduction in water use of up to 40 percent with no detectable deleterious effects on the plants. Comparative testing was done in the laboratory, but one treated corn crop, grown naturally, yielded over 100 bushels per acre. Chemical tests of this corn showed no apparent ill effect from large doses of hexadecanol added to the roots of the plants. The potential economic significance of these experiments is not presently foreseeable.

To sum up, the control or suppression of evaporation has been shown feasible in the laboratory and in certain small-scale experiments in the field. The economic feasibility (and hence the widespread applicability) of the method is not yet clear. In certain applications, where alternate sources of water are relatively expensive, the methods will be tried and evaluated as adequately as the inexact methods of determining evaporation will allow. Compared with the demineralization of water, the economics of evaporation suppression appear to be good for the same quantities of water: Potentially, capital and operating costs would seem to be much lower.

From a hydrologic standpoint, in contrast to weather control, no deleterious side effects should be anticipated. Evaporation from the land surface (and landlocked water) furnishes only a very small component of the vapor content of the atmosphere at any instant, and the maximum changes, even in this component, can be expected to be insignificant. In the final analysis, the point of evaporation may be moved very slightly both in time and space, but the total amount of atmospheric moisture at any point, over even a short period, should not be measurably different from what it would have been otherwise. It may be that some new type of monolayer, one with a silvery surface that would combine the reflection of energy with interference with the movement of water molecules, may be the answer to the problem of evaporation reduction. There is much potentially productive work to be done in this field.

NOTES

1. Am. Soc. Civ. Eng., Hydrology handbook, 1949, *Manual of Engineering Practice*, no. 28, p. 126.
2. Blaney, H. F., 1958, Evaporation from free-water surfaces at high altitudes, *Trans. Am. Soc. Civ. Eng.*, v. 123, pp. 385–404.
3. Engler, K., Thompson, D. G., and Kazmann, R. G., June, 1945, Ground-water supplies for rice irrigation in the Grand Prairie Region, Arkansas, *Univ. of Ark.*, *Agr. Expt. Sta.*, *Bul.* 457.
4. Hedestrand, G., 1927, The influence of thin surface films on the rate of evaporation of water below the boiling point, *J. Phys. Chem.*, v. 31, pp. 1917–1931; 1928, *Chem. Abstr.*, v. 22, p. 522.

5. Hickman, H. C., 1940, Evaporation experiments, *Trans. Am. Soc. Civ. Eng.*, v. 105, pp. 807–849.
6. Homan, W. R., May, 1961, Estimating potential evapotranspiration, *Proc. Am. Soc. Civ. Eng., J. Hyd. Div.*, no. HY-3, p. 112.
6a. Koberg, G. E., Cruse, R. R., and Shrewsbury, C. L., 1963, *Evaporation Control*, 1959–1960, *U.S. Geol. Surv. Water Supply Paper 1692*.
7. Kohler, M. A., Nordenson, T. J., and Baker, D. R., 1959, Evaporation maps for the United States, *U.S. Dept. of Com., Weather Bureau, Tech. Paper 37*.
8. Langmuir, I., 1917, Shapes of group molecules forming the surfaces of molecules, *Proc. Natl. Acad. Sci. U.S.*, v. 3, pp. 251–257; 1918, *Chem. Abstr.*, v. 11, p. 2422.
9. Leopold, L. B., 1959, Probability analysis applied to a water-supply problem, *U.S. Geol. Survey Circ. 410*.
10. Meinke, W. W. *et al.*, May, 1962, Reducing reservoir evaporation by use of monomolecular films, pt. II, *Water Works Engineering*, pp. 274–276.
11. Meyer, A. F., June, 1942, Evaporation from lakes and reservoirs, Minnesota Res. Comm., p. 12.
12. Penman, H. L., 1956, Evaporation: An introductory survey, *Netherlands J. Agr. Sci.*, v. 4, no. 1.
13. Roberts, W. J., October, 1961, Reduction of transpiration, *J. Geophys. Res.*, v. 66, no. 10, pp. 3309–3312.
14. U.S. Dept. of Int., Bur. of Recl., 1949, Central Valley Basin, Sen. Doc. 113, 81st Cong., 1st Sess., p. 107.
15. Yamaoka, Y., April, 1958, Experimental studies on the relation between transpiration rate and meteorological elements, *Trans. Am. Geophys. Union*, v. 39, no. 2, pp. 249–265.

4

Surface Water

THE RUNOFF CYCLE IN NATURE

Runoff from the land surface is, in a sense, the residual water of the hydrologic cycle. After encountering the land surface and before reaching the sea, there are many opportunities for a drop of rain to return directly to the atmosphere. It is this residual water—water that has not been evaporated by plants or has not infiltrated the surface of the ground—that is directly available for use by mankind. The quantity available is never certain because its distribution in time is not predictable with precision and reliability. Further, its mineral characteristics vary with the passage of time and differ greatly from place to place depending on the geological formations on which it falls and over which it travels. The "runoff cycle" designates a description of water and land and their interaction in the drainage area associated with a stream. The first phase of the cycle relates to the rainless periods, after surface storage has been depleted and when stream flow is maintained by outflow from natural subterranean storage. These are the conditions normally found at the end of one water year or the beginning of the next, usually in the driest period of the year. Figure 4.1 shows the first phase of the runoff cycle. Flow rates are low—the lowest of the year, usually; the water quality is relatively poor inasmuch as it is primarily ground water that has had time to dissolve minerals from the formations through which it has traveled. Various terms such as *effluent seepage, base flow, sustained flow,* or *ground-water flow* have been used to describe this outflow from underground storage. The ground-water table is commonly associated with valley-floor areas which are underlain by alluvial deposits. In mountainous areas, under different geologic circumstances, the flow may be maintained by drainage from consolidated rocks. In arid regions a water table may be entirely absent, and the stream may be ephemeral and flow only when there is overland runoff.

During the initial period of rain there is little, if any, runoff. Instead. raindrops that reach the land surface are absorbed by the structure of the uppermost layers of soil. Eventually water penetrates the soil, descending by virtue of capillary, molecular, and gravitational forces. Finally the infiltration rate of water into the soil is exceeded by the rate of rainfall, and surface runoff carries away the excess water. It should be noted that the possible

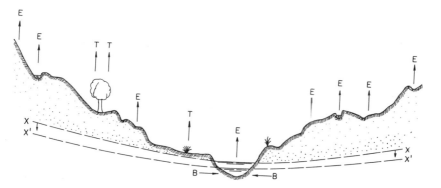

Fig. 4.1. First phase of the runoff cycle. During a rainless period the water table falls from XX to X'X' as the base flow (B) drains from the water-bearing formation into the stream. At the same time transpiration (T) and evaporation (E) are removing water from the ground.

infiltration rate into the soil is a variable, being at its maximum during the end of a dry period and generally reaching a more or less defined minimum after a long period of steady rainfall. As the rain continues, the overland runoff raises the stream level more rapidly than infiltration through the soil to the water table raises the water table. During this period of high stream level, water from the stream leaves the channel to enter the banks of the stream—this is known as "influent seepage." The situation is shown schematically in Fig. 4.2.

After the initial rise of the stream, many situations become possible. Generally the water table and the stream level rise and fall together; sometimes the rise in the river precedes the rise in water table, sometimes, due to local rain, the water table rises and this may or may not be followed by a rise in the river. During periods of surface runoff the rate of discharge of the stream is large and the mineralization of its water declines—the water quality improves.

This simplified description of the annual runoff cycle makes no mention of the effects of evaporation from the land surface or small bodies of surface water, ditches, or depressions, nor is cognizance taken of the effects of freezing and thawing and the effect of a snow cover that melts in the presence of warm rain and augments surface runoff. All of these influences and others such as geology, slope, and vegetation affect the runoff cycle and modify the quantity of surface runoff.

In its essence, however, the example is hydrologically correct: given the same sequence of meteorological and allied natural phenomena, the observations of flow and quality should repeat themselves. Thus, each observation is statistically meaningful, and from the record valid deductions

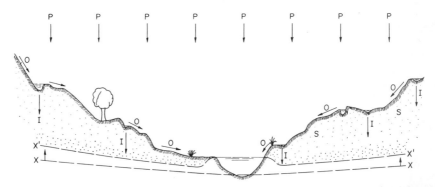

Fig. 4.2.   Final phase of the runoff cycle. The water table rises slowly from XX to X'X' as part of the precipitation (P) reaches the stream overland (O), part is held in storage (S) by molecular and capillary forces in the zone of aeration. A fraction of the precipitation infiltrates (I) and joins the ground water body and this raises the water table elevation. Next to the stream the "mound" of water in bank storage caused by infiltration of river water is clearly shown.

may be made as to probability of recurrence of water phenomena. Therefore, measurement of flow and stage, periodic sampling and analysis of water, and recording of water temperatures are carried on to define the hydrologic system in useful terms. With this end in mind we shall examine the history, methods, and limitations of hydraulic and hydrologic measurements and mankind's utilization of these measurements.

A BRIEF HISTORY OF MEASUREMENTS

Water has attracted the attention of mankind since long before the invention of an alphabet. The sparkle and force of flowing water, the health-giving properties of certain springs, the cool, blue depths of mountain lakes—these are but a few of the characteristics that have captivated man's imagination while sustaining his body.

Although only a tiny fraction of the fresh water on the earth's surface is moving in a watercourse at any instant, it is a very important fraction, and it is with this minute percentage that we are concerned in our measurements of surface-water discharge. We thus exclude in one fell swoop salty seas and oceans and the mighty rivers of salt water, such as the Gulf Stream or the Humboldt Current. Although relatively small in total volume compared with the immense volume of available subterranean water, lakes, reservoirs, rivers, and streams are subject to change, and our measurements seek to define these changes.

Flowing water always has fascinated man. Throughout the centuries profound thinkers have considered the source, movement, and quality of water and perceived serious problems. For instance, this question was posed: Although the rivers perpetually add more water to the sea, why does not the sea fill up and rise to cover the entire earth?

> The streams all flow into the sea
> But the sea they never fill,
> Though the streams are flowing still (*32*).

But this particular problem defied solution for almost 2500 years. Many laborious steps had to be taken before the hydrologic cycle was understood and the hydrologic equation balanced. The first step, which was soon forgotten, was the recognition by Hero of Alexandria, during the second century B.C., that the flow of a spring can be measured. The following passage from Hero's *Dioptra* contains the earliest known expression of a possible relationship between cross-sectional area, velocity, and time and may well be the first written instruction for stream gaging:

Given a spring, to determine its flow, that is, the quantity of water which it delivers . . . . Now it is necessary to block in all the water of the spring, so that none of it runs off at any point, and to construct a lead pipe of rectangular cross section. Care should be taken to make the dimensions of the pipe considerably greater than those of the stream of water. The pipe should then be inserted at a place such that the water in the spring will flow out through it . . . .

Now the water that flows through the pipe will cover a portion of the cross section of the pipe at its mouth. Let this portion be, for example, 2 digits. Now suppose that the width of the pipe is 6 digits. $6 \times 2 = 12$. Thus the flow of the spring is 12 digits.

It is to be noted that in order to know how much water the spring supplies it does not suffice to find the area of the cross section of the flow which in this case we say is 12 sq digits. It is necessary also to find the speed of flow, for the swifter is the flow, the more water the spring supplies, and the slower it is, the less. One should therefore dig a reservoir under the stream and note with the help of a sun dial how much water flows into the reservoir in a given time, and thus calculate how much will flow in a day. It is therefore unnecessary to measure the area of the cross section of the stream. For the amount of water delivered will be clear from the measure of the time (*10*).

These instructions, and the thinking behind them, were forgotten by Hero's successors; indeed, the whole science of hydraulics actually seems to have retrogressed for more than 1000 years (*38*). The practice of hydraulics as an art, however, advanced greatly. The Romans constructed aqueducts with only a vague idea of flow velocities and discharge rates; some still conduct water. In many European cities, fountains designed by Romans or their successors still bear witness to the architects' abilities.

During the sixteenth and seventeenth centuries, following Renaissance-inspired advances in mathematics and technology, the quantitative expression of the flow of water in channels was improved. Edmé Mariotte (1620–1684) computed the discharge of the Seine at Paris by measuring its width, depth, and velocity at approximately its mean stage. Velocity was measured by timing the movement of a float in the river as it moved between two points located at a predetermined interval.

During the eighteenth century considerable progress was made in the quantitative study of river flow. In 1732, Henri Pitot (1695–1771) described an instrument he invented to measure the velocity in different parts of the cross section of a river. This instrument, the Pitot tube, is still manufactured essentially as first designed. It was almost 100 years later, however, that detailed information concerning the daily flow of a stream or river over a period of several years was first obtained. This achievement is credited to Escher de la Linth, who gaged the Rhine River at Basel, Switzerland, for the years 1809–1821. Davenport stated:

> The art of measuring the rate and volume of flow of natural streams has developed essentially within the last 60 or 70 years . . . only a few reliable records of river flow in the United States exceed 50 years or even 40 years. The availability of long records of river flow is not materially greater in parts of the world where the progress of civilization and development of written records had been moving in advance of those in this country for hundreds and thousands of years (*12*).

An understandable comment in view of the history of the measurement of flow quantities summarized earlier. However, as noted previously, a long record of river stages for the Nile River is available (but not the rates of flow) as are significantly long records of stages of other streams, together with occasional records of extraordinary gage heights on many smaller, less important rivers.

THE GAGING OF STREAMS

The equation for the flow of water through a cross section of a stream can be written

$$Q = AV,$$

where Q is the rate of flow, A is the cross-sectional area of the stream at the selected location, and V is the average velocity of the stream. In English units, Q is expressed in cu ft per sec, A is the cross-sectional area in sq ft, and V is the average velocity of water in ft per sec. Many other consistent sets of units are used in addition to the English units, and many conversion tables for transforming data from one to another set of units are available.

As a practical matter, the simplicity of the equation of flow is deceptive, and actual river flow is difficult to determine with accuracy, although inexact approximations are easy to come by. The simplest way to measure the velocity of a river is to throw a chip of wood, or a float, into the stream and time its travel as it moves between two lines a known distance apart. Humphreys and Abbott, in their pioneer study of the Mississippi River, used floats (21). Floats are influenced by cross currents and wind, and there is no assurance that water velocity is uniform or that the movement of the float represents the average velocity of the current. Further, experiments have shown that the float method yields inconsistent readings and that there is no fixed relationship between the progress of the float at any particular interval of time and the average velocity of the stream.

The Pitot tube can be used to make a pattern of measurements along the cross section of a stream. With the velocity at many points known, a weighted average of velocity can be obtained and the flow determined. This has been accomplished several times experimentally. However the method is laborious and it is difficult to hold the inlet of the Pitot tube at the right elevation and direction, especially in swiftly moving deep currents. Furthermore, this method would be very expensive to use regularly in deep rivers, and sediment in the water causes additional complications.

Another difficulty, not unique to Pitot-tube measurements, is that natural streams are dynamically rising and falling and are rarely constant in stage. Thus, the velocity distribution will vary during the period of measurement, and the error from this source can never be known exactly. This error can be expected to be greater during flood periods when the water is sediment laden and turbulent—and when most of the discharge occurs—than during the comparatively steady flow of low-water periods. There are other methods for the measurement of river and stream flow. The inherent error involved in each method has not been extensively investigated, with the exception noted in a later section.

Federal agencies that measure river and stream flow in the United States include the U.S. Geological Survey, Division of Water Resources, the Corps of Engineers, the Tennessee Valley Authority, and the Bureau of Reclamation. Measurements are also made by state agencies—as the Illinois State Water Survey Division does in the course of studying specific localities—health departments, and interstate agencies such as the one in charge of the pollution-abatement program on the Ohio River.

The results of stream-flow measurements are available directly from the files of the agencies involved and are also published annually. Summaries covering longer periods of time are published at five- or ten-year intervals. A typical page from *Water Supply Paper 1105, the Hydrology of Massachusetts*, is shown as Fig. 4.3. It should be examined carefully; the data presented will be evaluated later in this chapter.

Location.- Water-stage recorder, lat. 42°09'38", long. 72°30'52", 1,000 feet downstream from West Street Bridge at Indian Orchard, Hampden County, and 1.1 miles upstream from Fuller Brook. Prior to November 1938, water-stage recorder at site 1 3/4 miles downstream, published as Chicopee River at Bircham Bend.

Drainage area.- 688 square miles. Prior to Nov. 1, 1938, 703 square miles.

Records available.- August 1928 to September 1945.

Extremes.- 1928-45: Maximum discharge, 45,200 second-feet Sept. 21, 1938, by computation of flow over dam; minimum daily, 16 second-feet (regulated) several times in 1929-31; practically no flow at times at former site when wheels were cleaned or repaired.

Remarks.- Flow regulated by power plants and reservoirs above station. Runoff in inches adjusted for diversions for Boston metropolitan district from 186 square miles in Swift River Basin and from 97 square miles in Ware River Basin, for industrial use in Springfield from Ludlow Reservoir, and for change in contents in Quabbin Reservoir (since August 1939) and Ludlow Reservoir (since October 1943).

Monthly and annual mean discharge, in second-feet (observed)

Water year	Oct.	Nov.	Dec.	Jan.	Feb.	Mar.	Apr.	May	June	July	Aug.	Sept.	The year
1928	-	-	-	-	-	-	-	-	-	-	-	1,090	-
1929	615	566	602	1,020	1,030	2,740	2,770	2,310	699	340	241	248	1,100
1930	254	355	420	715	834	1,300	1,110	647	524	530	236	163	589
1931	149	313	256	221	332	1,280	1,780	1,340	1,310	411	465	341	684
1932	277	314	666	1,270	1,130	1,190	2,250	858	398	276	271	301	764
1933	730	1,420	814	1,140	1,250	2,040	4,120	1,240	583	277	348	1,570	1,290
1934	1,103	815	785	1,366	647	2,465	3,221	1,685	1,003	c426	361	906	c1,234
1935	1,056	1,158	1,353	1,723	1,160	2,578	2,145	1,237	1,102	522	240	298	1,215
1936	217	356	491	1,035	649	5,993	2,823	1,315	691	319	245	364	1,213
1937	647	559	1,871	2,447	1,752	1,587	2,096	1,793	1,310	761	492	850	1,345
1938	715	1,559	1,900	1,931	1,902	1,588	1,771	1,232	1,358	2,458	1,609	5,474	1,952
1939	1,900	1,244	2,278	1,117	1,354	2,165	3,009	1,059	603	289	229	199	1,287
1940	187	417	443	403	378	877	3,064	1,241	860	447	218	190	725
1941	179	519	651	542	774	690	780	489	322	252	182	167	460
1942	131	258	325	464	458	1,714	898	658	644	511	300	209	549
1943	298	693	693	835	1,116	1,751	1,152	1,584	737	316	341	170	823
1944	281	803	453	252	432	1,040	1,338	732	784	458	206	425	599
1945	296	402	714	768	660	1,802	1,162	1,434	1,218	926	630	365	867

c Corrected.

Monthly and annual runoff, in inches (adjusted)

Water year	Oct.	Nov.	Dec.	Jan.	Feb.	Mar.	Apr.	May	June	July	Aug.	Sept.	The year
1928	-	-	-	-	-	-	-	-	-	-	-	1.73	-
1929	1.01	0.90	0.99	1.67	1.53	4.50	4.40	3.79	1.11	0.56	0.40	.39	21.25
1930	.42	.56	.69	1.18	1.24	2.13	1.76	1.06	.83	.87	.39	.26	11.30
1931	.24	.50	.42	.36	.49	2.28	3.39	2.34	2.22	.67	.76	.54	14.21
1932	.45	.50	1.10	2.26	1.78	2.03	4.02	1.42	.63	.45	.44	.48	15.56
1933	1.21	2.25	1.34	1.87	1.85	3.34	6.54	2.03	.92	.45	.57	2.49	24.86
1934	1.81	1.29	1.29	2.24	.96	4.05	5.11	2.77	1.60	c.70	.59	1.44	c23.85
1935	1.73	1.84	2.21	2.82	1.73	4.23	3.40	2.03	1.75	.86	.39	.47	23.46
1936	.36	.56	.81	1.78	1.00	10.00	4.48	2.16	1.10	.52	.40	.58	23.75
1937	1.06	.89	3.36	4.09	2.59	2.61	3.32	2.94	2.08	1.24	.81	1.35	26.34
1938	1.18	2.48	3.11	3.17	2.82	2.61	2.81	2.02	2.15	4.04	2.64	8.69	37.72
1939	3.11	2.02	3.82	1.87	2.05	3.63	4.88	1.81	.98	.48	.45	.36	25.46
1940	.38	.85	.99	.84	.75	1.90	8.04	3.10	1.92	.90	.34	.31	20.32
1941	.27	1.23	1.50	1.24	1.56	1.50	1.84	1.10	.64	.53	.24	.24	11.89
1942	.30	.56	.75	1.19	.91	4.95	2.05	1.43	1.42	1.05	.46	.38	15.45
1943	.58	1.69	2.29	1.94	2.27	4.50	2.94	4.18	1.87	.62	.73	.17	23.28
1944	.61	2.08	.91	.53	.93	2.83	3.64	1.65	2.50	.96	.27	1.08	17.99
1945	.46	.95	1.59	1.89	1.50	4.98	3.14	4.10	3.38	2.46	1.25	.62	26.32

c Corrected.
Note.- Runoff for period September 1928 to September 1930 recomputed on basis of revised drainage area.

Annual discharge, in second-feet

Year	W.S.P.	Water year ending Sept. 30						Calendar year	
		Observed			Adjusted			Observed	Adjusted
		Maximum day	Minimum day	Mean	Mean	Per square mile	Runoff in inches	Mean	Runoff in inches
1928	661	-	-	-	-	-	-	-	-
1929	681	5,120	16	1,100	1,100	1.56	21.25	1,040	20.02
1930	696	2,460	16	589	589	.838	11.39	563	10.88
1931	711	3,950	16	684	738	1.05	14.21	730	15.10
1932	726	4,990	16	764	805	1.15	15.56	905	18.31
1933	741	6,450	31	1,290	1,290	1.83	24.86	1,270	24.45
1934	756	5,660	31	c1,234	c1,234	c1.76	c23.85	1,306	25.24
1935	781	5,300	31	1,215	1,216	1.73	23.46	1,005	19.41
1936	801	19,200	31	1,213	1,226	1.74	23.75	1,383	27.33
1937	821	4,190	65	1,345	1,365	1.94	26.34	1,436	27.80
1938	851	37,000	105	1,952	1,952	2.78	37.72	2,059	39.90
1939	871	4,000	32	1,287	1,294	1.88	25.46	918	18.73
1940	891	5,530	35	725	1,027	1.49	20.32	750	21.10
1941	921	1,710	36	460	603	.876	11.89	407	10.50
1942	951	3,720	60	549	783	1.14	15.45	647	18.40
1943	971	3,190	32	823	1,180	1.72	23.28	793	22.32
1944	1001	5,920	65	599	910	1.32	17.99	589	17.39
1945	1031	3,130	120	867	1,334	1.94	26.32	-	-
1929 - 45	-	37,000	16	982	1,082	1.57	-	-	-

c Corrected.
Note.-Runoff for period September 1928 to September 1930 recomputed on basis of revised drainage area.

Fig. 4.3. Reproduction of a summary of discharge measurements made by the U.S. Geological Survey. (From C. E. Knox and R. M. Soule, 1949, *Hydrology of Massachusetts*, Water Supply Paper 1105, U.S. Geol. Surv.)

Flow measurement involves two principal steps. The first is measurement of the water velocity at a number of points on a cross section of the stream, usually at 10 or more points equidistant across the stream channel and at the 0.2 and 0.8 depths or the 0.6 depth at each point. This is usually done with a current meter; the river stage is measured simultaneously to make sure that major changes in level have not occurred during the period of measurement. (If the stage has changed, corrections must be made, but that is another story.) One type of current meter consists of a small screw-type propeller similar to that of an outboard motor, connected to a counter that clicks at each revolution. Another type, the Price Current Meter, substitutes a horizontal wheel, the perimeter of which consists of a number of cups, for the small propeller. Figure 4.4 shows these types of current-meter. The probable accuracy of current-meter measurements is, of course, of great interest to the engineering profession and has been the subject of several studies. The most recent of these, by Carter and Anderson, concluded that with care, and a sufficient number of points on the cross section of the stream, the discharge of a stream can be determined with an error of between 2 and 3 percent (9).

The current meter is lowered into position at the end of thin steel cable; its orientation during the period of measurement is maintained by the force of water against a rudder-elevator. The stream gager, using a stop watch, determines the rpm and, using a calibration curve, computes the water velocity of that point. The current meter must be calibrated by towing it through a long tank under controlled conditions, but at different velocities, and recording the rpm each time. From these data, a rating curve is prepared for the instrument. It is assumed that a turbulent stream, with its cross currents, will affect the meter in the same way as the still water of the laboratory, the movement of turbulent water around an unmoving current meter being considered as the equivalent of a moving meter in a body of stationary water.

The second step is to determine the profile of the river's cross section, which is accomplished by sounding. However, because of sediment load, great velocities, and complex irregularities of stream flow, there is no way to evaluate the accuracy of such determinations in some streams. For example, many alluvial rivers possess shifting beds, which do not necessarily stop shifting during floods while measurements are being made. Therefore the operator's skill and experience have great bearing on the accuracy of measurements. Stream-flow measurements often are not readily accomplished, and even the best stream gager will acknowledge the existence of unavoidable error in the results.

There are other, less direct methods of stream-flow measurement. A common method, used wherever possible, consists of finding—or building—a stable cross section across the stream bed. This control section is then gaged by use of a current meter and a correlation, or rating curve is obtained that

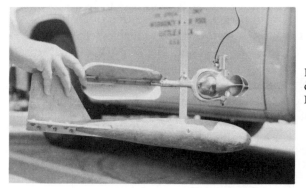

(a)

Fig. 4.4. (a) Price current meter. (b) Ott current meter. (Courtesy Watertown Instruments, Watertown, N.Y.)

(b)

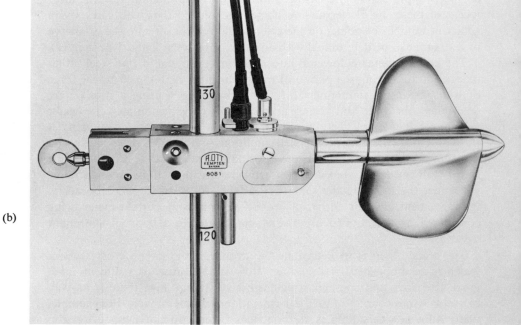

shows the probable rate of flow for any particular stage. The flow rate, however, will be different on a rising stage from what it is on a falling stage.
Under some circumstances this difference is trivial and is not important
compared with the inherent errors of measurement. It may require a number
of years of measurement to obtain a more or less complete rating for a given
station with a fixed control section. In rivers lacking a control section, it is
best to make measurements in a long, straight reach where turbulence and
cross currents are minimal.

Even after a rating curve has been developed for a particular station, it is necessary to keep track of developments above and below the control section. For example, the construction of dams or levees downstream may produce backwater effects on the stage at the control, raising it with no corresponding increase in flow. Sometimes, to add to the difficulty, backwater effects are variable, as when a dam is installed for purposes of hydropower generation and an erratic cycle of operation, with its associated backwater effects, may make the record of stage so questionable that it is invalidated for purposes of flow determination.

Under other circumstances, such as the measurement of stage and flow in an alluvial river that lacks a control section, the attendant complications reduce the accuracy of the measurements considerably, and the rating curve—developed to convert stage measurements into discharge measurements between gagings—changes from year to year or even between two successive measurements.

Kennedy commented on the errors caused by the use of rating curves in alluvial channels:

Most streams in central United States flow in unstable alluvial channels. Rating curves continually change both position and shape as channels scour, fill, and move laterally. Despite these conditions, and using average ratings, records of good (less than 10% error) quality are usual. The principal factor of accuracy of records for alluvial channel streams is frequency of current meter measurements. The writer knows of no technical reason that would prevent the collection of excellent records (less than 5% error) on streams with unstable ratings, though the cost would be prohibitive (23a).

Under such circumstances, or during flood periods when normal methods of determining flow are difficult, if not impossible, to apply, a method that combines observed river elevation with estimates of the constant in the Manning formula is employed. This is the so-called slope-area-discharge method which is based on the assumption that if no substantial inflow occurs between two gaging stations, then the rate of inflow into the reach of river is equal to the outflow, when allowance is made for the change in storage within the reach. The average velocity is computed from the Manning formula

$$V = \frac{1.486}{n} R^{1/6} \sqrt{RS},$$

where

V = mean velocity, ft per sec
R = hydraulic radius, ft (cross-sectional area of stream divided by its wetted perimeter, excluding the air-water contact)
S = hydraulic gradient
n = coefficient of roughness

In this equation, the slope at any time can be determined by the difference in gage height elevations divided by the river distance between the gages; the hydraulic radius can, more laboriously, be determined at many points and an average obtained. However n must be estimated, mostly by experience. Values of n may range from 0.025 in a natural stream channel with a straight bank, full stage, and no deep pools with no trees or other obstructions, to 0.080 in a sluggish, weedy river with deep pools. Values of n outside this range have also been encountered (*40*).

The probable error in slope-discharge measurements is impossible to estimate, but it is certainly higher that that of standard "good" measurements published by the U.S. Geological Survey. The Survey considers its good measurements to be within 5 percent of the true values. Estimates have been made that the error in slope-discharge measurements may range from 15 to 20 percent under the best circumstances. Of course it must be remembered that this is a method to be used when all else fails—under unusual and extraordinary circumstances or in instances where exact knowledge of discharge quantities is not essential. Under such circumstances a plus or minus of 20 percent may be acceptable if the information is used with this limitation in mind.

The measurement of flow in natural channels is an engineering art rather than an exact science; however, to measure the flow of water in pipes for municipal and industrial use, there are commercially produced flow meters with a guaranteed accuracy of plus or minus 2 percent. A variety of instruments is available to measure flow in pipes, including propeller meters, disc meters, and devices that depend on differential pressures like the sharp-edged orifice, the venturi tube or the Dahl flow tube, and the sonic, or magnetic mass-flow meter. But with regard to flow in man-made open channels, even under the best of circumstances where there is economic incentive to improve the types and methods of measurement, much remains to be done. This is particularly true with regard to the in-between situation found in the distribution of water to farms in open channels where the problem of measurement arises.

Although there have been few systematic studies of errors in the measurement of irrigation water, Thomas found that the errors in installation and gage reading, combined with the natural deterioration of measuring devices, had a tendency to cause the computed volume of flow to be less than the actual volume:.

In the case of a weir, discharge varies more rapidly than the head. The relationship given by many weir formulas shows that the discharge varies as the $\frac{3}{2}$ power of the head. Therefore, the volume of discharge obtained by reading the gage at intervals and averaging the readings will yield a discharge that is somewhat less than that actually passing the weir . . . . The error is negative as in many of the instances cited in the paper. Thus when waves are present [in the channel] more water is delivered through the weir notch than the gage readings of the mean water level indicate . . . (*47*).

Although Thomas drew no general conclusions, the tenor of the paper seems to be that there are substantial errors "built in" to the measurement of flow in irrigation systems. This is done inadvertently by faulty selection, installation, operation, and maintenance of the devices for measuring the irrigation water. The errors appear to be in the direction of understating the quantity of water delivered, with the magnitude of understatement ranging from 1 or 2 percent under good circumstance to possibly as much as 10 or 15 percent.

We may tentatively conclude that nonuniform flow in natural channels, as measured by the techniques outlined previously, may quite possibly be higher than the measurements indicate.

THE MINERALIZATION OF WATER

The mineral content of water can conveniently be divided into minerals in suspension and those in solution. The geological formations beneath a drainage basin are subject to attack by solution, oxidation, and hydration as well as to the mechanical effects of freezing and thawing and the disintegration caused by earth movements. Much of the material subject to these erosional forces eventually reaches the streams by the action of flowing water. Although all of the principal rock minerals are soluble to some extent, only a few of their constituents are present in solution in appreciable quantities in natural waters.

If we confine ourselves to the naturally occurring, water-borne minerals, the most important of those in solution are carbonates, sulphates, silica, and chlorides, which are usually combined with calcium, magnesium, sodium, and potassium. The carbonates are usually the decomposition products of feldspars and the solution of limestones. Sulphates are derived from beds of gypsum. Chlorides are present in small quantities in most surface water (possibly, in many instances, derived from salt swept into the atmosphere in spray that evaporates leaving tiny salt crystals that later form the nuclei of raindrops) and occur in higher concentrations in waters that drain regions of sedimentary rocks of marine origin or containing marine deposits. Calcium and magnesium usually predominate in waters draining carbonate rocks. Igneous rocks disintegrate very slowly, so that streams draining regions of exposed rocks of this kind carry relatively small amounts of suspended or dissolved material. Sedimentary rocks disintegrate more readily, and so streams draining such areas carry much suspended matter and have high concentrations of minerals. The rate of erosion is dependent in part on the climate. In humid regions, due to the growth of vegetation, erosion is reduced. In arid climates, where rainfall is infrequent but occasionally very intense, there is no vegetation to armor the land against the raindrops, and sedimentary formations are subject to much erosion and water courses are heavily laden with suspended material.

The evaluation of the role of water as agent of solution and transportation is complex. Here hydrology and geomorphology overlap, and the transformation of a descriptive science to a quantitative one has not yet been achieved. We will return to this relationship again and again as we try to understand hydrology and its man-made modifications.

The quality of water is determined in the laboratory by the chemical analysis, which includes mineral constituents and radioactivity, of a water sample. Water temperature is measured when the sample is taken. Many different methods of water sampling have been devised for a multiplicity of purposes. For a run-of-river water supply with no seasonal storage, daily or weekly composite samples at the proposed intake site may suffice. For a water supply involving major carry-over storage in a reservoir, an occasional sample during low water and samples during flood periods, when most of the stored water will be derived, will be adequate. For studies of river pollution or sediment accumulation in proposed reservoirs, samplings are made as the special circumstances require. The U.S. Geological Survey has collected and analyzed many water samples and compiled data on water quality from all over the United States (17, 30). The U.S. Public Health Service has established standards for drinking water (as medical knowledge accumulates and stream pollution gets worse, these standards are continually reevaluated and revised) and determines the biological and organic quality of bodies of water.

Suspended matter provides an entirely different problem when quantitative data is needed. During floods caused by rainfall of high intensity, the sediment burden of a stream may show a tremendous increase. Since the energy level of the stream is increased by increase in water volume and velocity, this is comprehensible. Howard discussed this matter in some detail (20), and Love, on the basis of studying 34 streams said:

... the greater part of the total load of suspended matter was removed from the drainage area in a very few days out of a total of about 450 days of record. In the area drained by Coon Creek at Coon Valley, Wis., 90 percent of the total load was carried in 10 days, and in the area drained by West Torkin Creek near Westboro, Mo., 90 percent of the total load was carried in 12 days (31).

This means that the period of sampling can be confined to flood periods for all studies of gross sedimentation. It also implies the existence of an organization that must do all of its field work at unpredictable times and for short, but critical, work periods.

Various types of samplers have been developed for the collection of representative samples. Basically, collection of a sample consists of inserting an empty container into a stream and removing a specimen of the fluid. But in deep water, where high velocities exist, special apparatus is needed. Solid material may drop into an open bottle after it is full, so any full bottle may contain material foreign to the original volume of sample. Some samplers close automatically after a sample has been collected.

If the measurement of flow in natural channels is inherently subject to error, the same is true most emphatically, when it comes to the evaluation of the suspended load of a stream. Cooperative studies of the methods of measurement and analysis of sediment loads in streams were planned and conducted jointly by the Tennessee Valley Authority, the Corps of Engineers, the U.S. Geological Survey, the Department of Agriculture, the Bureau of Reclamation, the Indian Service, and the Iowa Institute of Hydraulic Research. Five reports, each dealing with a separate phase of the problem were issued in 1940 and 1941 (23). Of course these reports did not constitute the last word on the subject. An indication of the civil engineering profession's continuing interest in the subject of sedimentation are 39 major papers published in the ASCE *Transactions* between 1935 and 1959, which elicited more than 100 separate discussions (1). All of these papers on sedimentation— its causes, effects, and control—are based to a considerable extent on the quantitative data derived from the sampling procedure.

THE USEFULNESS OF SURFACE-WATER DATA

General Analyses

There are, of course, two principal types of observations with regard to the occurrence of surface water: (1) the elevation of water level, or gage height, at each particular place and (2) the discharge, either measured or computed. When compared to the elevations of land surface, elevation may be interpreted in terms of flooding. Or, if compared to the elevation of the river bottom, elevation may be interpreted in terms of channel depth. Discharge may be interpreted in terms of available water supply, as a capacity for the dilution of water, or as a source of replenishment or drainage of surficial water-bearing formations.

The hydrograph, the simplest type of analysis, affords a view of the entire period of record. Gage height or stream discharge are platted, usually on a daily basis. However, when the period of record is long, sometimes the mean monthly stages or discharges are shown, and occasionally the values are platted as yearly averages. Figures 4.5 and 4.6 are examples of such graphs. Water quality, temperature, or other characteristics are readily platted in a similar manner.

But for long records of river stage or discharge the monthly hydrograph, although convenient, is not completely satisfactory. For example, it does not provide a convenient means of determining the number of consecutive-day periods that flood levels prevailed during a selected period or over the period of record. Nor can the percentage of time that the level was at or above any particular elevation be determined easily from such graphs. This information

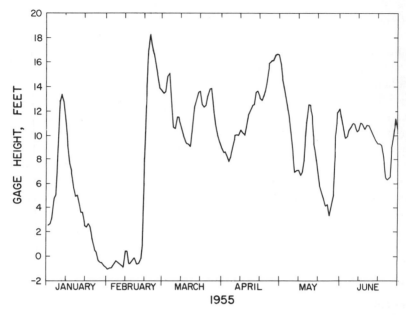

Fig. 4.5. Hydrograph showing mean daily stage of the Mississippi River at St. Louis, January–June, 1955. (Based on data from the U.S. Geological Survey, St. Louis, Mo.)

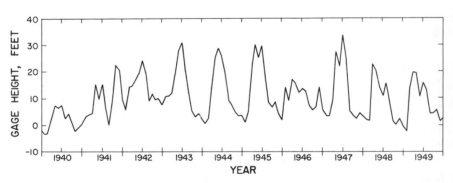

Fig. 4.6. Hydrograph showing mean monthly stage of the Mississippi River at St. Louis, 1940–1949. (Based on data from the U.S. Corps of Engineers, St. Louis, Mo.)

can be particularly useful in studying the possibilities of navigation, the proper level for water intakes, and ground-water replenishment. Figure 4.7 is a typical gage-height-duration curve that summarizes, on one graph, all of the data obtained during the 100 years (1861–1960) of observation at the Market Street gage in St. Louis. On the basis of the gage-height-duration curve it should be possible to compute the areas subject to flooding for various predetermined periods with reasonable accuracy, since a 100-year

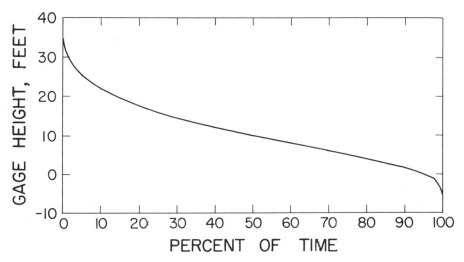

Fig. 4.7. Gage-height-duration curve, Market Street Gage, St. Louis. Curve shows percent of time indicated gage height was equalled or exceeded. (Based on daily stages recorded from 1861 to 1960 by U.S. Corps of Engineers, St. Louis, Mo.)

record of measurements is available. Referring to Fig. 4.7, if we can afford to be flooded 5 percent of the time, then our flood wall, or levee, should be built to a level of 25 or 26 ft on the gage. If we can afford to be flooded half the time, we can build on land where elevation corresponds to a gage height of 10 ft—parking lots on the river bank might be paved above that elevation. If the bank sloped at the rate of 10 ft per 100 ft of horizontal distance, then 100 ft inland from the edge of the pavement the lot would be wet only 14 percent of the time. However, if we didn't wish to be flooded at all, we would build protective works around our property to a level above 40 ft on the gage.

The duration curve can also be used as part of the base data for evaluating the ground-water yield of an area fed by a river—or one made influent by the offtake from wells located in a hydraulically connected aquifer. Such an aquifer, the American Bottoms area, exists in the flood plain of the Mississippi River opposite St Louis. The mean river stage at St Louis is apparently between 10 and 11 ft. Thus, if we take it to be 10 ft and base our computations of ground-water level on this figure, assuming that the annual fluctuations are cyclic around this elevation, we should not be too far from the truth.

Companies that maintain river intakes for purposes of water supply (power companies, water companies, or industries) are interested in the duration curve so that they can build their intakes at the proper elevation and select the pumps with the proper head-capacity characteristics. Such intakes are built low enough so that they won't go dry and high enough so that the floors on which the motors of the intake pumps rest are above flood.

Transportation companies that operate barges on the Federally maintained waterway are interested in the occurrence and duration of low water (it determines their periods of shutdown) and the probable duration of substandard water depths. The Federal Government is interested because the design of the locks and dams it operates is affected by low-water conditions and its dredges must maintain minimum channels for shippers and transportation companies.

It should be noted, however, that the duration curve furnishes no information concerning flood frequency, the occurrence of periods of low flow, the number of consecutive days that a flood of given elevation has occurred, or the average interval between the occurrence of such floods—it is only one type of statistical analysis, important though it may be. Hydrographs and their derivative analyses such as gage-height duration and discharge duration have many uses. The value of existing structures predicated on hydrologic data, while it can not be calculated precisely, surely runs into several tens of billions of dollars in continental United States alone. Discharge-duration curves, although similar statistically to gage-height-duration curves, are of completely different utility, For a company that discharges wastes into a stream, relying on dilution and natural purification to make them harmless, the percentage of the time that a discharge rate is equaled or exceeded is an important factor in economic and engineering evaluations. For a power plant that requires a tremendous volume of water for cooling purposes, knowledge of the minimum flow of the stream and the duration of low flows is essential—possibly a small reservoir may be needed to furnish water to supplement the minimums. For an irrigation project that requires its maximum water supply during the driest weather in the growing season, the duration of low flows may well be the governing factor in its planning and operation. The list of organizations interested in the duration of discharges (not to mention the chronological recurrence and probable recurrence period) is long and runs the gamut from recreational groups to farmers and industrial corporations. The data are used, basically, to anticipate future conditions, within the limits of probability. All sectors of the population and all interests have a need for such hydrologic analyses.

Floods

A flood can be defined as a relatively high stream flow as measured by either gage height or discharge rate. Whenever the stream channel in a reach is overtaxed, causing water to cover lands outside the usual channel boundaries, the stream is said to have reached flood stage. The benefit to be derived from the prevention of flooding and the consequent reduction in property damage is the principal justification of flood-control projects. Thus an important subcategory of statistical analysis deals with floods: the recurrence interval, the "design" flood, maximum probable discharges and stages, and so forth.

There is no general relationship between the annual water yield of an area and flood flow. Water yield may be defined as the flow rate divided by the area from whence it is derived. Thus, the average annual water yield of the Mahoning River at Youngstown is 0.91 cu ft per sec per sq mile (53). At the same place the flood discharge (for instance, the rate equaled or exceeded only 1 percent of the time) is 7.34 cu ft per sec per sq mile. A discharge rate that constitutes only a minor flood, or even the mean annual flow, in streams draining a humid region might be classed as a notable flood, far exceeding the maximum of record, in streams draining basins of equal size in arid or semiarid regions.

Flood flow results from intense precipitation; it is occasionally augmented by the rapid melting of snow cover or diminished by sudden freezes. Damaging floods sometimes result from an accident, such as dam failure when a reservoir is full or the sudden opening of a reservoir's flood gates after heavy rains, to draw down the storage so that runoff from a possible subsequent rain will not be passed without detention through a full flood-control reservoir.

The many formulas proposed to compute peak flows from data obtained during normal river conditions are inadequate because during peak flows unusual factors cause a flood and these are not usually reflected in the record of average flow. Consequently, no formula has been found that will enable the engineer to calculate the magnitude of the design flood for a drainage area based on the size of the average annual flood or the mean annual stream flow (16).

If a long, continuous record is available, one of the most convenient methods of analyzing the data is the following: All peaks above a selected base flow are listed, regardless of date of occurrence. This base should be chosen so that the number of peaks is at least equal to the number of years of record; but not more than four floods in a year should be used. Each peak should be associated with a separate and distinct meteorologic event. The peaks should be numbered in the order of magnitude starting with 1 for the highest. The recurrence interval, in years, is computed by the ratio $(N + 1)/M$, in which N is the number of years of record and M is the order of relative magnitude (*26*). The data are then platted on semilogarithmic paper, using the linear scale (ordinate) for the discharge and the logarithmic scale (abscissa) for the recurrence interval. A curve is then drawn to fit the platted points, as illustrated by Fig. 4.8.

This method of analysis organizes the data in convenient fashion, although to what extent extrapolation is possible is uncertain. It should be emphasized that "recurrence interval" is a statistical term and is not analogous to a railroad timetable; a recurrence interval of 10 years for a flood does not mean

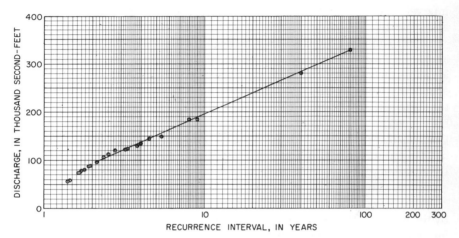

Fig. 4.8. Recurrence interval for flood peaks, Red River at Garland, Ark., 1872–1950. (Based on data from the Louisiana Department of Public Works.)

that every 10 years a flood of this magnitude will recur. It simply means that on an average interval of 10 years, over a very long period of time, a flood equal to or greater than the one specified will occur (*25*). Extended and excellent discussions of this matter, as applicable to all observed natural water phenomena, have recently been presented by two members of the U.S. Geological Survey (*3, 36*).

When asked about the probable size of the design flood to be used in planning the dams and spillways for the Damodar Valley Project in India, Dr. A. E. Morgan of TVA fame advised that it could not be calculated and would have to be assessed from rainfall-runoff data. He seriously recommended that spillway capacity should be so large that the only criticism left for future engineers would be that it was unnecessarily large! Statistical studies made to determine the recurrence interval of this design-flood resulted in figures ranging from 1000 to 90,000 years—thus illustrating the effect of assumptions on results. Ajwani summarized his experience with statistics by saying, "Meanwhile, we may continue to use statistics, but as a drunk uses a lamppost, for support rather than illumination (*2*)."

The sum total of all of this study of frequency and recurrence interval is

(1) that we really don't know what might happen, and (2) that our data, while probably inaccurate, may be adequate for design purposes if we are aware of its limitations (and our ignorance) and make reasonable allowances. In this connection, we are limited primarily by how much we think it is worthwhile to spend to achieve the sought-for benefit. Hydrologic calculations, while essential, are no substitute for judgement and experience.

Water Quality Data

Data concerning water quality is of great value in planning water developments. For example, the temperature of river water, and particularly the

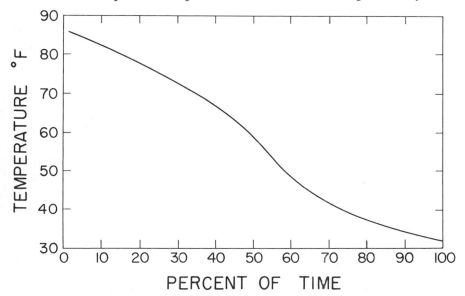

Fig. 4.9. Temperature-duration curve, Mississippi River at St. Louis, 1956–1962. Graph shows the percent of time that any given temperature was equalled or exceeded. (Based on data supplied by the Union Electric Company of St. Louis, Mo.)

duration and magnitude of peak temperatures, are of great interest to companies planning steam-electric generating plants. Water temperature data are needed for condenser design. Figure 4.9 is a temperature-duration curve prepared by a utility in the St. Louis area. Figure 4.10 is a thermograph of the average monthly water temperature of the Mississippi River observed at St. Louis.

Similar analyses could be made for hardness, chlorides, sulphates, and other significant constituents. Rorabaugh has published a graph comparing well-water quality with that of the river that was the ultimate source of the well water (37). Such data are used to determine the suitability of water for various purposes. For instance, a glance at the analysis of the water of the Arkansas River would show that it is too heavily mineralized to be economically suitable for making cigarette paper. Moreover, it is too mineralized

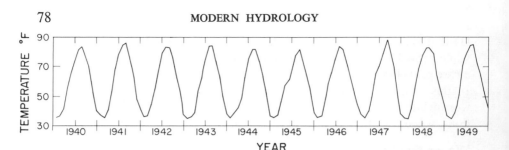

Fig. 4.10. Thermograph showing mean monthly water temperature, Mississippi River at St. Louis, 1940–1949. (Based on data supplied by the Union Electric Company of St. Louis, Mo.)

during the months that irrigation is needed for rice. The water presently contains too much gypsum and salt, although this may be changed through the operation of the Arkansas River reservoirs.

NATURAL FACTORS THAT INFLUENCE RUNOFF

In preceding sections we have examined the techniques of measurement, some of the records that have been obtained, and how these records are utilized. Despite inherent uncertainties, the measurements have proven to be useful, techniques for handling the data have been developed, and, based on the results of these studies, large sums have been invested. However, we have not considered the effects of geologic conditions on flow, nor have we noted how changes in topography affect the hydrographs or attempted any generalizations based upon, for instance, climatic conditions. Yet all of these factors and more enter into the quantities we measure. Thus, each drainage basin is unique, and the factors in addition to precipitation which control runoff constitute a puzzle to be painstakingly worked out so that water may be harvested in appropriate quantities when required.

Geology

Probably one of the most important factors governing runoff is the geology of the drainage basin. Geology, of course, concerns itself with chronology as well as with materials. There are ancient Cambrian sandstones and younger Pennsylvanian sandstones; there are Pliocene gravels and Pleistocene gravels that are hydrogeologically indistinguishable. For the surface-water hydrologist—and especially one concerned with occurrence and rate of flow geologic chronology is important primarily for purposes of identification. Whether the sandstone is 400 million or 50 million years old is not necessarily meaningful. Of interest is the physical character of the underlying rocks: Do they absorb water, or are they relatively impervious, like an asphalt pavement? Do they yield water readily like a clean saturated sand, or do they hold water stubbornly like mixtures of clay? Are the rocks weathered at the surface and cracked, or are they smooth and undamaged? Do they dissolve readily like limestone, or are they almost insoluble, like granite? The hydrologist is interested in the answers to these and other questions because he may then compare a new area with those that are similar geologically and look for the significant differences, thus facilitating his evaluation of conditions.

For example, in evaluating the utility of streams as a source of water much importance has been attached to high *base flows*, or sustained flows, during periods of drought. This phenomenon is encountered in rivers draining lakes or swamps and in streams that drain areas whose surficial geology includes geologic formations such as sandstones and unconsolidated sands and gravels. Such streams rarely go dry, and measurements of flow made after a long rainless period can be analyzed to furnish clues as to the nature of the geology underlying the drainage basins if the topography is known.

Areas whose surficial formations consist of unfractured igneous rock, clays, or shales do not produce good sustained flow. Moreover, of two adjacent drainage basins that have the same general meteorological history, the one underlain by the more impermeable formations will experience flashier and more violent floods and lower flows during drought periods. This is brought out by an examination of flow-duration curves of the Rocky River near Berea, Ohio (drainage area 269 sq miles), and Sandy Creek, at Sandyville, Ohio (drainage area 481 sq miles). The Rocky River drains an area of glacial till, essentially clay, whereas Sandy Creek drains an area underlain by surficial sands and gravels, which are widely known as water-bearing formations. The flow-duration curves, to make them comparable, have been platted on the basis of the observed discharge, in cu ft per sec divided by the areas of the respective drainage basins. No artificial storage distorts the records, so that natural conditions, basically, are reflected in these curves. Figure 4.11 is a plat of the data.

The peak flows of Sandy Creek are lower than those of Rocky River when expressed as flow rate per sq mile of drainage area. The low flows of Sandy Creek are far higher than those of Rocky River. The effect of geological conditions is apparent: Geology can be used to evaluate synoptic data from two watersheds, and, conversely, stream gagings can assist in the interpretation of surficial geology (*11*).

The effect of the geology of a watershed upon the quality of the water is readily apparent. Where hard, insoluble rocks constitute the land surface, water quality is good—the mineralization of the water is low. At the same time we can anticipate wide and rapid variations in stream flow (if there are no lakes) and only a small quantity of sediment in the water.

Water from rocky areas that are basically soluble limestones will be mineralized and a principal constituent will be calcium carbonate. The water will be palatable but much soap will have to be used for cleaning and so

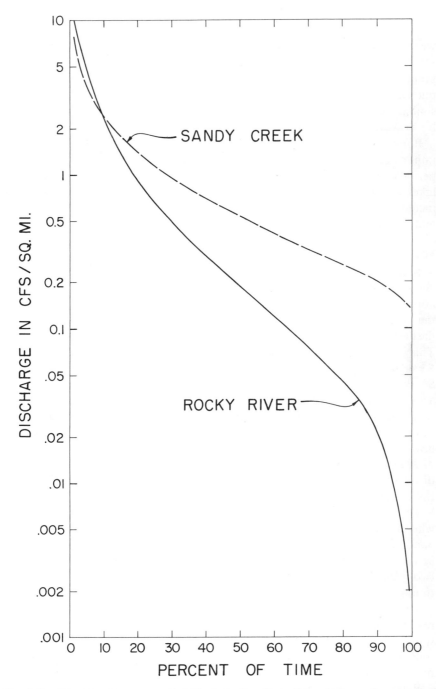

Fig. 4.11. Flow-duration curves that illustrate the effect of the geology of a watershed on stream flow. Curves show percent of time that indicated rate of discharge was equalled or exceeded. (Based on data from C. H. Wall and C. V. Youngquist, May, 1942, *Ohio stream drainage areas and flow-duration tables*, Ohio Eng. Expt. Sta. Bull., no. 111.)

forth. The Kentucky blue-grass region is typical of the geology that produces this type of water. In the headwaters of the Arkansas River lie the salty and friable Permian red-beds. The river water reflects these geologic conditions through its excessive mineralization and its load of sediment.

And so it goes—young unconsolidated or semiconsolidated formations in arid lands produce a great deal of sediment, as in the Elephant Butte Reservoir on the Rio Grande River (46). The old, consolidated rocks of a humid region such as the Appalachian mountains of the Tennessee River basin produce relatively little sediment. The gradations in geologic and climatic conditions are innumerable, as are the rates of erosion, even when works of man are excluded from consideration.

Topography

Topography is the second major factor influencing runoff. Topography is the result of geologic and climatic conditions—and the duration of time. The basic geologic matrix is acted upon by spectacular tectonic forces and the inconspicuous but dynamic forces of air, temperature, and water. The results are immediately available for inspection in the configuration of land forms. A detailed examination of the origin and changes in the land surface, part of discipline known as geomorphology, will not be undertaken here; rather, it will be considered only as it affects the rate, volume, and quality of flowing water.

Concentration time is an amorphous but extremely important concept in the field of hydraulic engineering. This is the time that it takes a particle of water to travel from the most remote part of the watershed to the gaging station, or point of interest. This time can be computed under various assumptions, but to the writer's knowledge it has not been directly observed. Despite this, the term is useful in that it gives the hydrologist the "feel" of a watershed, topographically speaking. When considering two watersheds of equal size and similar surficial geology, the steeper or more rugged the topography, the shorter is the concentration time—that is, the water gets away more quickly from one than from the other because of steeper energy gradients. Despite assumptions to the contrary the concentration time of a watershed can be influenced by man; hence, one is tempted to call it a pseudohydrologic concept.

Topography influences runoff by compressing the runoff period and raising the peak flow in proportion to the steepness of slope and ruggedness of terrain. When you read of a flash flood (one that occurs suddenly and creates damage through the energy of flowing water, similar to the results of a dam failure), you can be sure that the topography is rough and the contrasts in elevation are large. Conversely, if a flood causes damage because land is covered with water and things get wet, the topography of the drainage area is probably relatively flat and the drainage area of the stream comparatively large.

The effect of topography, expressed as concentration time, has been extensively employed by hydraulic engineers in preparing synthetic unit-hydrographs for use in the design of hydraulic structures. One of the assumptions made in computing the synthetic unit- hydrograph is that the rainfall period used must be smaller in duration than the concentration time of the watershed (*42*). Let it be noted that the unit-hydrograph is a useful empirical method of extrapolating available data based on a number of hydraulic, geologic, and hydrologic assumptions. It works best for small watersheds of uniform surficial geology and topography, and its technique is acceptable in analyzing the runoff patterns of natural watersheds greater in area than about 1 sq mile and smaller than 2000 sq miles (*13*).

This would seem to be a likely place to emphasize a point not often understood concerning hydrologic and hydraulic computations: For the most part these computations are based on extreme conditions—minimum flow, maximum flow, longest drought period, most intense rate of rainfall, and so forth. Thus, the approximate figures obtained from measurements can serve as the basis for design—the structures are based on the worst conditions to be expected with an additional factor added to compensate for ignorance. The data have proved to be reasonably adequate, and analyses have produced structures that are, all things considered, generally economical and satisfactory. Only when hydrologic measurements are to be used as the basis for direct economic decision do the inherent errors in the methods become vexing. Examples of this would be the operation of storage and distribution systems for municipal water supply based solely on stream gagings, calculation of the economic desirability of rain making (based on results of rain-making efforts), or computation of the effects of the suppression of evaporation in determining the practicability of such a program.

Climate

The last of the important factors that influence flow is climate, and the slow changes in climate that apparently occur. Of all known influences this is the most subtle and difficult to evaluate. If the climate changes cyclically and our records cover only a portion of one cycle, how valid are the statistical studies of hydrologic data? Of course the difficulties go further. Our longest continuous records of stream flow encompass 100 years. Most records of stream flow cover less than 50 years. Disregarding, for the nonce, the effects of diversions and other man-made changes in river regime, if the climate has been getting wetter for the past 50 years, then our predicted future flows will be too low; if it has been getting drier, we'll get less water than we expect.

Cyclic variation of stream flow has been widely discussed. A recent study by Williams (*54*) attempted to correlate sunspot activity with moving averages of annual stream flow (*54*). The results of this study do not seem to be conclusive, for while the mean annual number of sunspots seems to change cyclically with about 11 years between the peaks, the correlation with stream flow, even when 3-year moving averages are used, does not appear to be certain.

Linsley pointed out that while Williams noted that rigorous statistical tests failed to confirm a relationship between solar activity and world climate, still he set this evidence aside on the grounds that it "denies what the eye can see in graphs of data from all over the world (28)." To demonstrate that the eye can confuse normal statistical variation with cyclic activity (especially when 3-year moving averages are compared to an annual sunspot average), Linsley developed two random series, one with a standard deviation equal to one third of the mean and the other by flipping a coin, and compared a three-item moving average of each series with the graph of sunspot numbers. There is a remarkable visual, or apparent, correlation comparable to that obtained by use of precipitation data or runoff data. Linsley pointed out that such a coincidence "seems to show that the human eye provides far from conclusive evidence on this issue."

So, despite the probability of climatic fluctuations, and the impact of such fluctuations on the evaluation of all types of hydrologic data, the verdict must be "not conclusively demonstrated." And, inasmuch as the economic life of a water-development project is usually 40 to 100 years, if climatic fluctuations are important, the cycle is either too indefinite or too long to be demonstrated on the basis of a record spanning only 100 years or less. Our grandchildren will have to make the proper adjustments—we simply don't know enough to take action.

CONTROL AND UTILIZATION OF RUNOFF

We are now in a position to examine some engineering applications of the hydrologic data discussed previously. Small-scale applications like culvert design or the design of spillways for farm ponds will not be touched upon here because the effects are local and usually short lived. The U.S. Bureau of Public Roads is probably the largest agency concerned directly with this type of problem (35), although the Department of Agriculture, in its program for soil conservation, is a close second. The applications of hydrologic data to the most critical problems will be discussed first. The criterion as to which is most critical is economic: How much will people pay for the water itself, or to control it? Municipal and private water supplies, for example, are essential and local, and the value of the water substance is high. Next in value is water used for industrial supply; least in value is water used for agricultural purposes. But all water-supply uses are infinitely more valuable, as far as the monetary worth of the water substance itself is concerned, than any of the other uses: hydropower, navigation, flood control, or recreation. A municipal supply may be worth 20 cents per 1000 gal of water delivered—as much as 60 cents per 1000 has been found reasonable. On the same basis industrial water is worth, possibly, between 2 and 5 cents per 1000 gal. Agricultural water, even for high-value crops, commands less than 3 cents, usually between 1 and 2 cents per 1000 gal. Where the delivered price would exceed such a minimum, subsidies sometimes have been granted to stimulate crop production.

For hydropower the energy of the water, not the water particle itself, is the prize sought. A thousand gal per minute, passing through a completely efficient turbine under a head differential of 100 ft, yields about 20 Kwh per hr—valued at current bus-bar prices at 14 cents or less. So 60,000 gal of water are worth 14 cents, about 0.25 cents per 1000 gal. Even a bus-bar change of 1.5 cents per Kwh yields a gross water value of about 0.5 cents per 1000 gal. On the plus side of the ledger is the fact that the water itself is still available for use and that the head at the power site may be far greater than 100 ft, thus making the water even more valuable.

The value of water used for freight transportation is not calculable, but it is surely small. Moreover, the costs of maintaining the waterways are not chargeable to the users but are a general levy on the entire population. So whether the value of the water used for the floating of barges and tugs is high or low is everybody's business but no one's concern. Nevertheless it is the water itself that is valuable, and entire water supplies have been developed for navigation projects. One of the principal justifications for construction of the Gatun and Madden reservoirs is the need to supply water for navigation purposes to the lock canal at Panama (8).

Other important applications of hydrologic data in the use of water include fish and wildlife production, recreation, and the dilution of wastes. The value of water used for these purposes cannot be ascertained. It depends, for the most part, on climate and population density. The value of the water particle itself, inasmuch as it is utilized productively, is greater than zero. But the value of 1000 gal cannot be computed directly.

Hydrologic data are important, too, in planning flood-control projects. The cost of the water is negative—you're trying to keep it from doing damage, and the value of water is measured, perversely, by estimates of damage prevented rather than by the benefit derived in the process of use.

In taking a more detailed look at runoff and its control and utilization, we shall proceed from the highest positive value of water, although there can be no guarantee that all items are correctly ranked.

Water Supply

Man has always lived near a source of fresh water. Whether it was the water hole of the Australopithecines, the springs that fed the Roman aqueducts, or the waters of the Nile, the Yellow, or the Tigris-Euphrates rivers, the location of the fresh-water supply has determined the dwelling of man.

An index of the flowering of civilizations was a progressively more extensive and intensive use of water. And when systems to control and utilize water—systems financed with the small annual economic surplus of centuries of agriculture—have been destroyed, the people have moved or perished and the land has been made barren. The destruction of the elaborate irrigation systems in Iran and Iraq by the Mongols is the classic illustration of this.

Contrary to widespread belief, however, no functioning culture or civilization has been shown to have been ruined by mishandling its water supply. True, climatic changes that diminished water supply have forced abandonment of an area—as in the American southwest. And an example now coming to light is that of the cave painters of North Africa who apparently took over the Nile Valley when the springs and wells they had previously relied on diminished in output. But in neither case is there evidence that the abandonment of an area was due to misuse of a reliable water supply. The evidence indicates that circumstances beyond the control of the population overcame the civilization, not that the water resources had been mishandled. The seven-year drought in the southwest during the 1950s and the Dust Bowl of the 1930s come to mind as disasters comparable, on a very small scale, to those major climatic changes that caused the Indians in south-western United States and the to-be protodynastic Egyptians to move. Generally a water-supply system fails *after* the morale and organization of the builders have been weakened or destroyed—it is the result of the decay of a culture, not the cause of the decay.

Domestic and Municipal Water

Surface water—from rivers, lakes, and springs—is the obvious and oldest source of water. Wells are a relatively recent development. The first man-made well probably was built about the same time that writing was invented. We do not know when man first used spring water which generally was associated with religious rites and believed to possess medicinal properties. The Oxford *History of Technology* contains an illuminating discussion of early water-supply systems, together with maps, photographs, drawings, and paintings that have survived the millenia. (*43*).

A run-of-river supply requires a minimum of hydrologic knowledge. Philadelphia, Louisville, New Orleans, and St. Louis are typical of cities that use such supplies. Assuming that the climate is semihumid or humid and that the minimum river flow is far greater than the maximum potential water demand, the principal problems are water treatment and water distribution. Hydrologic measurements are not essential to planning or operating such a supply. Of course, even a run-of-river supply is not immune to changes in river regime: water diversions upstream may reduce flow, change the mineralization or temperature, or produce difficulties with intakes. But these are operating problems, and hydrologic measurements, while helpful, are not

Table 4.1. Water Statistics 1950, 1960

Supply	City	Population Served (Millions)		Income (Millions of Dollars)		Production (Billions of Gallons)[a]		Approximate Cost (Cents per Thousand Gallons)	
		1950	1960	1950	1960	1950	1960	1950	1960
Lake	Chicago	4.1	4.4	19	40	350	380	5	10
Lake	Cleveland	1.2	1.9	8	15	84	110	10	13
R—O—R	Philadelphia	2.1	2.0	10	19	125	120	8	15
	St. Louis	0.8	0.8	5	7	62	60	8	12
	New Orleans	0.6	0.7	3	6	37	36	8	16
	Louisville	0.4	0.6	3	5	22	29	14	17
	Cedar Rapids, Ia.	0.07	0.09	0.49	1.2	2.9	4.3	17	27
	New Kensington, Pa.	0.05	c	0.32	c	1.4	c	23	c
	Quincy, Ill.	0.04	0.05	0.33	0.6	1.2	1.8	27	33
	New Albany, Ind.	0.03	c	0.30	c	1.1	c	27	c
Imp.	New York City	7.5	7.7	42	52	344	441	12	12
	Boston	0.8	0.6	5	8.7	41	43	12	20
	San Francisco	0.8	1.5	11	15	39	61	28	25
	Tulsa	0.2	0.3	3.3	6.3	10	17	23	37
	Little Rock	0.1	0.2	1.0	2.2	5	7.7	20	28
G—W	Houston	0.6	0.9[b]	3.6	9.6	23	37.7	16	26
	Jamaica, N.Y.	0.5	0.6	2.8	5.5	14	19.8	20	28
	Memphis	0.4	0.6	2.8	5.7	15	25.1	19	23
	Canton, Ohio	0.1	0.15	0.6	1.6	6	7.2	10	23
	Manitowoc, Wisc.	0.03	0.03	0.2	0.23	1.5	1.8	13	13

[a] Total water production, including all water sold, given away, or lost through leakage.
[b] 76% from wells, 24% from surface source.
[c] Not available.

essential. A variation on this sort of water supply is based in a large body of fresh water, such as Lake Michigan. Chicago and Cleveland are good examples of cities using this type of supply. Again the hydrologic knowledge needed for design and operation is almost negligible.

In comparing water supplies, a useful indicator is the cost of water from different types of sources. The less hydrologic knowledge needed, the cheaper the water, and the larger the water supply, the cheaper the water. A large water supply requiring little hydrologic knowledge implies low-cost water. As more and more hydrologic understanding is required, demand for water is evidently approaching the limits of the readily available, firm supply, and costs may be expected to rise.

The American Water Works Association made two surveys of production and distribution data: for 1950 and 1960, and the results, summarized in Table 4.1, seem to support the foregoing generalizations (41, 1a). It should be noted that this table does not purport to show the average price paid for water by the consumer. It is based on the assumption that the annual revenue from a waterworks operation must approximate the average cost of production, including capital costs, distribution costs, treatment costs, and so forth. Thus, the gross income has been divided by the total volume of water produced to obtain an overall approximate cost in cents per 1000 gal. All production figures are the gross production figures. The quantity of water actually sold ranges from as little as 55 percent of the water produced by the water department in New Orleans to about 95 percent of the water produced by the water works in San Francisco. Unsold water includes leakage from the distribution system, water furnished free to public institutions, water not registered due to faulty metering, water for fire fighting and street cleaning and the like.

The effect of operation size on the run-of-river cost of producing water is shown in the table. For example, for Louisville (in 1950) there is a cost of 14 cents per 1000 gal, in New Albany, across the river, the figure is 27 cents per 1000 gal. The contrast in cost in 1960 between St. Louis (12 cents per 1000 gal) and Quincy, Ill. (33 cents per 1000 gal), neighbors on the Mississippi River, is also striking. Of course only parts of these differences are directly due to the size of operation. Plant age and ability of operators are also factors. But basically the overhead costs go down as the size of the operation increases, and this is reflected in the gross figures shown in the table. It might be well to refer to this table when the cost figures of other methods of producing water, such as saline-water conversion, are under consideration. An excellent discussion of the costs of saline-water conversion was presented by Koenig whose conclusions are still considered to be sound (24).

In contrast to the minimum knowledge of hydrology needed for the run-of-river or run-of-lake water supply, is the data that must be amassed to design a reservoir impoundment. Such a supply can be developed only after

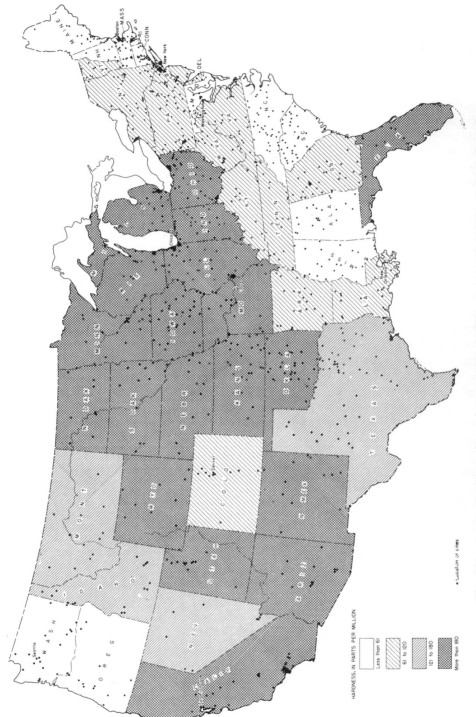

Fig. 4.12. Average hardness of raw water, by states (public water supplies). (After E. W. Lohr and S. K. Love, 1954, *The Industrial Utility of Public Water Supplies in the United States, 1952, U.S. Geol. Surv. Water Supply Paper 1299*, p. 24.)

HARDNESS, IN PARTS PER MILLION

Less than 61

61 to 120

121 to 180

More than 180

• Location of cities

a lengthy study of hydrology, including precipitation and runoff records accumulated over a long period of time. The two largest cities that use impounded surface-water supplies are New York and L.A. But cities located in other parts of the country—for example, Little Rock, Tulsa, and San Francisco—also use impounded water supplies. The raw water obtained from an impounded supply is generally better than that obtained from a run-of-river water source. The watershed is usually protected from contamination, the water remains in storage for a long time, allowing natural purification to take place and smoothing out abrupt changes in mineralization. Moreover, the city is generally at a lower elevation than the source so that water is delivered automatically by gravity as it is needed. Assuming that the basic engineering was well done, this is a most flexible and relatively maintenance-free source of water. The contrast in costs of impounded water shown in the table are due in part to geologic and climatic conditions (Tulsa being less humid and less favorably situated from a geologic standpoint than, for example, Little Rock).

The final grouping—"ground water"—is somewhat out of place here, and a fuller discussion will be found in the next chapter. However, the gross production costs for this water source are comparable to those for surface-water supplies.

Industrial Water

The industrial uses of water are many and varied. Grouped together under this category are the enormous quantities used for cooling the condensers of steam-electric generating plants and the minor quantities used for boiler-feed make-up water. The properties of water that are utilized differ from use to use. Heat transfer is an extremely important property of water: most industrial processes and all steam-electric generating plants rely on it. Energy transfer is another important property: The steam used in driving turbines or providing heat for certain chemical reactions illustrates this use of water. Water is also used in separating the materials obtained from ore bodies (after suitable reduction in size by grinding), for washing, dilution, as a raw material, and for sanitary purposes. Without belaboring the point, the industrial uses of water, if we exclude the cooling of condensers in power plants, is second only to the use of water in irrigated agriculture.

The average concentrations of dissolved solids in water, prior to treatment, is shown in Fig. 4.12. The map is based on an extensive state-by-state study of water quality by the U.S. Geological Survey. Tables 4.2 and 4.3 set forth some of the requirements as to quantity and quality of water for a number of industrial uses.

It should be noted that private industrial water sources are being increasingly predicated upon the study of hydrologic data. Such a study permits a sound evaluation of economic alternates: If a river is too small to supply water for a once-through use by condensers, then there are alternates that require less water. However, there is always a price: Once-through water is undiminished appreciably in volume, but raised in temperature. Make-up water for cooling towers uses about 5 percent as much water, but results in the discharge of highly mineralized wastes (the residue of evaporation and water-treatment chemicals).

Table 4.2. Industrial Requirements for Water[a]

Item	Unit	Water required (gal. per unit)	Item	Unit	Water required (gal. per unit)
Airplane engine	to test	50,000–125,000	Milk:		
Alcohol	gal.	100	Receiving station		180
Aluminum	lb.	160	Bottling works		250
Aviation gas	gal.	7–10	Cheese factory		200
Brewing:			Creamery	1,000 raw lb.	110
Beer	1 bbl.	470	Condensery		150
Whiskey	gal.	80	Dry milk factory		150
Buildings:			General dairy		340
Office	person	b/27–45	Oil, edible	gal.	22
Hospital	bed	b/135–350	Oil field	100 bbl. crude	18,000
Hotels	guest room	b/350–525	Oil refining	100 bbl.	77,000
Laundries:			Paper:		
Commercial	lb. "work"	4.3–5.7	Paper mill		39,000
Institutional	lb. "work"	3	Pasteboard	1 ton	14,000
Restaurants	meal	0.5–4.0	Strawboard		26,000
Butadiene	lb.	160	Deinking		83,000
Canning:			Paper pulp:		
Apricots		8,000	Ground wood		5,000
Asparagus		7,000	Soda		85,000
Beans:			Sulfate	1 ton dry	64,000
Green		3,500	Sulfite		60,000
Lima		25,000	Poultry	1 bird	b/1
Pork and		3,500	Rail freight	ton-mile	0.1
Beets		2,500	Records	1 disc	2.4
Corn		2,500	Smokeless powder	ton	50,000
Grapefruit:			Soap factories	ton	500
Juice	100 cases No. 2 cans	500	Steam power	ton of coal	c/60,000–120,000
Sections		5,600	Sugar refineries	lb.	0.5
Peaches, pears		6,500	Tanning:		
Peas		2,500	Vegetable	100 lb. raw hide	800
Pumpkin, squash		2,500	Chrome	100 lb. raw hide	800
Sauerkraut		300	Textile:		
Spinach		16,000	Cotton:		
Succotash		12,500	Sizing		820
Tomatoes:			Desizing		1,750
Products		7,000	Kiering		1,240
Whole		750	Bleaching		300
Cement	ton	750	Souring		3,400
Coke	100 tons	360,000	Mercerizing		30,000
Distilling, grain:			Dyeing:		
Combined wastes			Basic	1,000 lb. processed	18,000
Thin slop	1,000 bu. grain mashed	600,000	Direct		6,400
Tailings			Vat		19,000
Evaporator condensate			Sulfur		5,400
Distilling, molasses	1,000 gal. 100 proof	8,400	Developed		14,400
Distilling, cooling water..	1,000 gal. 100 proof	120,000	Naphthol		4,800
Electric power	kw.	80	Aniline black		15,600
Explosives	lb.	100+	Print works		4,500
Gasoline	gal.	7–10	Finishing		6
Iron ore (brown ore)	ton	1,000	Knit goods	lb. bleached	8
Meat:			Rayon manufacture	1,000 lb. produced..	135,000–160,000
Packing house	100 hogs killed	550	Rayon hosiery	1,000 produced	9,000
Slaughterhouse	100 hogs killed	550	Woolens	1,000 lb. finished	70,000
Stockyards	1 acre	160			

[a] Jordan, H. E., Industrial requirements for water, *American Water Works Assoc.*, v. 38 (1946), pp. 66–67.
[b] Per day.
[c] 60,000 for recirculating systems, 120,000 for nonrecirculating systems.

Thus, the cost of usable water may range widely from as low as 0.5 cents per 1000 gal (a low-head once-through cooling system) to more than 5 cents per 1000 gal for boiler-feed, make-up water. Quantity and quality characteristics of raw water are of great interest to industry—as is the cost of water production. However, the water requirements are not rigid, and the quantity of the water substance needed can be decreased by one or even two orders of magnitude at the expense of minor increases in the price of the end product

Table 4.3. Suggested Water-Quality Tolerances[a]
(Allowable Limits in Parts per Million)

Industry or use	Turbidity	Color	Hardness as CaCO₃	Iron (Fe)	Manganese (Mn)	Total solids	Alkalinity as CaCO₃	Odor, Taste	Hydrogen sulfide	Other requirements [b]
Air conditioning	--	--	--	c/0.5	0.5	--	--	low	1	No corrosiveness, slime formation.
Baking	10	10	--	c/.2	.2	--	--	low	.2	P.
Brewing:										
Light beer	10	--	--	c/.1	.1	500	75	low	.2	P. NaCl less than 275 ppm (pH 6.5-7.0.)
Dark beer	10	--	--	c/.1	.1	1,000	150	low	.2	P. NaCl less than 275 ppm (pH 7.0 or more).
Canning:										
Legumes	10	--	25-75	c/.2	.2	--	--	low	1	P.
General	10	--	--	c/.2	.2	--	--	low	1	P.
Carbonated beverages	2	10	250	.2	.2	850	50-100	low	.2	P. Organic color plus oxygen consumed less than 10 ppm.
Confectionery	--	--	--	c/.2	.2	100	--	low	.2	P. pH above 7.0 for hard candy.
Cooling	50	--	50	c/.5	.5	--	--	--	5	No corrosiveness, slime formation.
Food: General	10	--	--	c/.2	.2	--	--	low	--	P.
Ice	5	5	--	c/.2	.2	--	--	low	--	P. SiO₂ less than 10 ppm.
Laundering	--	--	50	c/.2	.2	--	--	--	--	
Plastics, clear, uncolored	2	2	--	c/.02	.02	200	--	--	--	
Paper and pulp:										
Groundwood	50	20	180	≤/1.0	.5	--	--	--	--	No grit, corrosiveness.
Kraft pulp	25	15	100	c/.2	.1	300	--	--	--	
Soda and sulfite	15	10	100	c/.1	.05	200	--	--	--	
High-grade light papers	5	5	50	c/.1	.05	200	--	--		
Rayon (viscose):										
Pulp production	5	5	8	c/.05	.03	100	total 50; hydroxide 8	--	--	Al₂O₃ less than 8 ppm, SiO₂ less than 25 ppm, Cu less than 5 ppm.
Manufacture	3	--	55	.0	.0	--	--	--	--	pH 7.8 to 8.3.
Tanning	20	10-100	50-135	c/.2	.2	--	total 135; hydroxide 8	--	--	
Textiles: General	5	20	--	.25	.25	--	--	--	--	
Dyeing	5	5-20	--	c/.25	.25	200	--	--	--	Constant composition. Residual alumina less than 0.5 ppm.
Wool scouring	--	70	--	?/1.0	1.0	--	--	--	--	
Cotton bandage	5	5	--	c/.2	.2	--	--	low	--	

[a] Moore, E. W., Progress report of the committee on quality tolerances of water for industrial uses, *New England Water Works Assoc. Jour.*, v. 54 (1940), p. 271.

[b] P indicates that potable water, conforming to U.S. Public Health Service standards, is necessary.

[c] Limit given applies to both iron alone and the sum of iron and manganese.

(4). Water is not usually the critical factor in the economics of the productive process, and it would be well to maintain a sense of balance in this regard, in view of currently popular alarmist talk of an impending general shortage of water.

Agricultural Water

The largest category of water use is undoubtedly agricultural—for crop irrigation. It is important to note that most irrigation projects are located west of the Mississippi River. Rice and row crops are irrigated in Arkansas and Louisiana, and irrigation is practiced wherever water is available as one proceeds to the West, culminating in the irrigation of cotton and fruit in California. Since 1950, increasing acreages of rice have been irrigated and supplemental irrigation of cotton is now practiced in the delta region of Mississippi. In recent years, supplemental irrigation has taken hold elsewhere in the East, subject to the availability of water during the growing season. This has resulted in an increase in the number of farm ponds and stream impoundments, not to mention the utilization of ground-water sources.

Reliable, accurate, and up-to-date statistics concerning the quantities of water used for irrigation are not readily obtainable. Indeed, this quantity may vary widely from year to year in the humid sections of the country. Boyer (6, 7) has approached the problem of agricultural water supplies in a

Table 4.4.   Areas Irrigated and Drained, by Regions, Continental United States[a]

Year (1)	Farm area, in acres (2)	Acres per farm (3)	Area irrigated, in acres (4)	Area drained, in acres (5)
(a) NEW ENGLAND (40,500,000 acres)				
1930	14,280,000	114		
1939			2,846	
1940	13,370,000	99		
1949			31,450	
1950	12,550,000	122		
1954	11,120,000	136	38,395	
(b) MIDDLE ATLANTIC (64,500,000 acres)				
1930	35,050,000	98		
1939			17,260	
1940	33,640,000	96		
1949			54,616	
1950	31,860,000	106		67,671
1954	29,900,000	116	135,886	
(c) SOUTH ATLANTIC (165,000,000 acres)				
1930	86,360,000	82		6,920,000
1939			128,037	
1940	92,560,000	83		6,810,000
1949			381,044	
1950	102,170,000	116		7,560,000
1954	98,260,000	114	536,195	
(d) EAST NORTH CENTRAL (157,000,000 acres)				
1930	110,890,000	116		33,480,000
1939			10,833	
1940	113,660,000	113		32,680,000
1949			36,237	
1950	112,100,000	126		36,020,000
1954	108,600,000	136	75,578	
(e) EAST SOUTH CENTRAL (115,000,000 acres)				
1930	72,820,000	68		4,170,000
1939			891	
1940	77,090,000	75		3,990,000
1949			6,950	
1950	79,580,000	87		4,680,000
1954	77,200,000	98	185,130	
(f) WEST NORTH CENTRAL (131,000,000 acres)				
1930	98,680,000	150		20,720,000
1939			6,286	
1940	105,490,000	157		20,240,000
1949			7,710	
1950	102,270,000	166		21,150,000
1954	100,520,000	179	44,601	
(g) WEST SOUTH CENTRAL (62,800,000 acres)				
1930	25,410,000	63		8,290,000
1939			573,381	
1940	28,040,000	76		8,810,000
1949			998,882	
1950	30,070,000	98		16,860,000
1954	29,380,000	115	1,564,557	
(h) GREAT PLAINS (408,000,000 acres)				
1930	325,310,000	282		5,980,000
1939			1,529,77b	
1940	345,410,000	338		7,640,000
1949			4,291,913	
1950	363,450,000	432		9,550,000
1954	365,770,000	482	6,446,142	
(i) ROCKY MOUNTAIN AND PACIFIC (751,000,000 acres)				
1930	217,980,000	433		4,780,000
1939			15,713,626	
1940	255,590,000	503		6,200,000
1949			19,037,333	
1950	324,520,000	703		6,080,000
1954	337,430,000	797	20,959,034	

[a] N. Eng.: Maine, Vt., N.H., Conn., R.I., Mass.; *Mid. Atl.*: N.Y., Pa., N.J.; *So. Atl.*: Del.,W. Va., Va., N.C., S.C., Ga., Fla.; *E. No. Cent.*: O., Mich., Ind., Ill.,Wisc.; *E. So. Cent.*: Ky., Tenn., Ala., Miss.; *W. No. Cent.*: Minn., Ia., Mo.; W. *So. Centr.*: Ark., La.; *Grt. Plns.*: N.D., S.D., Nebr., Kans., Okla., Tex.; *Rocky Mt. and Pac.*: Mont.,Wyo., Id., Nev., U., Colo., Ariz., N. Mex.; Wash., Ore., Cal.

Source: From M. C. Boyer, 1961, Irrigation and drainage potentials in humid areas, *Trans. Am. Soc. Civ. Eng.*, v. 126, pt. 3, pp. 190–191 general fashion and presented some pertinent statistical data (Table 4.4) (6, 7).

There is little doubt that the acreage under irrigation has grown since 1954, aided to some extent by efforts of the Federal Government to reduce the total acreage in cultivation. The success of the government in imposing acreage restrictions has been matched by the ingenuity of the farmers in increasing the productivity of their remaining lands by use of irrigation and fertilizer. Consequently the irrigated acreage has grown steadily and the use of water in agriculture has increased.

Thomas has estimated that an average water depth of slightly over 3 ft is required for every irrigated acre (48). In semiarid and arid regions, with a total of some 29 million irrigated acres in 1954, the water requirement was about 87 million acre-ft. In humid regions, where irrigation requires less water, the $\frac{3}{4}$ of a million acres under irrigation used about 1 million acre-ft. Inasmuch as most (possibly 90 percent) of this water is evaporated (consumed) and the average annual runoff in the United States is computed to be in the order of 1300 million acre-ft, the diminution in stream flow, were it uniformly distributed throughout the country, would have been approximately 7 percent. Of course during a dry year the stream flow would be far below average, and in humid zones the demand for irrigation water might, quite possibly, increase until it equaled the average of 3 ft suggested by Thomas.

The value of water for irrigation purposes differs from place to place. In arid regions, of course, no agriculture is possible without irrigation. Studies of humid regions have shown the net gain in crop production that may be attributed to supplemental irrigation (49). The cost of water used was between 5 and 7 dollars an acre-ft (between 1.5 cents per 1000 and 2 cents per 1000 gal) and the amount of water used ranged from 3 in. to 11 in., averaging about 7 in. during the study period. The net increase in value of crop production ranged from about 7 dollars to almost 400 dollars per acre. These figures yield an order-of-magnitude figure as to the economic value of the water supply: 2 cents per 1000 gal seems to be the maximum attractive cost of water for irrigation of such crops as grain sorghum and soy beans (net increase in value $7.30 and $6.80 per year, respectively). Crops such as sweet potatoes, tobacco, and cotton might support a charge of as much as 100 cents per 1000 gal (at this price the cost of water would just about equal the gross increase in income that was found, if the entire increase were due to irrigation).

We can tentatively conclude that under certain circumstances water for irrigation may sell for as much as 10 cents per 1000 gal (33 dollars per acre-ft) and still be attractive in humid regions. Higher valued crops such as truck crops are valuable enough to justify far more than this expenditure. However the total acreage of such crops is small and the total water use for the production of high-valued crops would probably be only a very small percentage of that used by all irrigated acreage. Field crops, on the other hand will probably not be profitably irrigable when the cost of water to the farmer in humid areas goes much above 2.5 cents per 1000 gal (8 dollars per acre-ft).

Hydropower

Harnessing running water has always been attractive to mankind. The Norse mill, first used to power millstones in the grinding of corn, was mentioned in a poem during the first century B.C. (*44*). Except for animal power, water power was the only supplement to human effort until the invention of the windmill (circa 1000 A.D.). The Norse mill produced only a small amount of power, possibly $\frac{1}{2}$ horsepower. It was a run-of-river device that did not require a dam and mill pond. Subsequent improvements in the harnessing of water power led to the development of the mill pond and increased the average power output to, possibly 3 or 4 horsepower, with an occasional giant installation having a maximum output of 30 horsepower.

In these early examples of hydropower utilization we can recognize the forerunners of run-of-river generating plants (such as those operated on the Susquehanna River) and power plants that use impoundments (such as those of the Tennessee Valley Authority or the great power projects of the West).

There is no early prototype of the newly devised pumped-storage hydroproject, where off-peak power, generated by steam, is used to pump water into an elevated reservoir. The pumps are used as turbines to generate energy when the stored water is released.

The largest plant of this sort will soon be built at Cornwall, New York, not far from West Point, by the New York Consolidated Edison Company. This pumped-storage project will necessitate the pumping of Hudson River water to an elevation of more than 1000 ft above river level, into a very deep 230-acre reservoir, during periods when surplus steam-generated electric power is available in the system. During weekday periods of peak load water will run down through the turbines (which are designed to serve either as pumps or turbines) and generate almost 1.8 million kilowatts (1800 megawatts). The project is scheduled to go into operation in 1966, and when it does it will be the second largest hydroelectric plant in the world, surpassed only by Grand Coulee. Figure 4.13 is a design of the project.

Hydrologists believe that run-of-river and pumped-storage hydropower plants do not seriously change hydrologic conditions. A negligible quantity of water is consumed or evaporated as compared to the unimpeded river flow. Large hydroprojects in the West, however, cause additional evaporation because of the large area of reservoir surface combined with the high rate of evaporation. For example, it is estimated that about 800,000 acre-ft of water are evaporated from Lake Mead each year. Its reservoir area is almost 250 sq miles when the lake is full. By way of contrast, in reservoirs operated by the TVA the annual precipitation ranges from 50 to 80 in., which exceeds the average annual evaporation of about 40 in. (Figs. 2.7 and 3.1). Thus, TVA reservoirs, by and large, do not suffer the net evaporation loss experienced by similar projects in the western states. The value of water consumed unproductively as an unavoidable evaporation loss from a multipurpose project cannot be ascertained. If used for irrigation, at a value of 40 dollars per acre-ft, then a water-consumption charge at Lake Mead of about 30 million dollars a year should be noted on the ledger. It is recognized, of

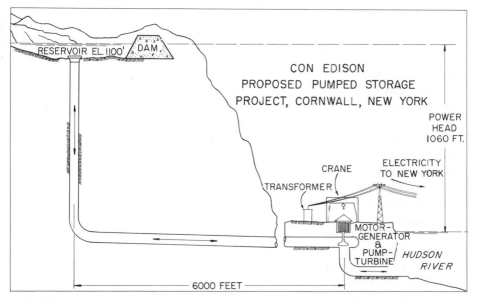

Fig. 4.13. Diagrammatic sketch of 1800 megawatt, pumped-storage project of Consolidated Edison Company of New York. (After October 4, 1962, Pumped-storage plant will set a record, *Engineering News-Record*, p. 34 © McGraw-Hill, Inc.)

course, that without water storage neither the power, flood control, nor domestic and irrigation water supply would be there as needed and that most of the water would go to waste. Yet the water consumption of the project constitutes a significant portion (6 percent) of the Colorado River's average annual flow of 13.5 million acre-ft and the consequences of evaporation include, of course, degradation of the remaining water due to its increased mineralization.

Navigation

The occasion of the first use of bodies of surface water as highways for the movement of men and materials is lost in antiquity. Until recently the principal requirement for the establishment of a city was its accessibility to navigable water. Thus, the largest cities of the world are located on sea coasts or inland waterways. Upstream from the navigable limits of rivers, cities are usually small. With the spread of rail transportation and the construction of highway networks, some inland cities—notably, Indianapolis and Columbus—have enjoyed a considerable growth despite their distance from navigable water. New York, Chicago, London, New Orleans, and Calcutta are examples of cities with a favored geographical location on navigable waters.

Where the natural flow of water is adequate, even if the seasonal period of satisfactory flow is short, a river channel can be used; however, it is not unusual to find that snags, sand bars, fallen timber, and other obstructions impede the movement of river vehicles. Thus, the earliest provision for the maintenance of navigation was the systematic patrol of the river channels by local people to find and remove snags and other impediments. Next came the dredging of channels through sand bars and the maintenance of predetermined channel depths. Finally, by constructing training works, such as dikes, and protective blankets to prevent bank erosion and the deposit of unwanted material in the channel, uniform and continuous channels have been created and maintained. Should these efforts prove to be inadequate, there is always the possibility of supplementing the low flow of the river by storing surplus water in an upstream reservoir and releasing it when needed. On the Missouri River, for example, the period of navigation is prolonged by this method.

A second method of providing a navigable waterway is to make a canal out of a natural river channel, providing the geology is favorable. Canals along a river are constructed by building dams to form a series of pools or lakes and by providing locks to by-pass the dams. This method may not require the release of water from upstream reservoirs for its successful operation, and the effects on the hydrology of a region are significant, even though the water requirement may be small. Navigation on the Ohio and Tennessee Rivers are examples of this method. The Arkansas River project, developed in a different geological environment, is also planned along these lines.

A third method of providing navigation is to construct an entirely artifical canal. This canal may run parallel to a river, as the present canal between Alton, Illinois, and Granite City, Illinois, or it may connect two different bodies of surface water. The Erie Canal, which connects the Great Lakes and the Hudson River, is the classic example of the latter. Among the earliest studies of hydrology in the United States was the one made by DeWitt Clinton (later governor of New York) to determine whether an adequate water supply would be available to maintain the level of the proposed Erie Canal. Under such circumstances a relatively small water supply may compensate for losses in lockage, leakage, and evaporation. By way of contrast, the Panama Canal probably requires a greater volume of artificially impounded water for its operation than any other canal in the world.

Flood Control

Flood control and land drainage are closely allied topics in one fundamental respect: Water is the common enemy and expenditures are made to abate a nuisance, not to utilize the water itself or its properties.

Drainage is accomplished by constructing ditches so that land of low elevation such as swamps and marshes may be drained, and by the improvement of existing channels so that they are made adequate to convey the water away from the drained areas at a more satisfactory rate.

Flood-control methods may include improving river channels, building levees or dikes to keep the water out, and building upstream reservoirs to hold back the flood waters for later release at nondamaging rates.

The most notable example of systematic channel improvement to reduce flood heights is to be found on the Mississippi River where, since 1929, a number of riverbend cutoffs have been constructed. These channel improvements have reduced the river length by some 150 miles and have resulted in a decrease in river stage. For example, at Arkansas City, the records of the Mississippi River Commission show that for a flow of 500,000 cu ft per sec the stage of the river was approximately:

Year	1930	1935	1940	1945	1950	1955	1960
Stage	26.5	23.0	18.5	17.5	16.8	16.0	15.2

At this location, over a period of 30 years for the same discharge rate, the improvements in the channel hydraulics have caused the stage of river to be lowered by about 11 ft. At Vicksburg, over the same period and for the same discharge rate, the stage declined from 24.0 ft to 15.5 ft on the gage. At this time we do not know what the end result of channel improvements will be; all we can be certain of is that the Mississippi River is not yet in a state of hydraulic equilibrium.

But even without the construction of spectacular engineering works such as cutoffs, the steady dredging of a channel, removal of snags, and installation of dikes to deflect and increase the current so as to reduce deposition can produce significant changes in the hydraulic efficiency of a channel and a corresponding reduction in gage height.

The summary in Table 4.5 has been compiled from the rating tables prepared for stream-gaging purposes by the Corps of Engineers and the U.S. Geological Survey over a period of 80 years at the Market St. Gage in St. Louis.

This table is extremely significant because it clearly shows the results of a program for the improvement of navigation and, later, the effect of a program for protection against flood. Between 1880 and 1910, for example, for a flow of 60,000 cu ft per sec the observed river level went from 5.8 to 3.0 ft. Had time-lapse photography been available (and used every time that a flow of 60,000 cu ft per sec was recorded), the resulting motion picture would show the river cutting its way down some 3 ft while we watch. Had this photography been continued for another 30 years, by 1940, the water surface would be seen to drop an additional 3.6 ft. By 1958, another drop of 1.4 ft would be witnessed.

Of course these channel improvements have been made to benefit navigation at the low discharge rates. And flood-protective works, mainly levees on the river bank at some distance from the channel at low flow, do not start to restrict flows until, possibly, a discharge of 500,000 cu ft per sec occurs.

Table 4.5. Gage Height and River Discharge at St. Louis, Mississippi River

Flow (cfs)	1880	1895	1910	1925	1940	1950	1958
20,000	0.4	−2.7	a	a	a	a	a
40,000	3.6	1.8	0.0	−3.7	−3.4	a	−5.1
60,000	5.8	4.5	3.0	0.3	−0.6	−0.8	−2.0
80,000	7.6	6.6	5.3	2.9	2.1	2.0	0.9
100,000	9.2	8.4	7.4	5.1	4.5	4.2	3.5
150,000	12.6	12.3	11.9	9.5	9.8	9.7	8.7
200,000	15.4	15.4	15.3	13.2	14.2	12.8	12.7
400,000	23.5	24.1	24.7	23.1	25.4	23.5	24.6
600,000	29.0	29.4	29.9	29.2	32.8	31.7	33.4
1,000,000	36.8	37.2	37.6	38.1	39.2[b]	46.6	a

[a] Data not available.
[b] For a discharge of 850,000 sec-ft, U.S. Geological Survey data.

The balance point—the discharge at which the same gage height has been observed throughout the period of record—is approximately 400,000 cu ft per sec. Referring to Fig. 4.7, this gage height has been equaled or exceeded about 7 percent of the time. So the ordinary program of river improvement has resulted in a cutting, or degrading, river that has already significantly lowered river stages more than 90 percent of the time.

A similar effect but in the opposite direction, has occurred at the high stages—for the same flows these stages are higher than they used to be. This has probably been due to the effect of levees in constricting the floods to a small fraction of the area formerly flooded.

Whereas the effects of channel improvements upon the stages of a river are usually readily determinable, the magnitude of the reduction in flood stage due to the construction of flood-control reservoirs is not directly measurable. The amount that the stage of the river has been lowered may be determined by mathematical and hydraulic calculation or from the study of small-scale models. Inasmuch as the movement of a flood wave down a river channel is not simply or reliably calculated, the most plausible reduction in stage is that indicated by a model study made after the event. Moreover the effect of storing flood waters becomes less and less noticeable as the distance from the reservoir increases. For example, in the floods of April, 1948, the reduction in stage of the Tennessee River at Chattanooga is reported to have been about 10 ft due to the operation of the TVA reservoirs. The reduction in stage of the Ohio River at Cairo is computed to have been between 1.5 ft and 2.0 ft (39). At Vicksburg, on the Mississippi River, the effect of the reservoirs in reducing the stage probably could not be demonstrated. At New Orleans the magnitude of the reduction caused by the TVA reservoirs would be a matter of conjecture and hope.

Other Uses of Water

Most bodies of surface water, unless grossly polluted or highly mineralized, will support aquatic life and may be used for recreation. In fact, recreation is becoming a reason in itself for the construction of lakes and reservoirs. The boating, swimming, skin diving, water skiing, and fishing made possible through the control of water appear more and more frequently as part of the justification for the building of multipurpose projects. In truth, as the population becomes increasingly urbanized, the need for outdoor recreational facilities grows apace. Among the foremost of these resort facilities are lakes and reservoirs, for the exercise they provide and for the fish and other wildlife they may harbor.

In the humid sections of the country, from the standpoint of hydrology, the effect of such developments is not great. Except for the possible increase in ground-water replenishment that occasionally occurs, the water balance is not seriously changed. Rainfall usually compensates for evaporative loss, and, anyway, the volume of water stored in reservoirs built solely for recreation is a minor portion of the total runoff. In the arid West, reservoirs built for recreational purposes alone are rare, the water loss due to evaporation is high, and the use of water purely for this purpose is rather expensive. For example, a net evaporation rate of 60 in. per year means an annual water-rent of 3200 acre-ft for each sq mile of reservoir surface—with a value, at the rate of $10 per acre-ft, of over 30,000 dollars per year. On this basis a small reservoir, covering 5 sq miles, would necessitate expenditure of $150,000 a year for water alone. If we assume that a fee of $1 per day per person would be charged for the use of the reservoir, it would require a constant load of 80 fisherman or water skiers per sq mile every day in the year merely to pay for the water lost in evaporation. This would not provide funds for maintenance and operation of the associated facilities. As any fisherman or water skier knows, this would be too intensive a use of a lake. There would also be the problem of the ever-increasing concentrations of minerals in the water that would result from continuous evaporation. The lake would tend to be transformed into a brackish water pond. There would be the added expense of completely changing the water of the lake periodically, much as one changes the water in a swimming pool.

It may be concluded that only under exceptional circumstances would fresh-water reservoirs be built solely for recreational purposes in arid regions. And it is not really necessary to point out that the cost of $10 per acre-ft for water is very nominal in a desert.

Another use of water that is becoming prominent is the addition of water for the dilution of wastes. Concentrations of mineral waste that would be objectionable if discharged into a river during a period of low flow might be tolerable if the low flow were augmented by the release of stored water. Some reservoirs have been built large enough to enable them to store water for this purpose.

Conflicts in Water Utilization

The widespread publicity given to multipurpose projects serves to obscure the hard fact that certain types of water utilization conflict with one another. Although no one can deny the potential economic advantages of multipurpose structures, there is a tendency to overstate these advantages—even to count them twice. To require the optimum operation of a project for *each* of several separate purposes is to pull simultaneously, with full force, in many directions. Flood control requires (1) an empty reservoir in advance of floods and (2) that the maximum volume of unused storage be maintained until danger of flooding is past. Power development requires that water levels be kept as high as possible at all times for maximum production. Irrigation operation demands a full reservoir at the start of the growing season and the release of water throughout the period of demand. Downstream navigation requires the release of water during the navigation season—and this water cannot be used for irrigation purposes. Recreational uses require a full pool during the vacation season—a period that usually coincides with the need to lower the pool to supply irrigation, power, and navigational needs.

It is apparent, therefore, that the essential feature of practical multipurpose design is compromise. This results in something less than the maximum possible benefits from any one of the uses, but it may realize the maximum benefits from the project as a whole. Multipurpose projects possess the distinction that the whole is considerably less than the sum of the individual parts when each is considered separately. It is the miscalculation of relative benefits that manifests itself as the major cause for mistakes in design—the engineering, as compared to the hydrology, economics, and planning is on relatively firm ground.

The operation of a multipurpose project demands accurate forecasts of water demands and, where possible, an accurate forecast of water availability. These in themselves are impossible requirements. Thus, it is almost never possible to operate a multipurpose project to anywhere near its optimum efficiency as determined by later analysis of the actual experience. From a practical standpoint, therefore, operation of a multipurpose project does not provide a full measure of all of the benefits advanced as selling points. In fact, even under the most favorable set of physical circumstances, such as those existing in the valley of the Tennessee River, the problem of getting the most out of the system is terribly difficult.

While a single dam-reservoir complex must contend with a single set of variables superimposed on a statistically sound hydrologic system, operation of a multiple-reservoir project on the same river superimposes a totally unpredictable, man-made hydrology on every succeeding downstream project. Even with the aid of hydraulic models and digital computers, system operation is a fly-by-wire process. Of course, no one can say that any decision taken at any time is wholly wrong—there is always some favorable aspect to any method of operation as long as no life is lost as a result of the decision. It is enough to say that many trials of various combinations of equipment and operating plans are required to determine which is most effective. And there is always the not-so-remote possibility that some unthought-of combination might be better than anything that had been considered.

Linsley has this to say about multipurpose water development:

Navigation, for example, requires a chain of reservoirs along a river. Enlarging the dams and installing power facilities makes it possible to generate power at these sites. However, such low-head reservoirs usually have relatively small flood-control capacity. This suggests the construction of headwater reservoirs for flood control storage. Here, too, is a potential source of power, and the stored water is available to increase power production on mainstream reservoirs during periods of low flow. [Power development, a source of direct revenue to the operating agency, is always in a preferred position as compared to flood control, whose benefits, though real, are indirect and can only be hypothetically determined by computation.] Thus it becomes progressively easier to justify each unit in the system as it contributes to the benefits of units already constructed . . . .

Once a system of reservoirs is started, there is a constant urge to add additional units because of the ease of justification . . . . Much highly productive farm land may be permanently flooded . . . with a corresponding disruption of local economy.

Far more serious, however, is the tendency for an increase in flood-peak flows . . . . Reservoirs greatly reduce the time of travel of flood peaks moving through them, and a system of reservoirs may cut several days from the normal time from headwaters to outlet . . . with resulting higher flood peaks in the lower basin . . . . Even if peak flows [downstream] are not increased, the reduced time to peak decreases the opportunity to take protective measures downstream (29).

This brief look at a navigation-flood-control-power project conveys some sense of the engineering complexity. It might almost be a summary view of the operation of the Tennessee River stream system development. Things get somewhat more complicated if we must, in addition, contend with the permanent withdrawal of water for irrigation purposes, the use of the reservoirs for recreational purposes, the operation of the system to insure mosquito control in the shallower portions of the lakes, and the losses due to evapora-tion. If, in addition, the system must carry over water from year to year—and no one knows what the runoff will be the next year—optimum operation can be justly regarded as never-to-be achieved goal and the mind reels.

As a practical matter, therefore, such projects are operated to satisfy the most important, or pressing, needs with the use of such judgement as the mortal man in charge may possess. Our understanding and sympathy for the unenviable position in which he has been placed will undoubtedly be wel-comed by such an individual. We may legitimately wonder, however, at the chain of circumstances that results in such a contretemps. Surely there must be a basic miscalculation somewhere, despite the billions of dollars spent for such projects.

SIDE EFFECTS AND FEEDBACKS

Although the terms *side effect* and *feedback* are not normally associated with the control and utilization of runoff, a moment of consideration will remove the unfamiliarity. For the unexpected by-products of a process, products that do not interfere with the process but give rise to unforeseen problems, are very familiar to us and are called side effects. And when the results of a process modify the process, possibly in an unexpected manner, and this in turn changes the results which in turn change the modification etc., etc., the system is said to have feedback. Side effects are generally associated with taking of drugs, feedbacks are generally associated with electricity or electronics whereby a fraction of the output of an electrical oscillation is returned to the input and thus exerts a control.

The terms are different in essence, because despite the side effect a process will continue unhindered to its conclusion. A drug may well go about its business and cure the disease despite the fact that the patient, cured of the disease, promptly develops drug poisoning. Feedback effects, however, modify the source of the process, the source is changed, the feedback may be lessened, and the system may reach the stage of "go" but at a far lower or higher level than was originally calculated. It may also become completely unstable, like the "excursion" of a runaway nuclear reactor or contrariwise, may come to a complete halt. In this section we shall examine a sampling of side effects and feedbacks as they apply to hydrologic observations and to the design of water development and other projects.

The science of hydrology, as it has been described in the preceding pages, is "classical" in that neither feedbacks nor side effects have been taken into account. Yet without an understanding of the techniques and theories of classical hydrology, modern hydrology must remain a mystery to even the well-educated citizen. It is the consideration of the feedbacks and the side effects of the development of water resources that has caused this book to be entitled *Modern Hydrology*.

Classical hydrology assumes that each measurement of discharge, stage, or water quality is a valid statistical unit that has resulted from a natural combination of circumstances. Consequently the observation will be repeated when the particular combination of natural events and antecedent conditions recurs. Thus, we can prepare maps showing the magnitude of recurrence interval for a particular rainfall intensity. The recurrence interval of flood peaks of the Red River has been subject of one illustration (Fig. 4.8). The concept of a flow-duration curve, or a gage-height-duration curve, has been set forth without much comment.

Yet, by this time the careful reader has already noted several short tables that have indicated that the gage height is not necessarily a constant for a given discharge rate of the Mississippi River at St. Louis or Vicksburg. The disturbing questions arise: What do the gage-height-duration curves really mean as to future probabilities? Are gage heights really to be classed as hydrologic data? Is there any reason to suppose that at St. Louis, despite a 100-year record of observed gage heights, the gage height will be at or above 10 ft half the time in the future? It is unlikely; the bed of the river has cut itself down to a lower elevation during this period.

We encounter a most ingenious paradox: At the very moment when statistical methods are reaching high levels of reliability and yielding many new insights into known relationships, the applicability of these methods to problems of water-resources development is being steadily, and rapidly, decreased. For the base data are no longer hydrologic, they are merely a record of numbers resulting from a mixture of operational and natural events.

Basic Data and Their Limitations

A look at the page from a Water-Supply Paper (Fig. 4.3) will reveal that this paradox is not new to the Water Resources Division of the U.S. Geological Survey which has been grappling with the problem for a long while, as the introductory commentary, discussed in detail below, indicates:

Drainage area—Chicopee River at Indian Orchard, Mass. 688 square miles. Prior to November 1, 1938, 703 square miles.

This looks interesting. What happened to change the drainage area? It turns out that this was merely the result of moving the location of the gage 1¾ miles upstream. Consequently the observed discharges before the date must be reduced by a small percentage to make the data comparable, on the assumption that all parts of the watershed contributed flow in proportion to the drainage area involved.

Extremes—1928–45: Maximum discharge, 45,200 second-feet Sept. 21, 1938, by computation of flow over dam; minimum daily, 16 second-feet (regulated) several times in 1929–31; practically no flow at times at former site when wheels were cleaned or repaired.

Well now, let's see . . . if we wish to drink water or irrigate during periods of low flow, how much storage do we need? How long a period of zero flow is likely to occur? The hydrologic data at the former site, at least, are incomplete—how long does it take to clean or repair a water wheel? As the water wheel gets older, will it take more or less time to effect repairs, to obtain spare parts? This information is needed for the proper planning of a storage reservoir for water supply immediately below the former site of the gaging station. Rain may fall in the watershed when it is needed, but the river won't flow past the intake if the water wheels are being repaired. Or, as part of the water-supply project, should plans be made to install a bypass around the water wheels so the flow will not be completely shut off during periods of repair? The answer to this is not contained in the Survey report, and yet without this information a reasonable engineering analysis of the situation cannot be accomplished. The data as published are incomplete and are not amenable to statistical analysis.

The maximum discharge rate is of interest should we desire to build a levee around property or to construct an industrial plant or house on high ground: How high is high enough? True, an estimate of the gage height for a flow corresponding to 45,000 cu ft per sec can be made, but is that figure of any value, and what is its recurrence interval? Were the upsteam reservoirs full at the time that the rainfall occurred that produced the observed maximum discharge? Did reservoir operation reduce the peak discharge or add to it, and how much? The tabular data indicate a reduction from a peak of 42,000 cu ft per sec to 37,000 cu ft per sec but the latter figure is the average for the day. If a similar rain occurred when all upstream reservoirs were full, what would the peak flow at the gaging station be? And to what elevation would the water rise? Suppose, unlikely though it may be, a dam gives way: at what level will the flood wave stand as it passes the property? In 1936, the National Research Council stated that (33) ". . . No less than 60 important dams have failed during the [past] 50 years as a result of overtopping by floods. . . ." Since that statement was published there have been additional instances where stored waters were suddenly released through failure of a dam (32a).

The next statement considered is;

Remarks. Flow regulated by power plants and reservoirs above station. Runoff in inches adjusted for diversions for Boston metropolitan district from 186 square miles in Swift River Basin and 97 square miles in Ware River Basin, for industrial use in Springfield from Ludlow Reservoir, and for change in contents in Quabbin Reservoir (since August, 1939) and Ludlow Reservoir (since October, 1943).

The tables are for the flow by months. Presumably any small reservoirs not included by name are low-head and useful mainly for maintaining a more constant daily flow. While this would affect the daily record more than the monthly record, it should be checked anyway.

The diversions are of great significance—anytime so large a fraction as 283 sq miles of a 688 sq mile watershed is subject to diversion, this must be considered. But how? Is all of the runoff in this diverted area presently used? Or is some water currently allowed to flow past the impoundment and to the gaging station. Are the diversions expected to increase as the water demand of the metropolitan area increases? Are the reservoirs kept as full as possible at all times, or are there legal requirements that provide for a minimum sustained flow below each dam? How repeatable are the data—if the meteorological conditions are repeated in ten or twenty years, will the recorded discharge at the gaging station also repeat itself? Or will it be less by a quantity equal to the growth in metropolitan district water demand during the interval? Even if the population served remains constant, does this mean that the diversions will remain constant, or is the per capita use increasing? Is there any limit to the area or population included in the metropolitan district?

Next comes "industrial use in Springfield." Is this water consumptively used? Is the sewage discharged into another drainage area? Is there any chance that the diversions will be increased? This too must be investigated—the data, as published, raise more questions than they answer.

There is no reason to investigate the question of change in reservoir contents. If the elevation, or water level, in each reservoir is known at monthly intervals and reservoir withdrawals are known, the remaining change in storage can be algebraically added to the hypothetical mean monthly stream flow. Of course on a daily basis this is not readily done because of the travel time of water between dams and gaging station.

This rather lengthy discussion of one data page of a Water-Supply Paper is intended to make this point: the observations of stream flow now being made all over the country must be used with caution. The data may consist of records of flow that are merely of historical interest and cannot be viewed as hydrologic data. And there is no real assurance that this historical data can be converted into reliable data for design.

There is also little reason to believe that a discharge-duration curve using observed data for this gaging station will be hydrologically meaningful. There is still less reason to believe that a "corrected" discharge-duration curve will have any value at all for purposes of design. We are dealing here with hydrologic data that have become *dirty*. The security of water supply for certain metropolitan areas has been achieved at the price of increasing the uncertainty (and cost) in the construction of engineering structures in the remainder of the drainage area. All engineering structures based on the control or utilization of the remaining water must be designed to overcome much greater extremes of flood and drought than would otherwise have been needed.

These questions are not academic, hypothetical, or alarmist. A recent illustration of this problem was contained in a story carried by the *Engineering News-Record* entitled "Engineers Erred in Bridge Failure." The story concerns the Big Sioux River Bridge at Sioux City, Iowa that was completed in 1959. Three of the five spans of this bridge, part of the Interstate Highway System, collapsed during a flood in early 1962. The U.S. Bureau of Public Roads investigated the failure and reached certain conclusions. The information pertinent to this discussion was reported by the *Engineering News-Record* as follows:

The failure of the bridge was the result of the floods of 1960 and 1962, which exceeded all previous floods of record in the Big Sioux River, combined with the fact that the four piers located in the channel were so placed that the effective waterway area was reduced by 35 to 40 per cent.

In arriving at the design of the bridge piers skewed to the natural flow in the channel, the state bridge engineers were undoubtedly influenced by a proposed channel improvement in the vicinity of the bridge site, authorized by an Act of Congress in 1946. At present . . . this channel improvement is quite uncertain.

The Corps of Engineers . . . perhaps misled the state's engineers, . . . through these two statements (made before the bridge was built):

"Flows on the Big Sioux River could approximate 42,000 cfs."

"The proposed construction will not materially affect the passage of floods . . . ."

Taking into account the floods of 1960 and 1962, a 50-year flood could have a discharge of about 60,000 cfs and a 100-year flood could be about 70,000 cfs . . . .

[The] recently constructed Fort Randall and Gavins Point Dams and Reservoirs . . . have changed flood flow conditions materially in the Missouri River (to which the Big Sioux is tributary).

The report contains several recommendations, two of which are:

In replacement of the collapsed upstream bridge . . . it be redesigned to provide a single span across the main portion of the channel. This would involve a main span length of about 225 ft.

This bridge washout brings to attention the need for more careful evaluation of bridge sites prior to the adoption of the final layout and design . . . . Also special attention should be given to the effect of flood control works on stream regimen so that damage to bridge and other drainage structures can be anticipated and prevented prior to actual failure (*15*).

This incident may be analyzed from the standpoint of modern hydrology and the conclusion can properly be reached that the bridge engineers were not to blame. They looked the situation over, obtained the best available estimate as to flood flow and the effect of their proposed bridge in constricting the channel, and then made an economical design. As part of the hydrologic data they were forced to ignore existing conditions, because of the hydrology contained in the Act of Congress which authorized construction of a differently aligned channel. In their analysis of the situation there can be no doubt that they recognized that they were obstructing the existing channel. But the authorized channel would not be obstructed by the new piers, since these were placed and oriented in accordance with the proposed channel realignment.

There is no way to determine the efficacy of channel improvements and improved drainage in the upper reaches of the Big Sioux River in decreasing the concentration time of the drainage area at the site of the proposed bridge. This might have been combined with a temporarily increased hydraulic gradient between the bridge and the extra-low Missouri River (owing to the storage of water in the upstream reservoirs at the time of flood) to further increase water velocities at the bridge. Presumably the figure of 42,000 cu ft per sec maximum flow, attributed to the Corps of Engineers, was high, a safe maximum to use based on available data. But it is difficult to blame anyone even if the increased flood was only the result of a normally high rainfall combined with a decrease in concentration time. Changes in concentration time are not to be calculated until after they have occurred: the interpretation of data always lags behind the reality. As to the passage of floods under the bridge, as far as the Corps of Engineers was concerned it would have been foolish to align the new structure in a manner not in accord with the authorized project.

It must be concluded that the headline "Engineers Erred . . ." is incorrect. Neither the Highway Departments of Iowa and South Dakota nor the Corps of Engineers can be held responsible for the results. All of these organizations used hydrologic and engineering principles in order to obtain an economical design: the greatest benefit for the least cost, all hazards considered. But the validity of the data they used had been ruined by upstream improvements, by water-storage operations on the upstream Missouri River, and by a statement of intention by Congress as to channel improvement, as shown by an authorization.

This analysis of the situation is borne out in the recommendation of the Bureau of Public Roads: Don't redesign the bridge with relatively cheap short spans that rest on piers. On the contrary, install a 225-ft clear span so that the flow, whether in this channel or that, 42,000 cu ft per sec or 70,000 cu ft per sec, can pass without damage. In short, overcome all of the uncertainty in the data by main brute force and awkwardness and the expenditure of enough money. Just what the cost of replacing the collapsed $250,000 structure will be, based on this new design criterion, has not been announced. Suddenly we seem to find ourselves on the edge of the situation previously envisioned for the distant future, when weather control has been perfected:

The situation with regard to control of floods, channel improvements, water supply, sewage disposal and all other forms of hydraulic and hydrologic engineering will then become one of increasing uncertainty. "Factors of Safety," already large, will inevitably be increased (and the increases will prove, in many instances, to be inadequate) and the cost of construction will mount. The economic evaluations that must precede construction will be totally unreliable inasmuch as they must be based on a political assessment rather than on observed facts and current (or probable) costs and benefits. This, of course, will lead to wasteful construction of uncertain utility and will not be beneficial to society.

A side effect of the large-scale development of water resources seems to be the need to substitute factually unfounded judgement for an analysis of facts. There were no firm hydrologic facts left in this instance. What remains? The intent of Congress, the desires of lesser political subdivisions, and historical information.

We turn again to the Water Resources Division of the U.S. Geological Survey, whose members have collected data on stream flow, water quality, ground-water levels, etc., since before 1900, and whose series of water-supply papers are standards in the field. At this writing the Water Resources Division is engaged in a campaign to secure wilderness areas that are not presently affected by man's activities and preserve them. The Survey argues that without such unspoiled areas climatic trends cannot be discovered because the hydrologic records are becoming too "dirty," or "noisy," due to man-made disturbance. Leopold, Chief Hydraulic Engineer of the Water Resources Division, put it this way.

There are direct practical reasons for our concern. The division of water of highly developed streams between bordering states is often based on the so-called virgin flow. What constitutes the flow unvexed by the hand of man cannot be determined at the council tables of negotiation, or even in the halls of justice without essential hydrologic facts . . . .

There is a vital need for a series of measurements of water discharge, ground-water levels, and other hydrologic parameters at selected places representing various environments, unchanged by and permanently protected from the effect of man's activities.

For long-term observations of the natural hydrologic regimen, the Geological Survey proposes to establish a network of "hydrologic bench marks" in areas which are as free as possible from man-induced changes (27).

The objective is laudable. For the engineer engaged in water-resource development, however, the proposed establishment of wilderness areas is principally of scientific interest. Classical hydrology is rapidly dying—modern hydrology has not yet been codified. The Leopold proposal is, in effect, a method of preserving the remnants of classical hydrology as a scientific curiosity, much in the manner that certain organizations preserve original strains of plants and animals for scientific observation and experiment.

Trends in the Mineralization and Temperature of Water

The nonhydrologic nature of observations of the mineral and thermal characteristics of rivers and lakes is popularly recognized in the term "stream pollution." Not only have there been increases in the concentrations of naturally occurring minerals, but substances that are entirely manmade, such as detergents, radioactive wastes, and complex hydrocarbons and phenols are found in ever-increasing amounts in streams and rivers.

Any systematic series of mineralogical analyses of surface water must be arranged in chronological order for study. For the data cannot be expected to repeat themselves since they have not resulted solely from naturally occurring, cyclic changes in the environment. The analyses merely serve to indicate the overall changes in the quantity and composition of the pollutants in recent years and the efficacy of antipollution measures in counteracting the trend of increase in the mineralization.

The so-called thermal pollution of streams has resulted primarily from the installation of steam-electric generating plants along our rivers. Water used for the cooling of condensers is heated and upon its return to the stream often produces a measurable rise in the temperature of the river. A secondary source of the temperature increase is found in the once-through cooling systems of industrial plants such as steel mills that require tremendous volumes of water.

The use of water for cooling in a once-through system raises the water temperature but has little, if any, effect on the mineralization of the river water. Use of cooling towers, however, results in highly mineralized wastes (products of evaporation and slime control) that may add to river pollution.

There is an inescapable price in natural-resource utilization that must be paid by machine civilization. This price is clearly expressed in terms of stream pollution. Nor is it even remotely conceivable that antipollution programs will restore the stream system to its original mineralogical innocence. The calcium chloride wastes from the salt-mining operations, the acid wastes of abandoned mines, the residues of agricultural fertilizers and pesticides, the waste heat of power plants and steel mills—all of these, and more, are invulnerable to the clean-up program that is pushed so hard by Federal, state, and local agencies.

We may conclude that one of the first victims of machine civilization is the hydrologic data pertaining to the quality of surface water. The practical result, for example, is that in a run-of-river installation to produce potable water the utmost vigilance must be maintained at all times and increasingly versatile equipment must be made available to monitor and control unexpected constituents in the water. This equipment must be improved constantly to keep pace with advancing technology and its new waste products. The ultimate in monitoring equipment is apparently biological in nature (*18*).

The Increasing Nonequilibrium of Rivers

It has already been noted that the relationship between stage and discharge on major stream systems is not constant. This is particularly true of alluvial rivers that flow over movable beds. It has already been shown that the records of daily discharge of small streams, streams subject to diversion for use, are not sufficient to define their performance. Hydraulic measurements cannot always be regarded as hydrologic data. For example, from the data presented previously, it is clear that a duration curve computed on the basis of steam flow measurements on the Chicopee River at Indian Orchard, Massachusetts, would be far from sufficient, in itself, for purposes of engineering analysis.

Yet it would seem at first glance that the volume of water issuing from a major drainage area, like the 700,000 sq miles of the Mississippi-Missouri River system above St. Louis, would be virtually immune to diversions simply because of the sheer volume of water involved—that even the largest diversions would be insignificant. And, until very recently, this was true.

But the extensive construction of reservoirs in the Missouri Valley has changed the situation. The approved Pick-Sloan Plan of development for the Missouri River Basin provides, among other things: (1) more than 100 multipurpose reservoirs on the Missouri River and its tributaries, with an aggregate storage capacity of more than 100 million acre-ft of water, and (2) the irrigation of some 5 million acres of new land and supplemental water for more than 1 million acres now receiving an inadequate supply.

This program may be placed in perspective when it is noted that the average annual discharge of the Mississippi River (1861–1950) at St. Louis was equal to approximately 130 million acre-ft. Thus, ultimately, the storage capacity of the reservoirs will be much more than half of the mean annual flow at St. Louis. The diversions for irrigation purposes may total 10 million acre-ft a year or more (if the Thomas criterion of 3 ft of water per irrigated acre is used). This 10 million acre-ft amounts to 7 percent of the natural mean annual flow of the Mississippi at St. Louis.

A complete hydrologic evaluation of such a program cannot be undertaken here. Several comments, however, can be made for the purpose of establishing a framework for understanding.

Geomorphology is the study of topographical features of the earth and how they have been produced. Excluding major tectonic movements, the changes in the earth's topography are chiefly caused by the action of air and water. Water, in its never-ending quest for the lowest possible elevation, is the principal agent of erosion. Thus, the control of water by man signifies interference with the action of a major geologic force. Consequently we can evaluate the water-development programs in terms of geomorphology. This discipline is fully capable of including the works of man within its scope on the same terms that it includes natural events.

A basic concept of geomorphology is the existence of hinge points, sometimes called fixed points, as controls for the flow and the erosive capability of water. For example, sea level is such a hinge point. The level of the sea determines the maximum potential of water at the moment it strikes the land surface and thus the slope of natural channels. If we assume that a river has cut its channel in a homogenous material and that the climate is uniform over a long period, then the sea-level elevation will determine the size and slope of the channel at any time. This slope will, of course, get flatter and flatter as the bed of the river erodes. The slope will approach the horizontal in the way that the floor of a descending drawbridge swings down on its steel hinge. Any abrupt fall in sea level will result in increased erosive force becoming available. Gradually the channel will scour and deepen. Any rise in sea level will result in a decrease in erosive force: the material being eroded from the land surface will not reach the sea to form a delta, but will be deposited in the stream bed, raising the channel and "aggrading" the flood plain.

This simplified picture of the geomorphology of rivers must not be allowed to remain unmodified. In subdrainage area after subdrainage area more or less temporary hinge points will appear, caused by differences in the nature of the underlying formations. Niagara Falls is the classic example of a temporary hinge point created by the tenacity and durability of the beds that outcrop there, as compared to those downstream. The Falls serves as the hinge point for the entire drainage area of the Great Lakes. No change in hydraulic conditions below the Falls, including small changes in sea level, has any influence on the upstream drainage area. Even if sea level were to rise as much as 50 ft the hydraulics of the Great Lakes Basin would not be affected by this. (Of course, the climatic changes accompanying such change in sea level would affect the rainfall in the drainage area, hence the hydrology.) Other, secondary hinge points exist between the individual lakes of the Great Lakes System—the bed of the Detroit River, for example.

These secondary hinge points, as long as they endure, control the basic hydraulics of the drainage area above them, to the next hinge point upstream. Alluvial streams have secondary hinge points only where they run on relatively unerodable bedrock. The Mississippi River, for example, has no hinge point on its main stem between the Gulf of Mexico and Thebes, Illinois, an airline distance of approximately 600 miles. The river distance of course is constantly changing and is approximately twice as great. Further upstream another important hinge point is the Chain-of-Rocks reach at St. Louis which controls the large drainage area whose discharge is gaged at the Market Street gage.

Let us consider each hinge-point elevation as being equivalent to a virtual sea level for the upstream drainage area, to the next upstream hinge point. Then the changes produced by water developments can be approximately interpreted in terms of changes in virtual sea level as far as the geomorphology of each upstream drainage area is concerned.

For example, an improvement in channel efficiency that lowers the stage of the river at low discharge can be considered as analogous to a lowering of virtual sea level for that reach of river. Levee construction, which constricts the flow at high discharge rates and raises the gage height, can be interpreted as a lifting of the virtual sea level. Thus river improvements can result in changing the geomorphology in two contradictory (but not counteracting) ways simultaneously.

The evaluation of reservoir construction is even more complex. The mere

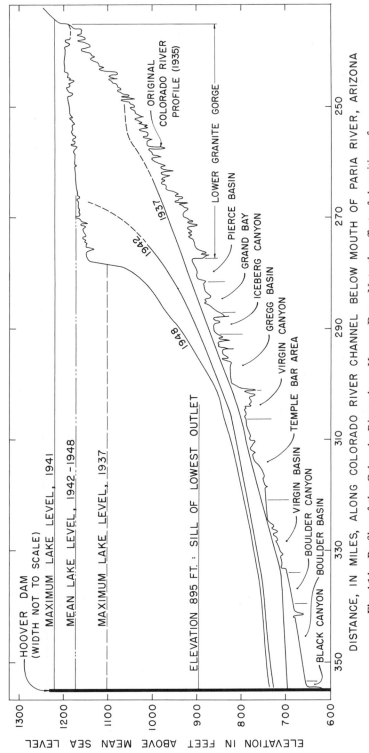

Fig. 4.14. Profiles of the Colorado River above Hoover Dam. Note the effect of deposition of sediment. (After H. E. Thomas, 1954, *The First Fourteen Years of Lake Mead, U.S. Geol. Surv. Circular 346*, Plate 1.)

construction of a reservoir inserts an additional hinge point into the drainage system, somewhat like the upheaval caused by a local earthquake in a hard-rock area. The equilibrium of the entire drainage area, to the next effective hinge point of the main stem and the secondary hinge points in the tributary streams, is changed. As with all geologic processes, many years must elapse before all of the effects can be recognized. In one sense we have raised the virtual sea level for the intervening drainage area. This implies the formation of a delta at the upstream edge of the reservoir. It also implies that the stream will deposit material on its banks upstream from the delta as the water velocity is reduced due to backwater effects, and the burden that the water can carry is also reduced.

However the stage of a reservoir is dependent upon its mode of operation—that is, on the quantity of water in storage for all purposes—and this depends on the rules governing its use. Consequently the observed water levels furnish no clue as to the future and are not subject to statistical analysis except in the crudest terms—the water levels of a natural lake created by an earthquake, by contrast, are amenable to analysis.

The aggradation of a river valley is usually accompanied by a rise in the upstream water table, the creation of poorly drained swampy areas, and an increase in flood heights above the reservoir. Clear-cut examples are difficult to find, because large projects have not been long in operation. However, the progressive formation of delta deposits in the original channel of the Colorado River is shown in Fig 4.14, and this may be considered as indicative of the results to be expected from impoundments of sediment-laden streams in arid regions. The history of Lake Decatur, Illinois, represents the outcome in a flat, more humid region. In the early life of an impoundment, when it functions as a very efficient silt trap, the erosive force of the water issuing from the reservoir is large, and downstream erosion occurs, enlarging and deepening the channel below the dam. Later, as the reservoir fills with silt, its storage capacity decreases and its effect on the river flow becomes less.

Thus as a matter of short-term geomorphology the construction of a dam raises the virtual sea level upstream and lowers it downstream, the exact zone of influence in each case being dependent on local geologic and topographic conditions.

The existence of a reservoir can also be evaluated climatically, in terms of drier climate in the area downstream. For the overall contribution of water to the atmosphere may be increased, whether usefully for irrigation purposes or wastefully to the vegetation subsisting directly from the raised ground-water table. This directly reduces the mean annual discharge of the stream below the dam, and the importance of this reduction is greater during dry years than it is during wet years.

There is another effect to be considered when the contents of a reservoir are used to maintain river flow either for navigation purposes or to empty the reservoir in advance of the next flood season: the increase in the duration of bank-full flow which is accompanied by an increase in the rate of river-bank erosion. The ever-increasing expenditures for revetment (to "permanently stabilize" eroding river banks) are testimony to the power of geologic forces in this connection.

It can readily be perceived that as a result of widespread large-scale dam construction our major river systems and their associated channels and flood plains have been placed in a geologically unstable condition. Added to this is an associated secondary instability that might be termed feedback. This stems from the inevitable attempts by the planners and system operators to counteract the unstable geologic conditions that have been created.

The claim will be made, with some justification, that taken all-in-all the construction program in the water-resource field has improved the human condition, at least for the time being: More water is available during low flows, some flood heights have been reduced, river navigation has been improved, and power has been generated more or less cheaply. And these claims are substantially correct. Substantially, but not entirely; temporarily, not permanently. At the real extremes of drought and flood, the extremes that are the primary concern of hydrology, there is some question.

Let us briefly examine the workings of a large and complex hydraulic and hydrologic system. The Missouri River above its junction with the Mississippi River will serve admirably as an example.

The Missouri River

Whereas the flow of the Missouri River is controlled substantially by the construction resulting from the Pick-Sloan plan, the main stem Mississippi River above St. Louis is pooled by a series of low navigation dams, and the flow in the Illinois River, its most important tributary, is augmented by a diversion of water from Lake Michigan. Thus, the hydrograph of discharge of the Mississippi has not been seriously affected by construction, although the discharge hydrograph of the Missouri River has been drastically changed.

The manner in which the discharge rates of the Missouri River are determined and the means by which the different demands upon its flow are reconciled are of interest. Students of political and economic theory might profitably consider to what extent the principles of majority rule are appropriately applied in deciding whether to generate power rather than store the water for navigation or water supply. By any reckoning, the machinery is cumbersome and whether the results are of optimum benefit to society is a question to be decided at some future date.

The waters of the Missouri River Basin are controlled by the Coordinating Committee on Missouri River Main Stem Reservoir Operations. This is a large committee, and is described by Pafford in the following words:

Since the inception of the coordinating committee in 1953, representatives of the states (Colorado, Iowa, Kansas, Missouri, Montana, Nebraska, North Dakota, South Dakota, and Wyoming) and federal agencies (Federal Power Commission; Corps of Engineers, United States Department of the Army; Weather Bureau, United States Department of Commerce; Public Health Service, United States Department of Health, Education, and Welfare; and Bureau of Reclamation, Fish and Wildlife Service, and Geological Survey, United States Department of the Interior) directly interested in mainstem operations have actively participated in its functions. The state representatives (governor-appointed) are generally the state water engineers.

The committee functions through general meetings, usually twice a year, and through interim contacts with and reports from the Reservoir Control Center. An annual meeting is held, usually in September, to review tentative annual operating plan schedules that have been prepared during August by the Reservoir Control Center. At this meeting the views of all interests are given full consideration, and a specific set of advance operating plans is agreed on and made final by the committee as a basis for actual operations. A second committee meeting usually is held in April of each year to review actual operations during the remainder of the year based on April 1 forecasts; revise the operating plan if necessary; and outline operational objectives to be considered by the Reservoir Control Center in setting up the tentative operating plans for consideration at the September meetings. In addition, special meetings are held to consider possible modifications of previously adopted annual operating plans should unforseen conditions arise that might warrant important modifications. Such a special meeting was held on November 1, 1956, in connection with the Mississippi River low-water crisis which threatened St. Louis industry.

Each committee member is responsible for ascertaining and fully presenting and supporting the viewpoints of his agency or state at these meetings. The committee members are in an effective position to make the various desires and requirements known and to have them integrated equitably into practical plans for operations (*34*, 388–389).

The outside observer can do no more than speculate as to how the Geological Survey and the Weather Bureau would cast their votes in the event of a dispute between South Dakota and Kansas. The attitude of the Fish and Wildlife Service with regard to deciding whether water should be conserved for irrigation purposes for the following year or used to prolong the navigation season of the current year cannot be predicted. A possible clue to the resulting output may be found in Pafford's statement of the guiding principles of the committee:

1. Flood control will be provided for by observing the requirement that predetermined upper blocks of storage space in each reservoir will be vacant at the beginning of each year's flood season. This space is available for annual regulation of flood control and all conservation uses in every normal and wet year, but must be vacant at the beginning of the next year's flood season.
2. Allowance will be made for all irrigation and other upstream tributary water uses during each year. This allowance also covers the effects of upstream tributary reservoir conservation operations, as anticipated from their advance operation plans.

3. Provision will be made for downstream urban water supply and stream sanitation requirements.

4. The remaining available water supply will be regulated so that the outflow from the lowermost reservoirs conforms to the seasonal requirements of navigation, with internal adjustments within the reservoir system and minor adjustments in overall releases from the system to provide for the generation of the maximum useable power consistent with the foregoing uses.

5. To the fullest extent possible, without serious interference with the foregoing primary functions, the reservoirs will be operated for maximum benefit to recreation, fish and wildlife, and other secondary purposes (*34*, 387).

In the Fall of 1956, before all of the reservoirs were completed, even before all of the completed reservoirs had been filled, a long dry period occurred. At St. Louis the flow of the Mississippi River was low, and during the last week of October the river level stood at −2.6 ft on the Market Street gage, and there was every indication that in the absence of rain upstream the discharge and river level would fall still more.

In this instance there had occurred, simultaneously, a number of circumstances that had not been foreseen by private, local, or Federal engineers. Two separate crises resulted from the low water.

The first pertained to navigation on the Mississippi River between Cairo and St. Louis. In that reach of river the decrease in discharge was expected to reduce the water depth to the point of interfering with the movement of barge traffic. Much of the cargo transported consisted of coal and fuel oil. The ultimate destination of much of the fuel oil was the Chicago area which would need it for the winter season. To counteract this decrease the Corps of Engineers lowered the pools of the Mississippi and Illinois Rivers above St. Louis so that the discharge of the Mississippi would be increased by the water taken from storage within the pools, thus enabling barges to move upstream from Cairo for a slightly longer time.

The second crisis involved the hydrology used to compute the elevations of river intakes in the St. Louis area: The river elevations were far lower than had been anticipated when the pumping stations of power companies, industrial plants, and water companies had been installed. It seemed very likely that power production in the area would be curtailed, that water would be short in the East St. Louis area, and that even the production of so essential a product as beer might be curtailed.

The *Engineering News-Record* discussed the situation and its implications under the headline "Low Flow a Threat on the Mississippi".

This week in St. Louis, time was running out on Ol' Man River.

With the water at 2.6 ft below the established datum, if there's no rain by Nov. 20 the Mississippi will drop to −6.2 ft to match the record low water level set in 1940. And assuming there's no rain by Dec. 1—the only safe assumption—a −7.0 level is predicted.

Below −5.5, municipal water supplies in the East St. Louis area would have real trouble getting water, while in St. Louis and its surrounding county the problem would be in treating it.

At −7.0, navigation, already hampered by low water, will cease for all practical purposes, causing serious shortages of fuel oil and coal in the Chicago and upper Mississippi Valley areas.

Below −7.0, power generation, needing cooling water, will be cut to an emergency degree in the St. Louis metropolitan area.

Below −7.0, industries needing water for process or cooling will feel the pinch along with steam-power stations . . . .

Missouri River flow helps a good bit. Without it, the stage at St. Louis would have been down to −6.0 last week. But the Missouri, too, has felt the effect of prolonged drought, and this is the time for the big main-stem dams on the river to begin their seasonal pinchdown on flow to increase storage. Summer release of 34,000 cfs at Gavins Point Dam is being cut to 15,000 cfs. On Nov. 15, this is to be cut further to 7500 cfs.

HELP FROM UPSTREAM

On the Mississippi itself the Corps began last Friday to drop the depth of 26 navigation pools from Alton, Ill. (just above St. Louis) all the way up to Minneapolis-St. Paul. This will be accomplished by Nov. 15. The upper river will be lowered from 9-ft to 8-ft navigation depth from the benefit of downstream St. Louis and the 175-mi reach of the river from there southward to Cairo, Ill. (Confluence with the Ohio there relieves the problem.)

The Illinois River, with its canal connections to Lake Michigan at Chicago, is a hope for improving low flow in the Mississippi. But Chicago is already helping all it can—legally.

Beginning Tuesday last week, and for 10 days at least, the Chicago Sanitary District is increasing the diversion of Lake Michigan water into the Illinois waterway system to 2600 cfs. Maximum allowable set by Supreme Court order is an annual average of 1500 cfs. However, according to figures compiled by Brig. Gen. Paul D. Berrigan, Division Engineer, North Central Division, the Sanitary District's diversion so far this year has averaged only 1488 cfs. This cushion of 12 cfs over the past 10 months will permit the 2600 cfs diversion temporarily without violating the court's limitation.

Normally, diversion this time of the year is at the rate of 900 cfs which means that the rate of diversion has been nearly tripled for the past 10 days. Army Engineer figures reveal that this increased diversion will raise the water level in the Mississippi River at Alton, Ill., just above St. Louis, by $2\frac{1}{2}$ in.—and in barge operation even $2\frac{1}{2}$ inches more navigable depth is important.

In Chicago, Gen. Berrigan issued this statement: "The situation is critical, and the pools are being lowered only as a last resort. Navigation has already been severely reduced because of inadequate depths over the lower sill of the Alton Lock (Dam 26). Furthermore, as the tailwater (river below the dam) continues to fall, it also becomes advisable to lower the pool above the dam to protect the structure from excessive hydrostatic pressure."

The St. Louis-East St. Louis area is faced with a serious water supply problem if natural flows in the Missouri, Mississippi or Illinois Rivers are not materially increased as a result of substantial rainfall. Two-thirds of the water in the Mississippi River at St. Louis has come from the Missouri River; largely from Corps of Engineer storage reservoirs, Fort Peck, Garrison and Fort Randall. However, this discharge was to be reduced to less than half its present volume beginning about Oct. 26 as Missouri River reservoirs were scheduled to go into winter operating schedules. An early freeze-up would reduce flows still farther and increase the severity of the problem.

In Omaha, the position of Maj. Gen. G. E. Galloway, Missouri River Division Engineer, is that he can not cut loose Missouri River water to help St. Louis. Dams on the Missouri were built as part of the Pick-Sloan Plan for benefit of the Missouri Basin. The manner in which Missouri River water is allocated is set out a year ahead by co-operative agreement among the ten states and seven federal agencies represented on the Missouri Basin Inter-Agency Committee.

Aside from legal restrictions on its manipulation, the Missouri itself is short of water. Storage at its four dams today is about 13.5 million acre-ft. This is less than the 16 million acre-ft stored behind Fort Peck Dam alone in 1953. There have been three years of drought in the area. Navigation had to shut down a month early, and reduced flow of the Missouri hit its mouth, near St. Louis, last week.

In Washington, there is only confirmation of what the district and division offices can and cannot do to alleviate conditions around St. Louis. Nobody in the Chief of Engineers office has come out and said it, but it is indicated that releases from the Upper Missouri might be ordered if it came to a matter of life and health.

The problem will be in determining what constitutes such a situation. Domestic water famine would presumably call for drastic action, but it is anybody's guess at this point whether power loss or industrial water scarcity would call for a high level decision on the Mississippi's low water problem.

Part of St. Louis' problem is described as failure to support proposed lower Missouri Basin dams on such tributaries as the Osage, and Gasconade Rivers, both in the State of Missouri.

TROUBLE FOR INDUSTRY

Union Electric is the most vitally concerned industry in St. Louis. Its five coal-burning steam plants in the area have a combined generating capacity of 1,270,000 kw. They need 1.2 billion gallons of cooling and make-up water daily.

A spokesman for Union Electric described for ENR the extent to which company operations might be affected and the means by which Union Electric hopes to keep the worst from happening. He said the company had never faced such a shortage. (They look for the Mississippi to drop down to -8.0 or -8.4.)

"At -6.0," he said, "we lose one of our old power plants, the Ashley plant . . . for generation of power." At -7.0 the losses would reach 10 to 15%; the company has reservoirs that can make up this difference. But at -8.0 fully a third of generating capacity would be lost and it would be necessary to "shed industrial load." This would mean industries in the St. Louis area would shut down at least in part for want of power.

Even before things reached this point, industries would be suffering from direct loss of water. The intake for the big Anheuser-Busch brewery will be out of water at -5.5.

Heavy rain in the right places would be the best help. Beyond that it will be up to the river controllers to do what they can within their fairly rigid legal limitations (14).

Before the water shortage ended, the Supreme Court of the United States had to authorize the temporary diversion of 7000 cu ft per sec from Lake Michigan. This was in addition to the 1500 cu ft per sec that Chicago had previously (in 1930) been authorized to divert into the Illinois River from the lake for sanitary purposes. The increased diversion of water combined with some rain in the watershed of the Mississippi River maintained a minimum discharge of 45,000 cu ft per sec in the river at St. Louis—a minimum gage height of −4.8 ft.

The lesson to be learned from this incident is that in the face of a stream system in a state of nonequilibrium, the hydrologic extremes cannot be foreseen, partly because the actions of agencies controlling the water cannot be predicted. For one can be sure that the river intakes affected by the crisis were originally designed by competent, conservative, engineers who thought that they were "safe"—and on the assumption that their data were hydrologic they were undoubtedly correct. But even the newest structure mentioned in the *Engineering News-Record* story, the lock at Alton, constructed in the years following World War II, proved to be falsely premised with regard to tail-water elevation.

As yet there is no method to determine whether the geomorphology produced by Congressional action will operate in one way or another. Even under a rigid operating schedule, based purely on water levels in reservoirs, a number of years must elapse before the results of the changes brought about by altered geomorphology become apparent in the regime of the rivers that have been affected. Under arbitrarily varying operating schedules, sound forecasts simply cannot be made.

Trends in Surface-Water Development

Water is a natural resource, resembling in some respects an agricultural crop: it is a naturally recurring "good" that must be used as it is available. When there is a surplus, it may also be stored for future use against the time of drought.

As with other natural resources, water may be brought into the productive process by individuals, private organizations, local and state organizations, or agencies of the Federal Government. At present this can be accomplished under a number of different legislative doctrines, no two of which are completely compatible. Humid regions have produced legal theories that differ from those developed in arid regions. Legal theories vary also according to origin of civil law—for example, Roman as opposed to English common law. In the United States, unique doctrines have sprung from interpretations of the Constitution, particularly the Federal Government's power to regulate commerce, to make treaties, and to promote the general welfare. Two basically different lines of development have thus taken place: political and economic.

The political development of water resources has, itself, taken two paths. According to the first, the primary importance of water was as a medium for transportation and commerce. Later this doctrine was expanded to include all circumstances wherein water interferes with commerce, and to work to abate the nuisance. The other path of development considers water to be a useful raw material but assumes (1) that the cost of water should be forcibly maintained at a historically low level and (2) that the profligate use of water resulting from (1) will continue at the same rate in the future, thus threatening the country with the specter of water shortage.

It is the writer's viewpoint that water will be and should be "short" for wasteful or uneconomic uses. The argument that there are water requirements wholly independent of water costs and that can thus be predicted by mechanical extrapolation of historic trends has resulted in premature and excessive construction to meet "indicated" shortages. Indeed, the argument is not valid. A recent book on water supply contains an excellent discussion of the effect of economics and technology on water policy and elucidates the relationships noted above (19). A more general approach to the evaluation of all phases of water development, not restricted to water supply, has been outlined by Fox and Herfindahl (16a).

The economic development of water resources treats water as one of a number of natural resources to be utilized by society. This approach to the development of water resources tends to balance the economic value of water against the nonwater resources sacrificed for water-development purposes. This is normally accomplished by calculating profit and loss for one as compared to other lines of expenditure. Without such an analysis marvelous structures for water control may be built—and be as productive and enduring as the pyramids. Such useless structures negate hydrology and engineering.

All of these economic and political doctrines must be included in any discussion of modern hydrology, together with stream-flow measurements and other physical information. They may, semihumorously, be classified as a new cause of potential earthquakes as far as hydrology and geomorphology are concerned, with the doctrines of Constitutional origin grouped as major diastrophic forces and the other doctrines considered as lesser forces.

In legalizing the use of surface water, there are two principal doctrines: the riparian doctrine and the appropriation doctrine. Under strict riparian doctrine only the owner of land riparian to a stream (touching it) may make use of its waters, and only on condition that the waters passing his land proceed essentially undiminished in quantity and unchanged in quality (22). This doctrine has been modified in many respects. It originated in a humid region where the actual consumptive use of water was small and where bodies of water were more important as the dwelling of fish or as the medium for cheap, convenient transportation, than as a supply of H_2O, the raw material. Basically the riparian doctrine acts to prohibit the utilization of water, inasmuch as any large-scale use of water must inevitably change both the quantitative and qualitative characteristics of the water substance permitted to pass downstream.   In an attempt to adapt it to modern conditions of water use, riparian doctrine has been modified to what is called the doctrine of correlative rights. This means that the use of water for irrigation purposes, for example, by a riparian owner must be reasonable in relation to the needs of other riparian owners. If all wish to use water at the same time, then, essentially, each may have an equal or proportionate share. Of course, the greater the number of riparian owners whose rights are involved, the more difficult it will be to reach agreement. But one principle is definitely established: No proprietor can absorb all the water of the stream and thus allow none to flow down to his neighbor. The strict application of this doctrine means that in a dry year even if the stream carries enough water to supply sufficient irrigation water to half of the riparian owners, each will suffer a crop failure since the water available to each will only be half enough. As a result, the gamble involved in making investments that require an assured water supply becomes prohibitive, and water developments are made to appear economically unattractive. Thus, the riparian doctrine (and its variations) are primarily notable as giving rise to vested interests in the waste or nonutilization of water. Nothing will be said here concerning the effect of this doctrine on the operation of industry that must dispose of its waste products or the operation of steam-electric generating plants that contribute thermal pollution.

The appropriation doctrine of water development, on the other hand, rests on the proposition that beneficial use of water is the basis, measure, and limit of appropriative right. The first in time is prior in right. The right is forfeited or lost by abandonment of use or change in utilization. This doctrine, at least, allows the water substance itself to be consumed if need be. By affirming a property right in water, it encourages private and local investments in water development.

However, there is no uniformity in the detailed provisions of the various state laws based on this principle. Some legal codes grant certain "higher" users priority or preference over other "lower" users, transfers from higher to lower users being hindered thereby. Hirshleifer notes that the arbitrary classification of uses into higher and lower dates back to Hammurabi and that, in this connection, the California Water Code defines the use of water for domestic purposes as highest and for irrigation the next highest (*19*). Hirshleifer considers this example a remarkable demonstration of the persistence of error, and the writer is forced to agree. For it is obvious that under drought conditions the use of water domestically for elaborate baths, air conditioning, lawn sprinkling, car washing, and so forth would be a grievous error if the same water could be used for irrigation to produce badly needed crops. Similarly, using water for irrigation, when power plants faced shutdown because they lacked cooling water, would be wrong. This higher-lower use definition simply acts to limit, arbitrarily and capriciously, the perfection of property rights in water. And although the effects of these provisions on geomorphology and hydrology are not immediately apparent, they nevertheless exist.

With all of its shortcomings and operational faults, however, appropriation doctrine is potentially capable of serving as a sound framework for the development of water resources. Inasmuch as the productivity of the water use must be greater than the energy (money) spent to bring it into use, the diversions by individuals or private corporations, or even municipal corporations, are limited and more or less sound. Appropriation doctrine has been adopted as law by most of the western states and is even making inroads into states having a humid climate such as Mississippi.

The appropriation and riparian doctrines are the outgrowth of common law—a grass-roots development. From the standpoint of geomorphology, only relatively limited changes can be attributed to this cause.

The political development of water resources has been preempted by the Federal Government and, as we have already noted, is a powerful force of geomorphology. The semiindependent, sometimes conflicting laws governing Federal development of water resources have been well summarized by the Commission appointed by President Truman in 1950 (50). For our purposes, suffice it to say that channel maintenance and improvements and their hydrologic effects stem from the commerce clause of the Constitution: "To regulate Commerce with Foreign Nations, and among the several states, and with the Indian tribes." In 1865, the Supreme Court, in Gilman v Philadelphia stated:

> Commerce includes navigation. The power to regulate commerce comprehends the control for that purpose, and to the extent necessary, of the navigable waters of the United States . . . . This necessarily includes the power to keep them open and free from any obstruction to their navigation . . . to remove such obstructions when they exist . . . (51).

Subsequent decisions of the Court have interpreted "navigability" to include any water tributary to navigable water and apply this reasoning to any project having to do with water diversions, such as the upholding of a Federal injunction against the construction of an irrigation reservoir in New Mexico because of the diminution of navigability downstream.

Flood control also has been approved by the Court as a legitimate exercise of power by the Federal legislature to "protect the various arteries of interstate commerce from the disasters of floods (52)". Reclamation projects are based on the ownership of lands by the United States and its right as proprietor to develop them.

The only matter more or less clear is that from a Constitutional standpoint —judging by interpretations of the Supreme Court—the highest use of water is as a medium for navigation—a historically understandable priority but, possibly, technologically obsolete. (There recently has been an acknowledgment of the superior benefits to be derived from utilization of the water substance by agriculture as compared to navigation, in areas west of the 100th meridian.) It might reasonably be expected, therefore, that with the passage of time these independent schemes of legislation, court decision, and subsequent water development would give rise to an increasing number of conflicts over water utilization. And they have.

The student of hydrology, as well as the engineer concerned with the design and construction of safe and adequate hydraulic structures, will find little comfort in the conditions of modern hydrology described above. No clear-cut, simple, overall plan for the study, control, and utilization of water resources on a national scale can even be visualized. The "politicalization" of hydrologic data is difficult even to describe adequately, much less to evaluate. But one does not have to be a profound student of economic and political life to grasp, almost intuitively, that political decisions concerning resource development, even when supported by hypothetical and academic "benefit-cost" ratios, cannot be economic—that is, materially beneficial to society—in an enduring way. Such evaluations are not purposeful in the sense that an assessment of tangible benefits and costs is, when the assessor must hazard the loss of his property and wealth as the penalty for mistakes. The construction of structures in response to a mere counting of heads (political pressure) is basically irresponsible and can be considered childish behavior. The consequences of such behavior are deleterious in exact proportion to the energy expended. The effect on hydrologic data has been noted and must be taken into account.

The men intimately involved in the magnificent engineering works associated with water-supply impoundments, irrigation projects, and flood-control planning have usually been too close to the physical details of geology, hydrology, and construction for them to have placed their efforts in overall perspective. Nevertheless on one memorable occasion they did, and their remarks are still worth repeating. The occasion was the publication of a paper by J. C. Stevens, a consulting engineer, at that time President of the American Society of Civil Engineers, and the views of 24 discussors on the "Future of Lake Mead and Elephant Butte Reservoir" (46). The student of modern hydrology would do well to become familiar with this paper, because in rudimentary form there appear in it many of the issues formally presented in this volume.

One of the eminent contributors, Dr. Charles P. Berkey, was then a consulting geologist and Newberry Professor Emeritus of Geology at Columbia University. He was consultant to the New York Board of Water Supply on the Catskill, Neversink, and intermediate developments of New York's water supply, including the dam sites and the geology of the proposed tunnels. The list of Berkey's accomplishments is too long to detail. His long and active involvement in engineering and geologic studies had left little time for contemplation as to their significance, direction, and implication. An aura of astonishment, almost shock—call it "recognition"—seems to have filled him as he sat down in his office on the Columbia campus and set down these words:

Although the principles involved in the paper by Mr. Stevens are well known, it is not certain that the implications are fully appreciated by many even in responsible relation to them. The factual data had been long known to the writer, but no statement before this one had brought so forcibly to mind their importance and bearing on long range planning. This does not apply only to Elephant Butte or Boulder, but to the entire enormous undertaking of recovering lands by irrigation. The United States has virtually set up an empire on impounded and redistributed water. The nation is encouraging development, on a scale never before attempted, of lands that are almost worthless except for the waters that can be delivered to them by the works of man. There is building up, through settlement and new population, a line of industries foreign to the normal resources of the region and they appear to be doomed to a limited life . . . .

Effort to use water on desert lands is not a new adventure by any means; but a program involving development of a great region—inviting thereby a large new population under conditions that carry elements of certain future destructive encroachment in limited and computable time—that is new. Not only is it new, but in some of the implications it is fairly astonishing. As a public policy probably nothing like it has ever been faced—certainly not on such a scale. The nearest thing in that respect was the settlement of the western high plains in earlier days by people who believed that these dust-bowl lands could be farmed in the same manner as those they came from in the Central Mississippi Valley, and no voice was raised to warn them. That was to be vast and prosperous empire, too.

For the first time, after reading this paper, the long-range significance of the suffocating effect produced by accumulating silt in all these reservoirs was borne down on the writer. He had been so much taken with the fine things being done that he had not fully appreciated the fact that the program carries elements of destruction sure to bring some kind of ending. It was always evident, of course, that there were severe limitations, but it was too easy to overlook or belittle this element of damage from within.

The experience of founding, in difficult surroundings, settlements which finally grew into influence and power is not new; and neither is their decline, and even their ending. In the past, however, none of them carried, along with the agents that built them up, such relentless elements of destruction as in the present reclamation of arid lands. The astonishing thing is that the life of these relief works promises to be so short. One could forget it if the time vista were indefinite, or if there were promise of a thousand years. In that time most human subsistence and economic lines take new turns and become adjusted; but in some of these projects, typical of the average more or less, the beginnings of decline loom already and will certainly grow into a serious problem in three or four generations. One wonders how many settlers gathering around these projects appreciate what it means.

Of course, if one is able to divorce his interest from the future, there is nothing to worry about. In this generation, and the next and the next, an upgrade can be maintained. One can claim (and it is true) that much has been added to the world; but the longer range view in this field, as in many others, is threatened by apparently incurable ailments and this one of slowly choking to death with silt is the most stubborn of all. There are no permanent cures. All are familiar with the simple elements of the matter; but the writer had faced all of that evidence without feeling greatly disturbed. The thing that did most to create a real shock was the figure on Bridge Canyon. The only time that site was visited, after mushing through thirty miles of silt-laden soupy river to get there, such close attention had to be given to the dam site itself that the silting of the proposed new reservoir was almost forgotten; but the paper by Mr. Stevens brings it out, and is a fair and timely reminder, that the problem is of the first magnitude. Although there are ways of postponing the end stages of these developments, there is no permanent cure, for the final contest transcends engineering skill. It has all the elements of a last stand (5).

Another eminent engineer of Berkey's generation, Dr. G. E. P. Smith, considered the situation: the proposed harnessing of the Colorado River, and the silting of the reservoir that would inevitably result. In his own way, he displayed recognition of the problems of public policy created by the operation of geologic forces:

> In the realm of history, two or three hundred years is a brief period. Structures and other normal investments can be amortized in a predetermined number of years, but a population settled on land with accessory rural institutions has never yet been amortized successfully. One can picture the farmers of the Colorado River Projects clinging to their houses and hoping for exceptionally well distributed river discharges to enable them to raise a few more crops. Perhaps the present civilization has been too uncharitable in its criticism of the civilization that once flourished in the valley of the Tigris and Euphrates Rivers. In some spots the present civilization is not too secure (45).

The geologic and morphologic implications contained in the large-scale construction of dams and reservoirs are only now beginning to be recognized by those most directly involved. In one very real sense there stands revealed a program for the continued and endless expenditure of ever-increasing sums of public money to combat the effects of geologic forces, as these forces strive to reach positions of relative equilibrium in the regime of rivers and the flow of water. It may be that future research in the field of modern hydrology will be primarily to find a method of extricating ourselves from this unequal struggle with minimum economic loss to the Nation.

If this appraisal seems unduly pessimistic, it is submitted that the student of hydrology had better reexamine the evidence. The facts of the situation, including the bridge piers of the Big Sioux River, the waterless intakes at St. Louis, the silt in Lake Mead, and the destruction of the hydrologic character of hydraulic data, are not in question and are symptomatic. This chapter has merely brought together, in one frame of reference, these facts and the tendencies—hydrologic if you will—that produced them. The forces involved in the situation are comparable to those met by a boy who builds a castle on the sandy ocean beach, next to the water, at low tide. And it is not pessimism, merely an objective evaluation, to predict the destruction of the castle by the action of water. In this instance good advice would consist of telling the boy to build his structure above the level of high tide. In the real world the problem is to decide on the appropriate time scale, to determine the proper elevation for construction, and to decide how to salvage a maximum from the existing situation.

NOTES

1. Am. Soc. Civ. Eng., 1961, *Cumulative Index to Am. Civ. Eng.*
1a. American Water Works Association, 1964, *A Survey of Operations Data for Waterworks in 1960.*
2. Ajwani, N. J., June, 1961, Discussion of "A new approach to peak-flow estimation," *J. Geophys. Res.*, v. 66, no. 6, p. 1996.
3. Benson, M. A., November, 1962, Plotting positions and economics of engineering planning, *Proc. Am. Soc. Civ. Eng.*, v. 88, no. HY 6, pp. 57–71.
4. Berg, B., Lane, R. W., and Larsen, T. E., 1963, Water use and related costs with cooling towers, *Ill. State Water Surv. Circ. 86.*
5. Berkey, Dr. C. P., 1946, Discussion of J. C. Stevens, "Future of Lake Mead and Elephant Butte Reservoir," *Trans. Am. Soc. Civ. Eng.*, *Paper No. 2292*, v. 111, pp. 1295–1297.
6. Boyer, M. C., 1959, Water supply versus irrigation in humid areas, *Trans. Am. Soc. Civ. Eng.*, *Paper No. 2978*, v. 124, pp. 280–290.
7. Boyer, M. C., 1961, Irrigation and drainage potentials in humid areas, *Trans. Am. Soc. Civ. Eng.*, v. 126, pt. 3, pp. 184–193.
8. Browder, E. M., and Brown, E. D., December, 1962, Water supply for the Panama Canal, *Proc. Am. Soc. Civ. Eng.*, *J. Power Div.*, v. 88, no. PO 4, pp. 69–81.
9. Carter, R. W., and Anderson, I. E., July, 1963, Accuracy of current-meter measurements, *Proc. Am. Soc. Civ. Eng.*, v. 89, no. HY 4, pp. 105–115.
10. Cohn, M. R., and Drabkin, I. E., 1948, *A Source Book in Greek Science*, New York, McGraw-Hill, p. 241.
11. Cross, W. P., 1949, The relation of geology to dry-weather stream flow in Ohio, *Trans. Am. Geophys. Un.*, v. 30, pp. 563–566.
12. Davenport, R. W., 1942, from *Hydrology* by Oscar Meinzer. Published by Dover Publications, Inc., New York 14, N.Y. and reprinted through permission of the publisher.
13. Davis, C. V. (ed.), 1952, *Handbook of Applied Hydraulics*, New York, McGraw-Hill, p. 1189.
14. *Engineering News-Record*, Nov. 1, 1956, Low flow a threat on the Mississippi, New York, McGraw-Hill.
15. *Engineering News-Record*, Sept. 6, 1962, Engineers erred in bridge failure, New York, McGraw-Hill.
16. Foster, H. A., 1959, Technical problems of flood insurance, *Trans. Am. Soc. Civ. Eng.*, v. 124, pp. 366–380.
16a. Fox, I. K., and Herfindahl, O. C., May, 1964, Attainment of efficiency in satisfying demands for water resources, *Amer. Econ. Rev.*, v. 54, no. 3, pp. 198–206.
17. Hem, J. D., 1959, Study and interpretation of the chemical characteristics of natural water, *U.S. Geol. Surv. Water Supply Paper 1473.*
18. Henderson, C., and Pickering, Q. H., June, 1963, The use of fish in the detection of contaminants in water supplies, *J. Am. Water Works Assoc.*, vol. 55, no. 6, pp. 715–720.
19. Hirshleifer, J., DeHaven, J. C., and Milliman, J. W., 1960, *Water Supply: Economics, Technology and Policy*, Chicago, Univ. of Chicago Press.

20. Howard, C. S., 1942, from *Hydrology* by Oscar Meinzer. Published by Dover Publications, Inc., New York 14, N.Y. and reprinted through permission of the publisher.

21. Humphreys, A. A., and Abbott, H. C., 1861, Report on the physics and hydraulics of the Mississippi River, *Corps of Top. Engineers, Prof. Paper 4*, Philadelphia, Lippincott.

22. Hutchins, W. A., 1942, Selected problems in the law of water rights in the West, *U.S. Dept. of Agr. Misc. Pub. No. 418*, p. 39.

23. Iowa Institute of Hydraulic Research, Report on Cooperative Studies, 1940–1941: Report No. 1, Field practice and equipment used in sampling suspended sediment, 1940; Report No. 2, Equipment used for sampling bed-load and bed-material, 1940; Report No. 3, Analytical study of methods of sampling suspended sediment, 1940; Report No. 4, Methods of analyzing sediment samples, 1941; Report No. 5, Laboratory investigations of suspended sediment samples, 1941.

23a. Kennedy, E. J., September, 1964, Streamflow records by digital computers (author's closure), *Proc. Am. Soc. Civ. Eng.*, v. 90, no. IR3, p. 75.

24. Koenig, L., July, 1959, Economic boundaries of saline-water conversion, *J. Am. Water Works Assoc.*, v. 51, no. 7, pp. 845–861.

25. Langbein, W. B., December, 1949, Annual floods and the partial duration flood series, *Trans. Am. Geophys. Un.*, v. 30, no. 6, pp. 879–881.

26. Langbein, W. B., 1960, in T. Dalrymple, Flood-frequency analyses, *U.S. Geol. Surv. Water Supply Paper 1543A*, pp. 48–51.

27. Leopold, L. B., 1962, A national network of hydrologic bench marks, *U.S. Geol. Surv. Circ. 460B*.

28. Linsley, R. K., May, 1962, Discussion of Cyclical variation in world-wide hydrologic data, *Proc. Am. Soc. Civ. Eng.*, v. 88, no. HY 3, p. 246.

29. Linsley, R. K., Kohler, M. A., and Paulhus, J. L. H., 1949, *Applied Hydrology*, New York, McGraw-Hill, p. 612.

30. Lohr, E. W., and Love, S. K., 1952, The industrial utility of public water supplies in the United States, *U.S. Geol. Surv. Water Supply Paper 1299* (east of the Mississippi River); 1954, *U.S. Geol. Surv. Water Supply Paper 1300* (west of the Mississippi River).

31. Love, S. K., 1936, Suspended matter in several small streams, *Trans. Am. Geophys. Un.*, pt. 2, pp. 447–452.

32. From *Hydrology* by Oscar Meinzer. Published by Dover Publications, Inc., New York 14, N.Y. and reprinted through permission of the publisher. Verse is from Ecclesiastes 1:7 (Moffat).

32a. Middlebrooks, T. A., 1953, Earth dam practice in the United States, *Trans. Am. Soc. Civ. Eng. Paper No. 2620*, v. CT, pp. 697–722.

33. National Resources Committee, September, 1936, Deficiencies in basic hydrologic data, *Report of the Special Advisory Committee on Standards and Specifications for Hydrologic Data, Water Resources Committee*, p. 3.

34. Pafford, R. J., Jr., 1959, Operation of Missouri River mainstem reservoirs, *Trans. Am. Soc. Civ. Eng.*, v. 124, pp. 387, 388–389.

35. Potter, W. D., 1961, Peak rates of runoff from small watersheds, *Bur. of Pub. Rds., Hyd. Design Series No. 2*.

36. Riggs, H. C., January, 1961, Frequency of natural events, *Proc. Am. Soc. Civ. Eng.*, v. 87, no. HY 1, pp. 15–26.

37. Rorabugh, M. I., 1956, Ground water in Northeastern Louisville, Ky., *U.S. Geol. Surv. Water Supply Paper 1360B*, p. 133.

38. Rouse, H., and Ince, S., 1957, *History of Hydraulics*, Iowa Inst. of Hyd. Res., ch. 4.
39. Rutter, E. J., 1951, Flood-control operation of Tennessee Valley Authority Reservoirs, *Trans. Am. Soc. Civ. Eng., Paper No. 2443*, v. 116.
40. Seelye, E. E., September, 1953, *Design* (*Data Book for Civil Engineers*), 2nd ed., New York, Wiley, pp. 5–26.
41. Seidel, H. F., Johnson, A. S., and Dencker, D. O., December, 1953, A statistical analysis of water-works data for 1950 and a survey of operating data for water works in 1950, *J. Am. Water Works Assoc.*, v. 45, no. 12.
42. Sherman, L. K., 1942, from *Hydrology* by Oscar Meinzer. Published by Dover Publications, Inc., New York 14, N.Y. and reprinted through permission of the publisher.
43. Singer, C., Holmyard, E. J., and Hall, A. R. (eds.), October, 1954, *A History of Technology*, v. 1, London, Oxford Univ. Press, ch. 19 by M. S. Drower, pp. 520–555.
44. Singer, C., Holmyard, E. J., and Hall, A. R. (eds.), 1956, *A History of Technology*, v. 2, London, Oxford Univ. Press, p. 593.
45. Smith, G. E. P., 1946, Discussion of J. C. Stevens, The Future of Lake Mead and Elephant Butte Reservoir, *Trans. Am. Soc. Civ. Eng., Paper No. 2292*, v. 111, pp. 1270–1273.
46. Stevens, J. C., 1946, The Future of Lake Mead and Elephant Butte Reservoir, *Trans. Am. Soc. Civ. Eng., Paper No. 2292*, v. 111, pp. 1231–1342.
47. Thomas, C. W., 1959, Errors in measurement of irrigation water, *Trans. Am. Soc. Civ. Eng.*, v. 124, pp. 319–340.
48. Thomas, R. O., 1960, Water—a limiting resource, *Trans. Am. Soc. Civ. Eng.*, v. 125, p. 104.
49. U.S. Dept. of Agr., 1955, Water, *The Year Book of Agriculture*, p. 256.
50. U.S. Government, 1950, Water Resources Law, Report of the President's Water Resources Policy Commission, v. 3.
51. U.S. Supreme Court, 1865 (3 Wall, 713, 724–725).
52. U.S. Supreme Court, 1941 (313 U.S. at 527–528), Dennison Dam opinion.
53. Wall, C. H., and Youngquist, C. V., May, 1942, Ohio stream-drainage areas and flow-duration tables, *Ohio State Bull., No. 111*, p. 56.
54. Williams, G. R., November, 1961, Cyclical variations in world-wide hydrologic data, *Proc. Am. Soc. Civ. Eng.*, v. 87, no. HY 6, pp. 71–88.

5

Ground Water

OCCURRENCE

Ground water includes all of the waters found beneath the surface of the ground. Ground-water hydrology, however, is concerned primarily with the movement of potable subsurface water caused by a difference in potential or head. This, in turn, is expressed as the difference in water-level elevations between two tightly cased wells screened in the same water-bearing formation, or aquifer.

Of only minor concern to the ground-water hydrologist is subsurface water that moves in response to capillary forces, water that moves under conditions of partial saturation (vadose water), in porous media above the zone of saturation, or water bound to the internal surfaces of a soil or rock complex by the forces of molecular attraction. It is only when, under special circumstances, such water adds to or subtracts from the main body of ground water that it becomes, briefly, the object of study.

Water existing under conditions of saturation and water moving under differences in head is important in engineering works (foundations, mines, tunnels, and so forth) and water-supply developments. The occurrence of water in the zone of saturation, its mode of accretion to this zone, its movement, and the methods or ways that it leaves, are the subjects of this chapter.

The physical properties of rock formations control and influence the movement of water within them and modify its chemical characteristics. The quantitative expression of these relationships under conditions encountered in the field is the subject of hydrogeology. Hydrogeology is not importantly affected by the geomorphology of the land surface. Changes in the

129

shape of the rock-air, or rock-water, interface affect the hydrogeology little, if at all. The basic rock matrix, although vulnerable to changes at the surface, is intractable in its heart. Large streams have been dammed, but the construction of subsurface dams to impede the movement of water underground has rarely been accomplished, and then on a limited scale and only under highly favorable circumstances.

The term *hydrogeology* is sometimes used as a synonym for *geohydrology*. Geohydrology is concerned with that phase of the hydrologic cycle that takes

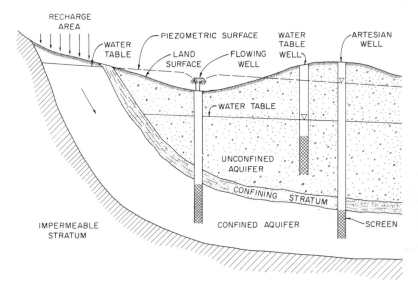

Fig. 5.1.   Unconfined and confined aquifers.

place beneath the surface of the earth. However, we know of many water-bearing formations that contain brine or fresh water and are *not* part of the hydrologic cycle because of geologic changes that have isolated them. Such formations possess certain test-determinable characteristics; they fall within the province of the ground-water engineer, but they do not participate in or affect the hydrologic cycle. The characteristics possessed by these formations are inappropriately termed geohydrologic. They are properly called hydrogeologic. When a hydrogeological system possesses natural or artificial boundaries that associate the water within it with the hydrologic cycle, the entire system may properly be termed geohydrologic.

A water-bearing formation, termed an *aquifer*, may be drained, but generally the rock materials, save for the lack of freely moving water, remain unchanged. Sometimes the dewatering of an aquifer is accompanied by a slow subsidence of the land surface, as in the San Joaquin Valley of California, or the Houston and Galveston areas in Texas. But, although water be squeezed out of the overlying beds, still the rocks from which the water was withdrawn remain unaltered. Figure 5.1 illustrates the hydraulic conditions encountered in two principal types of aquifers: a confined, or artesian, aquifer, and an unconfined, or water-table aquifer.

The Properties of Aquifers

For our purposes, any rock materials may be considered to have three basic microproperties and three basic macroproperties. Microproperties are those you can measure in the laboratory if a sample of material be brought in for testing: the porosity, permeability, and specific yield. Macroproperties are those possessed by the aquifer acting as a unit: transmissibility and storage coefficient, or "storativity" as Jacob has recently named it (15a). These properties are associated with one another, but there is no fixed, predictable relationship between them.

To explain these terms by means of an analogy, let us imagine that an airplane has lost a wing in a ground accident and that someone has brought us a possible replacement of roughly the right size, which was cannibalized from an unknown plane. We can take a small sample of the wing and test it for strength, examine its crystalline structure, determine its chemical composition. The microproperties of the material will then be known. Then we can assume an internal configuration of struts and that the same metal was used throughout and compute the strength and thus the capability of the replacement to function as a wing. And, if we make another set of assumptions, we can arrive at another, equally valid, answer. Thus, it is evident that we really do not know—and cannot determine without a test on the whole wing—its actual characteristics, for the internal arrangements within the replacement are unknown. Nor will the most careful examination of samples reveal what the gross structural arrangements really are. There is evidently only one thing to do: Test the entire wing and see how it acts as a unit. The tests of samples have yielded information that will help to clarify the results of the gross-testing procedure, but by themselves they cannot be relied upon to predict the performance of the wing.

As we all know, wind-tunnel tests of prototypes of airplanes are not unusual. And even though these are extensively accomplished and the designs later tested in the field, yet now and then some structural weakness remains hidden, as with the early Comets, and planes are destroyed by unforseen and unrevealed design flaws.

The philosophic statement of the operational approach to evaluation (as contrasted with the laboratory approach) is credited by some to the late Field Marshall Jan C. Smuts. He held that in nature determination is by wholes, and not by constituent parts. The whole is invariably something different from the result of a mathematical combination of properties of the parts. This doctrine is termed *holism*.

Porosity

Probably the most fundamental concept in hydrogeology is that open spaces, or voids, exist in rocks. This property of material is called porosity. The voids range in size from the minute and microscopic to the solution channels and caverns of limestone terranes. Such void spaces are very likely to be filled with fluid—usually water, but sometimes gas, oil, or brine.

Figure 5.2 shows the various types of porosity. The quantitative expression of porosity is the percentage of the total volume not occupied by solid

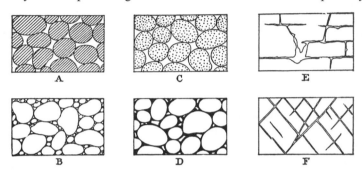

Fig. 5.2. The various types of porosity: (A) well sorted sedimentary deposit possessing high porosity; (B) poorly sorted sedimentary deposit of low porosity; (C) similar to A but consisting of pebbles that are themselves porous, so the porosity of the deposit is very high; (D) also similar to A but the porosity has been diminished by the deposition of mineral matter in the interstices; (E) rocks rendered porous by solution; and (F) rocks rendered porous by fracturing. (After O. E. Meinzer, 1923, *The Occurrence of Ground Water in the United States, U.S. Geol. Surv. Water Supply Paper 489*, p. 3.)

material. The diagrams (A), (B), (C), and (D) show primary porosity, or microporosity—porosity that can be determined in the laboratory. Diagrams (E) and (F) show secondary porosity, or macroporosity, because there is no way to determine by laboratory tests the original volume of cracks, or solution channels, that existed before the sample was removed from the parent formation. Let it be noted at this point that the evaluation of the quantity of water contained in aquifers possessing secondary porosity is not easy to accomplish, nor is one method applicable to all sets of circumstances.

Coefficient of Storage

Storage coefficient, a macroproperty of aquifers, may be defined as the volume of water that an aquifer releases from, or takes into, storage per unit horizontal surface area of aquifer per unit change in head. Figure 5.3 is a graphic representation of the concept. It should be evident that the coefficient of storage for the situation shown in Fig. 5.3A cannot be determined in the laboratory. Under these circumstances the coefficient quantifies the elasticity of the aquifer, the confining beds, and the water. It does not describe

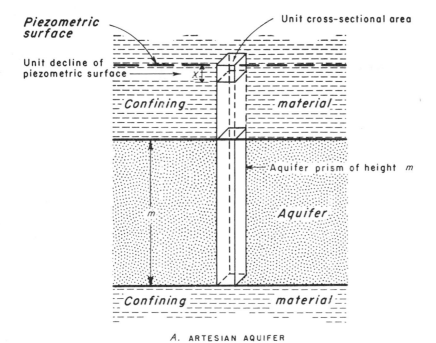

A. ARTESIAN AQUIFER

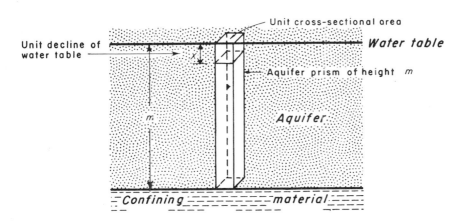

B. WATER-TABLE AQUIFER

Fig. 5.3. Diagrams showing coefficient of storage. (From J. G. Ferris *et al.*, 1962, *Theory of Aquifer Tests, U.S. Geol. Surv. Water Supply Paper 1536-E*, p. 77.)

the water obtained from the drainage of aquifer material, because under artesian conditions the formation remains completely saturated at all times.

Under the condition depicted in Fig. 5.3B, by way of contrast, if the aquifer is homogeneous and composed of granular materials, laboratory tests of the relative quantity of water yielded from a sample of the aquifer should approximate the results of a field test of the aquifer. If the aquifer contains water in cracks and crevices (Figs. 5.2E and 5.2F), the laboratory results will be meaningless.

When a sample of saturated material is allowed to drain under the action of gravity, some water usually is obtained. The volume of water so obtained depends, fundamentally, on the structure of the sample and particularly on the surface area of rock in contact with water. This surface area holds water by molecular attraction and capillarity, and the water so held will not drain in response to the force of gravity. Clay with a porosity of 50 percent yields little if any water to gravitational drainage; gravel with a porosity of 20 per cent will yield water totaling as much as 18 percent of its gross volume. One of the earliest experiments to demonstrate the efficacy of slow drainage was performed by King who found that the finer the sand, the more water is retained (22). The finest sand King tested was completely saturated and had a porosity of 34 percent. It yielded only 10 percent of its total volume in the first 24 hr of drainage, a cumulative total of approximately 13.5 percent after 10 days of drainage, and only slightly more water thereafter. The total quantity of water drained after a very long time divided by the original volume of material is called the *specific yield*. *Specific retention*, a term occasionally encountered in the literature, is equal to the porosity minus the specific yield.

The specific yield of an aquifer under the conditions shown in Fig. 5.3B can be considered the maximum value of the coefficient of storage of the aquifer. Thus, the figure for the coefficient of storage found by a field test of short duration will inevitably be smaller than the actual coefficient that would be calculated from observations after a long period of drainage.

The coefficient of storage, or storativity, of an aquifer that is under artesian conditions may be as little as 5×10^{-5}, or as much as 5×10^{-3}. This would indicate that a large pressure change over an extensive area is required to produce a substantial quantity of water.

The coefficient of storage, or storativity, of an aquifer under water-table conditions may be as little as 10^{-2}, or as much as 3×10^{-1}, and can sometimes be approximated by the specific yield of the materials of which it is composed. A more detailed discussion of this question is contained in a book by Todd (56,°23–31).

Permeability

The permeability of a material is a measure of its capacity to transmit water or another fluid through its interstices. As used here, *permeability* is

considered to refer solely to water. The *coefficient of permeability* is defined as
the rate of flow in gallons of water per day through a cross-sectional area of 1
sq ft under a hydraulic gradient of 1 ft per ft at a temperature of 60°F. In
Fig. 5.4 this would be the flow of water through area A, which is 1 ft sq.
In field practice, the adjustment to standard temperature is usually ignored

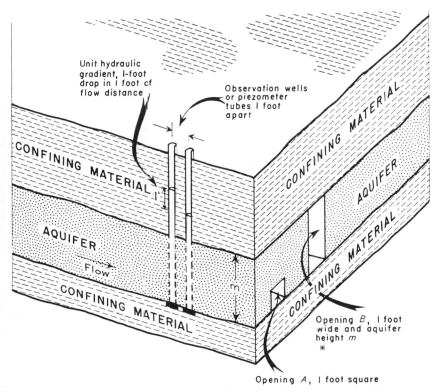

Fig. 5.4. Diagram showing the coefficients of permeability and transmissibility. (From
J. G. Ferris *et al.*, 1962, *Theory of Aquifer Tests, U.S. Geol. Surv. Water Supply Paper
1536-E*, p. 72.)

and the permeability is commonly understood to be a field coefficient at the
prevailing water temperature (which is measured and noted). Another
term frequently encountered is *coefficient of transmissibility*, first introduced
by Theis in 1935 (*51*). This is equal to the coefficient of permeability multiplied by the thickness, m, of the aquifer. In Fig. 5.4 this would be the flow
through area B under the same hydraulic gradient of 1 ft per ft.

Again, we encounter the difference between the micropermeability and the
macro-, or effective, permeability of an aquifer. The micropermeability of a
sample of formation may be determined in the laboratory by the methods
described by Fishel (*9*). But water-bearing formations are rarely, if ever,

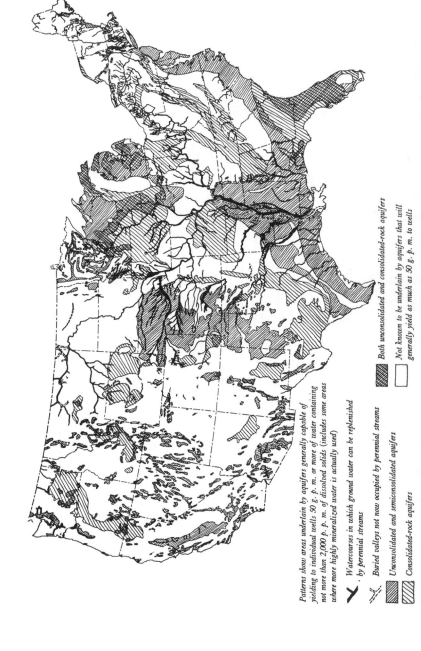

Patterns show areas underlain by aquifers generally capable of
yielding to individual wells 50 g. p. m. or more of water containing
not more than 2,000 p. p. m. of dissolved solids (includes some areas
where more highly mineralized water is actually used)

⤝⤙ Watercourses in which ground water can be replenished
   by perennial streams

⟋⟍ Buried valleys not now occupied by perennial streams

▨ Unconsolidated and semiconsolidated aquifers

▧ Consolidated-rock aquifers

▦ Both unconsolidated and consolidated-rock aquifers

☐ Not known to be underlain by aquifers that will
  generally yield as much as 50 g. p. m. to wells

Fig. 5.5. Ground-water areas in the United States. (From H. E. Thomas, 1955, Water, *U.S.
Department of Agr. Yrbk.*, Washington, D.C., Government Printing Office, p. 66.)

homogeneous, so there is no sure way of combining the laboratory perme-abilities of very small samples of aquifer to arrive at the transmissibility of the entire aquifer.

In present-day ground-water studies primary reliance is placed in the re-sults of field testing, from which the effective permeability and transmissibility of a large area of the aquifer may be computed. There are some circumstances under which even these figures are valueless for computational purposes, and where the performance test must serve directly as a calibration test of the aquifer, with extrapolations being made directly from the test data.

Along parallel lines, in recent years, the reservoir engineers of the petroleum industry have begun to question the adequacy of tests on cores in predicting reservoir performance. Wyllie recently commented:

... What matters is the rock unit and not samples of arbitrary size that may have been taken from it.
This approach may be exemplified particularly by the use of special well tests. Thus, pressure build up or fall-off analyses give directly the fluid transmissibility of a reservoir as a unit which exists in situ. Such a measurement represents an approach to reality which, as Warren *et. al.*, have shown is often very different from conventional arithmetic averages of permeability measurements made on cores (66).

The Classification of Aquifers

Two basic qualifications must be met by any geological formation that is to be classed as an aquifer: It must contain water in its interstices and it must be capable of yielding this water to wells. If it contains water but will not yield it to wells, it is probably a saturated clay. If it possesses the proper porosity and permeability, but does not contain water, it is not an aquifer. It may once have contained water which may have drained as a consequence of some geologic upheaval or have been pumped out by man. If so, the for-mation was an aquifer and may again become an aquifer, but it cannot presently be classified as such.

Aquifers can be classified in the light of their ability to yield water to a single well. They can also be classified according to their source of replenish-ment, which can be either rainfall on the outcrop of the aquifer or the seepage from a stream or lake. Ground-water areas in the United States, as shown in Fig. 5.5, have been classified by the use of both of these criteria. Such a map, on a larger scale, can be used as a point of departure for the selection of plant sites for industries that need water, for steam-electric generating plants, or for military camps or ordnance plants.

Another scheme for the classification of aquifers was proposed by Meinzer, whose classification was based primarily on the geology and rock type as related to the yields of wells (32). Geologic age, state of consolidation, nature of the interstices, and depth to aquifer were the criteria Meinzer employed. His descriptions and classifications can be used to supplement the data of Fig. 5.5.

With respect to their water-producing properties, the most productive unconsolidated formations consist of clean, coarse gravel, the coarser being the more productive. Ranking next are the uniform coarse sands. Then, each being evaluated separately, some mixtures of sand and gravel, sediments of finer grain such as fine sand and loess, many mixed alluvial deposits containing small fractions of silt, and finally, the products of rock decay that are still in place. The thickness of each formation is an extremely important factor when its ability to yield water is finally evaluated. A very thick deposit of fine sand will often yield more water to a well than a thin layer of coarse gravel.

Generalized statements about consolidated rocks are not too informative. In rocks that possess primary (micro-) permeability, such as consolidated sandstones, well productivity depends on the degree to which the sand grains are cemented together. Most consolidated formations also contain cracks and fractures and even volumes of shattered rock. The degree of cementation may vary greatly from place to place, thus changing the trans-missibility (and productivity) of the formation from the laboratory-computed figure.

As a class, sandstones are the most valuable water-bearing formations among the consolidated rocks. Next rank limestones which yield most of their water from the channels and passages produced by the solution of rock material. A well must intersect one or more of these openings for it to be productive. Lava rocks, that are permeable because of intersticial spaces in clinker or flow breccia, cavities between beds, shrinkage cracks, and other open joints resulting from the rapid cooling of solidified masses, match limestones in their ability to yield water to wells. Most of the other hard rocks—for example, granite, quartzite, shale, slate, schist—yield small amounts from joints or zones of decayed rock. The most completely unproductive of all materials are the true clays and fine silts, whose original interstices are too minute to yield water and which are too soft to have joints or other secondary openings. It is true, however, that these materials, when acting as aquifer boundaries, may replenish an aquifer when major changes occur in the water pressure of the aquifer. This type of aquifer replenishment is a one-time thing that results from "squeezing" the water out of the parent material, with a resultant irreversible change in the internal structure of the clay.

Origin and Discharge of Ground Water

In our study of ground-water hydrology, it is assumed that all of the fresh water found beneath the surface of the ground is of meteoric origin—that the water first reached the surface of the earth as precipitation and later infiltrated through the soil and subsoil to accumulate in water-bearing formations.

The earth's water-bearing formations can be considered to be conduits for the transmission and storage of water. The interface between water and land can be regarded as a natural filtration plant that removes all suspended matter from the water particles that finally reach the main ground-water body.

Movement of water from the land surface into a water-bearing formation involves (1) the penetration of the soil or rock surface, (2) the downward movement of water through a partially saturated medium—the zone of aeration, and (3) the accretion of the incoming water to the zone of saturation, which results in a rise of the piezometric surface of the aquifer.

Penetration of the water-soil interface results from a combination of molecular, capillary, and gravitational forces. The first two are more important when the soil is dry or partly saturated; gravitational forces govern the movement of water under conditions of saturation. When the supply of soil moisture in a given place is fully replenished, any additional water received from the surface is carried downward under the influence of gravity, either directly to the water table or to the intermediate belt of the zone of aeration: this phenomenon is termed the "recharge" of an aquifer.

A water-bearing formation may also be replenished by the percolation of water from a stream which occurs when the water table of an aquifer is at an elevation lower than stream level. Streams that provide water to aquifers in this manner under natural conditions are called *influent* streams. Such streams are generally encountered in arid regions. In the relatively humid eastern part of the United States most perennial streams receive water from subsurface sources and are termed *effluent*. A stream that is naturally effluent (aquifer fed) may become influent in certain reaches, as the water table is lowered through the operation of wells or infiltration galleries. Such recharge, termed *induced infiltration*, tends to sustain the offtake rates of wells producing from the aquifer.

Recharge from Precipitation

Wherever an aquifer outcrops at the land surface, the outcrop will be rained upon. Some of this impinging water can be expected to percolate downward and to reach the main body of ground water and thus raise the water table. The process of recharge and the influences that affect it are best illustrated by an example. Figure 5.6 has been prepared on the basis of data published by the U.S. Geological Survey concerning a potential productive area in which no large wells were operating (23). Shortly after the report was made, a well field with a capacity of 20 million gal a day was placed into operation, thus masking and distorting the precipitation effects. However, the record shown in Fig. 5.6 is long enough to illustrate details of the recharge of an aquifer by rainfall.

The Survey measured well 117, a 45-ft deep abandoned house well situated south of Hamilton, Ohio, 2100 ft south of the intersection of Symmes Road and River Road and 100 ft east of River Road. Land-surface elevation is approximately 580 ft mean sea level (msl), and the elevation of the water in the well varied, in response to natural conditions, from a low of 552 ft to a high of approximately 563 ft. The original gradient of the water table was to the west, toward the Miami River. Most of the year the elevation of the nearby river varied between 545 and 550 ft msl.

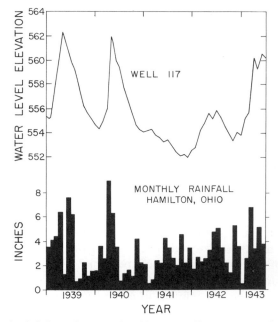

Fig. 5.6. Effect of rainfall on the water level in an aquifer. (Based on illustrations from F. H. Klaer and R. G. Kazmann, July, 1943, *A quantitative study of the well fields of the Mill Creek Valley Water Supply Project*, Butler County, Ohio, U.S. Geol. Surv., open file rept.)

An extensive study of geologic conditions and the logs of nearby wells established that the underlying material, excluding a 6-in. layer of sandy top soil, is sand and gravel, in varying proportions, from the surface down to bedrock, some 200 ft below the surface. A detailed report on the geology and ground-water conditions throughout the entire area has been published by Klaer and Thompson (*24*).

Figure 5.6 permits a direct comparison between the water-level elevation in well 117 at the end of each month and the rainfall recorded during the month at the U.S. Weather Bureau gage at nearby Hamilton, Ohio. Although there is no precise correlation between water-level elevation and rainfall, the data clearly show the accretion of water to the water table and establish, moreover, that the same quantity of rain will not always produce the same change in water level.

Normally, water levels are low and the soil is dry by the end of December. The ground may be frozen, although this is not certain. In 1939, 3.5 in. of precipitation were recorded in January and the water table rose about 0.2 ft. Either the precipitation was in the form of snow which did not melt, or, if it melted, most of it was held in the 20 ft of sand and gravel above the water table. In February, it rained more than 4 in. The water level rose a little more than 2 ft. In March, about 4.5 in. of precipitation resulted in another 2-ft rise in water level. In April, slightly more than 6 in. of rain raised the water level almost 3 ft. All of this time, remember, water was draining from the aquifer into the Miami River, about 6500 ft away from the well. May was a dry month; only 1.2 in. of precipitation fell, and the water level dropped more than 1 ft. In June, despite the heaviest rainfall of the year, 7.6 in., the water level fell another foot. Evidently plant root systems intercepted percolating water and prevented very much water from reaching the water table. The decline in water level, of course, was due to the discharge of water contained in storage in the aquifer into the Miami River. (During April, 1940, by way of comparison, 9 in. of rain resulted in a water level rise of about 6 ft.) The decline continued on a relatively uniform basis throughout the rest of 1939 despite variations in rainfall. The reduction in rate of decline is analogous to the reduction in rate of output from a freely discharging storage tank that results from a decrease of head in the tank.

The following year, 1940, was a repetition of 1939. But in 1941 the precipitation during the first four months was far below normal; the soil was dry and remained dry. The root systems of the crops (mostly corn) did not develop properly. Water levels continued to decline, but at a decreasing rate—the rate of decline can be expressed as a decay curve—as the quantity of water in storage in the aquifer above spillway elevation was reduced.

The entire process may be summarized as follows: In the winter and spring when the ground is unfrozen and vegetation is dead or dormant, precipitation reaches the water table and replenishes the aquifer after soil-moisture demand has been satisfied. Water reaching the water table immediately begins to move to areas of lower elevation, where the natural discharge of the aquifer supports stream flow. After planting, with the onset of warm weather, little if any precipitation reaches the water table. Plant root systems take up the water almost as fast as the rainfall is absorbed by the soil surface. The energy gradient of the soil (pF) works against the force of gravity. Even water that has passed through the root zone may move upward as vadose water under partly saturated conditions when the uppermost soil layers become dry enough. In the fall rainfall is minor, and the dryness of the upper layers is sufficient to keep water from reaching the ground-water body—water is held by molecular attraction and by capillary forces in the upper zones of material. Then, in the winter and spring, recharge occurs again.

Surface-Water Infiltration as a Source of Recharge

When an aquifer outcrops directly in a lake or stream, the outcrop area sometimes remains permeable due to the scouring action of moving water. Water from the stream will then enter the aquifer if the water level in the stream rises above the water in the aquifer. Among hydraulic engineers this phenomenon has long been recognized as bank storage (Fig. 4.2). It is usually associated with floods. Cooper and Rorabaugh have published an elegant mathematical analysis of the hydraulics of this phenomenon (*6a*, *45a*).

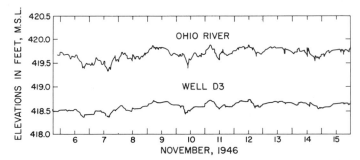

Fig. 5.7. Water levels in the Ohio River at Louisville, Ky., and water levels in a nearby observation well. Note that the maximum amplitude of river-level fluctuation is approximately 0.7 ft and the associated change in well level is approximately 0.4 ft. (After M. I. Rorabaugh, 1956, *Ground Water in Northeastern Louisville, Kentucky, U.S. Geol. Surv. Water Supply Paper 1360-B*, plates 10, 11.)

Water stored in the aquifer in this manner drains readily when the river level falls. Occasionally the bank storage of the sediments bordering on a lake can constitute a respectable fraction of the water stored in the lake.

After a comprehensive study of the water budget of Lake Mead that included a long period of observation of all inflow and all outflow (including evaporation losses), Langbein concluded that "the water storage beneath the reservoir sides and bottom when the lake is filled to capacity is about 3,200,000 acre-feet" (*26*). This figure may be compared with the volume of some 27,000,000 acre-ft that is the above-ground storage of the lake at maximum stage.

When a well is near the area of recharge, almost all changes in river level may be reproduced on a smaller scale as changes in well level. Figure 5.7, based on Rorabaugh's work (*45*) in Louisville, shows how the minor changes in the river level at Louisville, on the order of 0.2 ft (0.07 psi), caused by operation of the locks, are reflected in the levels of observation well D-3, situated about 150 ft from the area of recharge (*45*). Ground-water levels are, in many instances, extremely sensitive to minute changes in pressure, and these are transmitted over surprisingly long distances. On a larger scale the Mississippi River at Baton Rouge performs a similar function in replenishing aquifers that are in hydraulic contact with it. Figure 5.8 shows how the considerably larger changes in the stage of the Mississippi River are reproduced in an observation well two miles from the river. Meyer and Turcan commented: "The fluctuations between river stage and ground-water level have a different magnitude and there is a slight lag in the rises and declines of water levels in well EB-242 from the fluctuations shown for the river; however it is obvious that there is a direct relation between river stage and ground-water level" (*33*).

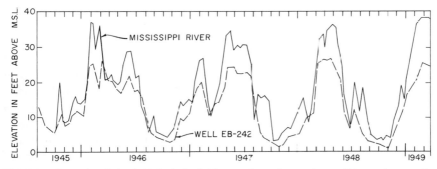

Fig. 5.8. Water levels in the Mississippi River and an observation well located two miles from the river. (After R. R. Meyer and A. N. Turcan, Jr., 1955, *Geology and Ground-Water Resources of the Baton Rouge area, Louisiana, U.S. Geol. Surv. Water Supply Paper 1296*, p. 20.)

Natural Discharges from Aquifers

The discharge and replenishment of aquifers under natural conditions are complementary phenomena. We have already seen how water from precipitation may enter an aquifer where storage space is available and how it may be discharged into a river. Under similar conditions of storage, surface water may also enter aquifers—the bank storage phenomenon has been noted—and quietly drain back into the reservoir or stream.

The best known discharges from aquifers, however, are those found under the classification "springs." These occur in great variety and some are very spectacular—hot springs and geysers come to mind immediately. Although the origin of springs always has been somewhat of a mystery, the purity of their waters has been legendary. But we now consider spring water as being in need of testing and possible sterilization. Water gushing forth from the rock also has been believed to possess medicinal or curative properties. Many places are identified by the word "Spring" in the place name—for instance, Hot Springs, Arkansas, White Sulphur Springs, West Virginia, and Warm Springs, Georgia.

The largest springs are found in rock country whose underlying formations are basalt or limestone. The aquifer intake outcrops at the land surface at a much higher elevation than the spring; this difference in level provides the motive power for water movement. The aquifer usually rests on an impermeable formation, so the aquifer has a natural spillway where this impermeable bed outcrops. This point of discharge is the spring. When the rate of discharge is very low, such a discharge is sometimes called a natural seep. For our purposes, we may note that an aquifer discharging through a spring is in an overall state of natural hydraulic equilibrium, the annual volume of discharge oscillating about a long-term mean rate. This, of course, assumes that the intake area is sufficiently permeable and sufficiently high above the water table to accommodate all of the recharge. Thus, over a period of years a systematic series of discharge measurements at a spring may actually enable computation of the natural annual recharge to the aquifer.

But there are many instances where the water table is at, or very near, the land surface. Thus, after a brief period of rainfall the water table and lowest part of the land surface may coincide. If the outcrop is a relatively low area, surrounded by lands of a slightly higher elevation, we may have a swampy condition or even a shallow lake in the area. Since the rainfall is already reaching the aquifer in excess of the aquifer's capacity to remove the water under existing hydraulic gradients, we encounter the phenomenon of *rejected recharge*. Under existing hydraulic conditions the aquifer, thick and permeable though it may be, cannot accept all of the recharge for lack of storage space. This surplus water manifests itself as a change in the swamp or lake level, or as discharge from the lake's spillway, or both.

Sometimes, especially in arid regions of artificially high water table (above the delta of a large reservoir such as Elephant Butte, for example), the aquifer can accept all of the water reaching it. The hydrogeologic system may be able to transmit all of the recharge. However, this necessitates high water-level elevations in the outcrop to create the necessary hydraulic gradients. Under such circumstances water-loving vegetation, with root systems deep enough to reach the water table, may flourish. This type of plant has been named a *phreatophyte*—from Greek root-words meaning a "well plant." Such a plant is literally a natural well with pumping equipment that lifts water from the zone of saturation. The most widespread of the desert phreatophytes in the United States are salt grass, greasewood, mesquite, and salt cedar. All occur in valley bottoms and along streams (*58*).

Salt grass will survive when the water table is as much as 12 ft below the land surface. Greasewood grows best where the depth to water table does not exceed 15 ft. Mesquite has been known to send its roots 40, 50, or even 100 ft to water. Salt cedar, willow, and cottonwood prefer localities where the depth to the capillary fringe is from 10 to 20 ft—this means that, depending on the fineness of the material, the water table may be 30 ft or more below land surface. In 1958 Robinson, of the Geological Survey, estimated that 16 million acres of western land were covered by phreatophytes that used a total of almost 25 million acre-ft of water annually (44). This water if not rejected recharge, was at least wasted recharge, since it was not available for use by man. Fletcher and Elmendorf, of the Department of Agriculture, have outlined methods to control this type of vegetation (10).

The magnitude of water usage by phreatophytes may be properly evaluated by comparison with the annual evaporation losses from the 50 reservoirs and regulated lakes with the largest amounts of evaporation. Meyers estimates the annual loss to the atmosphere from these bodies of water to be slightly more than 9 million acre-ft a year (34). This compares to the 25 million acre-ft wasted annually by phreatophytes.

The reader who is interested in ground-water conditions in his State as well as in the entire United States will find detailed information and a comprehensive list of references in a recent book by McGuinness (30a).

MEASUREMENTS

In the study of the occurrence and movement of ground water we are interested in two types of measurements: water level (or pressure), and discharge. When the depth to water is less than 200 ft, the simplest, most convenient way to measure it is to chalk the first 3 ft of a steel tape and to lower the end of the tape into the well until it is beneath the water surface. A ft-mark of the tape is held and slowly brought down to the measuring point. Then the tape is reeled in, and the water leaves a mark on the chalked tape. The distance from the end of the tape to the mark is recorded and subtracted from the ft-mark held at the measuring point. The difference is the depth to water.

For example, if you hold the 150 ft-mark to the measuring point and the water mark is 1.47 ft, then the depth to water is 148.53 ft. Sometimes several trials may be required to find the water level in a well. The procedure is repeated until the level has been measured. Field notes are usually recorded in the following tabular form:

Date	Time	Well	Held	Wet	D. W.
1/16/62	1243	H-15	150	1.47	148.53
	1347	H-16	175	2.68	172.32

The matter is discussed in detail because even so simple and fundamental an operation as obtaining the correct water level in a well is not always apparent, even to an educated man.

For intensive studies of ground-water conditions, individual water-level measurements may be replaced with the record furnished by an automatic water-stage recorder. This device is generally a float-actuated mechanism that turns a drum in proportion to the change in water level. At the same time, clockwork pulls a pen across a chart attached to the surface of the drum.

At any instant, therefore, the pen will record both time and water level simultaneously. This record can then be analyzed for any time interval of interest. Figure 5.9 shows one type of water-stage recorder in common use. It yields one chart per week, and is actuated by an 8-day clock. A variety of chart intervals, ranging from 1 hr to 1 month, can be obtained from the same mechanism by the simple device of gear changing and clock alteration. A variety of gage scales are available, so that a 1-ft change in water-level

Fig. 5.9. Water-stage recorder. (Courtesy Leopold and Stevens Instruments, Inc., Portland, Oregon.)

elevation can be represented by a chart distance as small as 0.05 ft or as large as 1.0 ft.

Where the water level is known to be of great depth, and where repeated trials of depth to water with a steel tape would be time consuming or unnecessarily tiring, an electric water-level indicator, which consists of a battery, voltmeter, a calibrated two-wire cable, and an electrode, is used. When the electrode is immersed in water, the circuit between the two wires is completed and the voltmeter signals the passage of current. The depth to water is then read directly from the calibrations found on the cable. This device is also useful in wells that are wet from condensation or have water leaking from pump columns—under such conditions the tape-chalk combination is not satisfactory because the chalk can get wet before the end of the tape reaches the water surface.

Another method of measuring water levels, used primarily in wells that are producing water, is the so-called "air-line" method. As the pump is installed in the well, a copper, plastic, or steel tube is attached to the top of the pump bowls. Then as the pump is lowered, tubing is added so that the pump discharge column is paralleled by a $\frac{1}{4}$-in. steel, plastic, or copper tube. At the land surface this small tube is connected to a hand-operated tire pump or to a small air compressor with a pressure gage installed in the line. Air is pumped into the tube until the pressure gage indicates a maximum pressure. This means that the air pressure within the tube is equal to the water pressure in the well at the tube's outlet. Inasmuch as the elevation of the end of the tube is known by measurements made during its installation, the pressure can be converted into feet of water above the end of the tube. The depth-to-water or water-level elevation can then be computed for any given pressure reading.

The accuracy of water-level measurements made with a steel tape or electric water-level indicator is usually within 0.02 ft. The accuracy of an air-line or pressure-gage measurement depends primarily on the accuracy and condition of the gage but is normally within 1 ft of the true level as determined by means of a steel-tape measurement. The air lines themselves, however, have been known to become clogged with mineral deposits or bacterial growth or to develop leaks and consequently yield false information. A series of airline measurements should be checked periodically by the use of a steel tape or an electric water-level indicator.

Measurements of ground-water discharge are accomplished by a variety of devices. Most of these are designed to measure the flow of water through pipes. For purposes of test the most commonly used device is the sharp-edged, freely discharging, circular orifice, This is simply a plate with a circular hole cut in it. The edge of the hole has a 45° bevel on the downstream side. This plate is inserted concentrically at the end of a long, open-ended, horizontal pipe (it is usually held in place with a thread protector) and the head produced by the constriction in the flow is measured by means of a piezometer located at least one pipe diameter upstream from the orifice plate. The only qualifications are: (1) that the ratio of the orifice diameter to the pipe diameter be 0.75 or less and that a full pipe of water be available, (2) that the orifice plate be perpendicular to the pipe and, (3) that the plate be clean and the edge sharp. It is necessary that the 45° bevel start at a distance of $\frac{1}{16}$ in. from the upstream face of the orifice plate. Tables are available to show the discharge in gal per min for any given head on the piezometer above the center line of the pipe.

Other devices commercially available include weirs, propellor meters, venturi tubes, sonic and magnetic flow meters, and a venturi-type device known as a Parshall flume.

The discharges of industrial or municipal well fields are usually recorded by the operating personnel. The actual measurements are made with

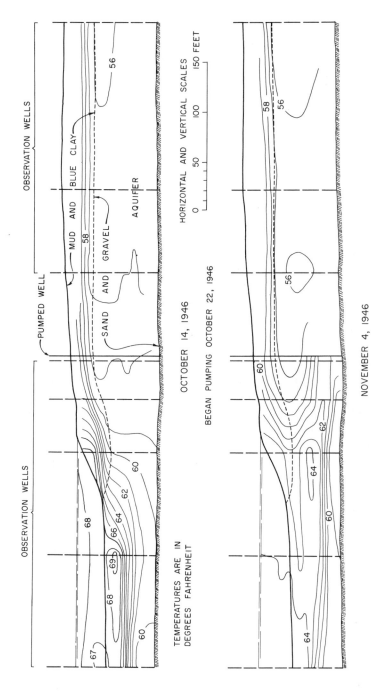

OBSERVATION WELLS

PUMPED WELL

OBSERVATION WELLS

MUD AND BLUE CLAY

SAND AND GRAVEL

AQUIFER

68 69 66 64 62 60 68 67 60 58 56

OCTOBER 14, 1946

BEGAN PUMPING OCTOBER 22, 1946

TEMPERATURES ARE IN
DEGREES FAHRENHEIT

HORIZONTAL AND VERTICAL SCALES

0   50   100   150 FEET

58 56 56 60 64 62 60 64

NOVEMBER 4, 1946

PUMPING STOPPED NOVEMBER 5, 1946

Fig. 5.10. Temperature distributions in a river-fed aquifer associated with the removal of water from a well on the bank of the river. (After M. I. Rorabaugh, 1956, *Ground Water in Northeastern Louisville, Kentucky, U.S. Geol. Surv. Water Supply Paper 1360-B*, plate 17.)

commercial flow meters and may be considered as being within 2 or 3 percent of the true values.

In areas where ground water is used for irrigation, a flowmeter is rarely operated on a well. Estimates of total discharge are based either on tests of a representative sampling of operating wells or on a determination of the area irrigated combined with a study of water useage, or a combination of both. This can sometimes be checked by the record of power use (if electric power is used) and by appropriate computations made on this basis. Under the most favorable conditions such approximations may be within 10 percent of the true offtake.

There are other, indirect, methods of determining the total pumpage of ground water over a large area. These methods are based on the preparation of piezometric maps of the underlying water-bearing formations which are then evaluated by using the results of performance tests made on the aquifer. Under certain conditions the year-to-year change in areal ground-water levels multiplied by the average coefficient of storage may yield an estimated total of ground-water offtake. The average slope of the piezometric surface at a bounding contour, shown on a piezometric map, multiplied by the average transmissibility of the aquifer and the length of the contour will yield an approximate figure of input through the circumference. The change in storage within the area bounded by the exterior contour line plus the input should be equal to the total offtake.

Intensive studies of ground-water conditions invariably include a systematic sampling of well water and its subsequent analysis in the laboratory (*13, 42*). Ground-water temperatures are also measured inasmuch as the temperature of water may be of great importance both for diagnostic purposes and for evaluation of the suitability of the water for industrial or other uses. Temperature measurements may be made at single wells over a long period of time, or a study may be made of the distribution of water temperatures within the aquifer at various levels. Rorabaugh's classic study of the movement of water from a river to a nearby discharging well included a number of aquifer cross sections, like those shown in Fig. 5.10 (*45*). These cross sections show the change in temperature in the aquifer caused by the infiltration of warm river water. Prior to the October 14 test, river water was slowly replenishing the aquifer as a result of gradients caused by water withdrawals more than a mile away. The temperature changes in the aquifer caused by pumping the test well for two weeks at an average rate of about 1100 gal per min are clearly indicated.

MOVEMENT
Theory

When ground water moves, it usually moves slowly. A lazy snail would have no difficulty in keeping up with the most rapid movement of ground water under natural conditions. Of course this statement applies only to flow through porous media and excludes the rapid flow of water in the solution channels of cavernous limestone or the cracks and fissures of a basalt aquifer. In hydraulic terms, ground-water flow through porous media is usually laminar. This type of flow is sometimes called streamline, or viscous. In each thread of laminar movement there is an endless procession of water particles, linked together by molecular forces, following the same streamline path. These threads are propelled by the differential head that overcomes the friction with the adjacent threads and with the thread of more slowly moving particles near the wall of the interstice. The movement of a particle of water is not constant, for it speeds up gradually when approaching the neck of a pore space and slows down where it enters the larger space.

Under these circumstances the mean, or average, velocity of the water varies directly as the hydraulic gradient—a relationship discovered by Poiseuille in his work with capillary tubes and found, by Henri Darcy, to be applicable to flow through filter sand. Later work has shown that the relationship holds for Reynolds numbers that are less than 1 (46). The Reynolds number, R, is the ratio between the inertial and viscous forces operating in the flow of a fluid. Reynolds number is expressed as:

$$R = \frac{\rho v D}{\mu}$$

where ρ is the fluid density, v the velocity, D the diameter (of a pipe), and μ the viscosity of the fluid. To adapt this criterion to flow in porous media, the apparent or average velocity of the fluid is used for v, and average diameter of the grain, d, is substituted for D. Of course grain diameter is only an approximation of the average pore diameter. However, it is difficult, from a practical standpoint, to measure a pore, and, in any event, the Reynolds number is only a rough criterion of the limit of laminar flow. As with many other hydraulic measurements the criterion is a limiting one and is used as a caution rather than as an exact quantity in itself. When the Reynolds number reaches an order of magnitude of $10°$, then the possibility that Darcy's law may not be applicable must be taken into account.

Darcy's Law

Darcy's law states that the flow rate through porous media is proportional to the head loss and is inversely proportional to the length of the flow path. This law can be stated in mathematical terms as follows:

$$v = \frac{Ph}{l}$$

in which v is the velocity of water, at the observed water temperature, through a column of permeable material, h is the difference in head between the ends of the column, l is the length of the column, and P is a constant that depends on the character of the material, especially on the size and arrangement of the grains.

In the laboratory all of the variables except P, the coefficient of permeability can be measured directly. Thus, the value of P can be computed and a consistent hydraulic system can be defined. The system holds good until v exceeds a critical value. This value causes the Reynolds number to exceed unity, and the value of permeability determined under these conditions then becomes meaningless. Fortunately, in the overwhelming majority of instances the value of R, the Reynolds number, is far less than unity, and Darcy's law holds. It is only in connection with water flow in the vicinity of discharging wells that R exceeds unity, the flow is often turbulent and Darcy's law does not apply.

Considered mathematically, Darcy's law is merely one expression of the well-known Laplace equation that describes steady-state conditions in certain homogeneous fields. This has made it possible to prepare models, or analogs, of aquifers and to use mathematical relaxation methods in studying problems of ground-water movement (56, 307–325). The methods have certain limitations that must be understood. In many instances the results of model studies serve merely to show that actual conditions differ from those assumed in building the model—but this too is valuable information.

Darcy's law may also be considered to be the special end case resulting when a state of unsteady flow decays to steady-state conditions. This is approximately similar to an equation that describes the action of a spring under compression as a sudden load is applied. Such an equation would describe the action of the spring at all times, but as time increases, the change resulting during successive intervals is reduced until, finally, it becomes negligible and the end condition (steady state) has arrived. So with the change in the piezometric surface in the vicinity of a well that derives its water from storage within an aquifer: At first water levels change rapidly; then as offtake continues, the change in water levels near the well becomes smaller and smaller, finally arriving at a state approximating equilibrium.

The branch of field theory now used in analyses of ground-water movement was first used in studying the flow of heat in solids, and the mathematical work that described the flow of heat has been successfully adapted to describe ground-water flow. Pioneer in this work was Theis who, in 1935, published his famous nonequilibrium formula for the flow of ground water (51). The Theis formula introduced the factor of time into the basic equation of ground-water flow and made it possible to predict the rate of change of ground-water levels at various points in an aquifer due to any assumed rate and distribution of offtake. The well-known Thiem formula can be obtained by applying Theis' equation to obtain drawdowns at two points and allowing t, the duration of pumpage to become infinitely large.

A convenient form of the Theis equation, or nonequilibrium formula, is

$$s = \frac{114.6Q}{T} W(u),$$

where

$$u = \frac{1.87r^2S}{Tt}$$

s = observed drawdown, ft
Q = constant well offtake, gpm
T = transmissibility, equal to permeability P, in gpd per sq. ft, multiplied by the aquifer thickness, m, in ft.
r = distance from point of offtake to point of observation, ft
S = coefficient of storage of aquifer (dimensionless)
t = time, days, since the start of offtake
$W(u)$ = "well function," elsewhere termed negative exponential integral, designated as $-Ei(-u)$. (Tables of this function have been published in *Geol. Surv. Water Supply Paper 887*, *Water Supply Paper 1536-E*, and in many other books and publications on ground water. An inverse table of this function is found at the back of this book.)

Innumerable studies based on this equation have been made of the effects of additional well offtakes in partially utilized aquifers. Recently, electrical analogs of aquifers have been constructed that simulate hydrogeologic constants by use of transistors, resistances, and capacitances. These networks, in conjunction with wave-form generators that simulate the offtakes of wells, are used to study nonequilibrium conditions. Read-outs (the drawdowns at any point) are obtained by using a probe connected to an oscilloscope. The trace resulting on the oscilloscope is often photographed for later study. The validity and reliability of the results are directly dependent on the soundness of the field work and interpretation of aquifer tests (in terms of hydrogeology and geohydrology), since these constitute the raw data for the analog. This work, still in its infancy, undoubtedly will increase in importance.

Evaluation of Permeability and Other Aquifer Characteristics

Many methods have been developed to evaluate the characteristics of aquifers. The applicability of the methods, and their limitations, should be understood by the hydrologist since the information so obtained may serve as the basis for planning the development of ground-water resources.

An aquifer may consist of one or more identifiable geologic units operating as a hydraulic entity. If regarded as a mechanism for the supply of water, a number of questions should be asked about this entity. Among the most important of these are the qualitative or semiqualitative questions: How widespread is it in area? What is its thickness? Is it a uniform, homogeneous deposit or is it hydraulically discontinuous because of faults, permeability pinch-outs, or excessive stratification? What are its boundaries? Is it being replenished? Where and when does recharge occur? Is it possible to alter the rate of recharge? These questions may be answered, in part, by geologists without special training in the quantitative methods of hydrogeology.

To obtain more complete answers, however, the qualitative determinations must be supplemented by quantitative evaluation. The two principal methods are laboratory work on samples and in-place field tests of the water-bearing formation. The limitations of laboratory methods have been discussed previously and will not be repeated here.

The field methods used in the study of the movement of ground water are many and versatile. They divide into two basic groupings: mass effect and individual.

The mass effect methods depend on gross measurements of offtake and drawdown. The results place numerical values upon effective or average aquifer properties. While they tell us little, if anything, about the movement of an individual water particle, they tell us a great deal about the effect of force fields on the overall movement of underground water. These field methods of aquifer evaluation are designated, broadly, as aquifer-performance tests. An outstanding summary of these tests and their application to the solution of specific problems has been prepared by Walton of the Illinois State Water Survey (61).

The other category of field tests deals with the movement of the individual water particles through the formation. This type of test consists of injecting a tracer of some sort into the aquifer and sampling the aquifer at a distance from the point of injection to determine the time that it took for the tracer to arrive at the point of sampling. This is a valuable technique when applied to aquifer-contamination problems and has great applicability in the study of the underground disposal of radioactive wastes, one of the major problems of our era.

Field Tests

Aquifer Performance

An aquifer-performance test consists of pumping a well at a constant rate of offtake and measuring the elevation of the piezometric surface at one or more points in the vicinity of the discharging well. During the test the offtake is maintained at as constant a rate as possible and water levels in the observation wells are measured at predetermined intervals of time. The time and water level are carefully noted after each measurement is completed. In addition samples of water are collected and the well-water temperature is measured periodically.

The analysis of an aquifer-performance test does not merely yield usable

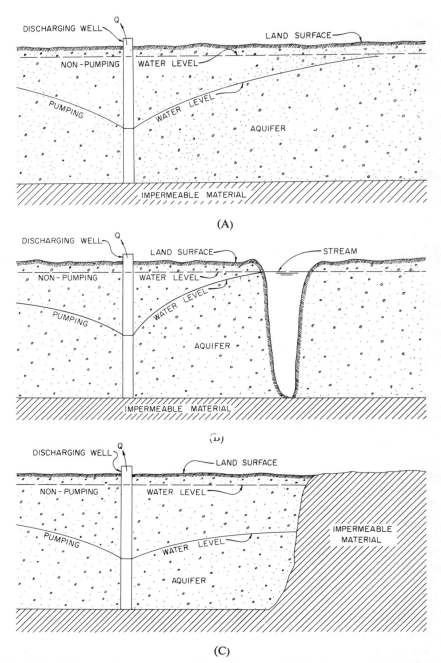

Fig. 5.11. Basic situations encountered in aquifer-tests: (A) Profile of cone of depression created by a well pumping water from a thick, extensive aquifer that has no nearby boundaries; (B) profile of the cone of depression created by a well pumping water from a thick, extensive aquifer that is replenished by infiltration from a stream located near the well; (C) profile of the cone of depression created by a well pumping water from a thick, extensive aquifer that is limited, on one side, by a subsurface, impermeable wall, near the well.

figures for the effective transmissibility and the coefficient of storage of the aquifer. It may also demonstrate the existence of hydrogeologic boundaries, such as impermeable discontinuities, or structures that reduce the areal extent of the aquifer, or of potential recharge boundaries, such as the beds of perennial streams, that assure the permanence of the supply. A theoretical treatment of aquifer tests, summarizing and combining material formerly widely scattered in the technical literature, was recently published by the U.S. Geological Survey (8).

There are two principal methods of analysis: (1) analysis of the rate of change of drawdown and (2) analysis of the distribution of drawdown in the aquifer at any time. Theoretically, the results obtained by the use of each method should be the same; in practice this is rarely so, for the geologic and hydraulic characteristics of aquifers rarely coincide completely with the assumptions made in the derivation of the formulas. Consequently, the results of the tests must be interpreted with discretion and with an eye on the end use of the data. For example, in analyzing data for purposes of evaluating a potential ground-water supply, the computed quantity of water should be based on a pessimistic interpretation of the results. Any time there is doubt, it should be resolved in favor of the smaller water supply. On the other hand, in a mine-dewatering problem all data should be interpreted in favor of the maximum quantity of water being obtained. In this way the pump capacity will be adequate to dispose of the water, the mine will not be flooded out, and no one will drown.

The basic situations encountered in aquifer-performance tests are (1) a thick, extensive aquifer with no nearby boundaries, (2) the same aquifer with a perennial stream replenishing it, and (3) the same aquifer with an impermeable boundary cutting it. These situations are shown in Fig. 5.11. Figure 5.12 shows the distinctive shapes of the time-drawdown curves that result from measurements in a nearby observation well; in each instance the observation well is assumed to be located in the same position relative to the discharging well.

These basic situations form the components of the practical problem of the evaluation of ground-water resources. An infinite variety of conditions is possible here from the standpoint of aquifer geometry and geology and well location. Moreover, interpretation of the geohydrology may be complicated by the periodic disappearance of recharge (the stream may go dry, or the stream bed may become more or less impermeable due to siltation), by recharge from rainfall, and by the arbitrary and unpredictable operation of unknown wells in an area.

The effective transmissibility of an aquifer under such circumstances may not remain constant. A decrease in the saturated thickness of aquifer may occur owing to water-level declines created by pumpage. Or, even without aquifer dewatering, the transmissibility may vary if the source of recharge is a river. This latter condition comes about because the transmissibility term in the equation of flow contains within it the assumption of constant water viscosity. The change in transmissibility varies as the viscosity of water changes. A change of water temperature from 34°F to 90°F, accompanied by a decrease in viscosity from 1.70 to 0.77 centipoises. At 68°F the viscosity is 1.005 centipoises. Thus, the transmissibility of a formation changes by about 1.5 percent per degree Fahrenheit in the temperature range normally encountered

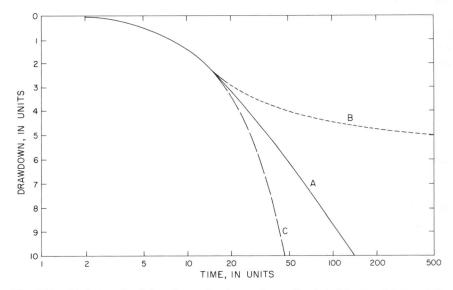

Fig. 5.12. Hydrograph of drawdowns in observation wells placed in the vicinity of the discharging wells under the circumstances depicted in Fig. 5.11. The drawdown scale is arithmetic, the time scale is logarithmic. Curve *A* shows drawdown in an idealized, infinite aquifer; *B* shows the result of the infiltration of river water; *C* shows the result of the cut-off wall.

in ground-water work. The yield of a well at constant drawdown that produces water that infiltrated the aquifer from a nearby stream may be expected to vary cyclically, during the year, as the effective temperature of the water in the aquifer changes.

To sum up: Aquifer-performance tests are an invaluable tool in the evaluation of the hydrogeology of an area. They have been developed to yield information on geohydrological boundaries as well as the formation constants, *T* (transmissibility) and *S* (storage coefficient). They serve as the basis for well-field design and for predictions of water levels under any assumption of well offtakes. By placing another set of constraints on the interpretation of the geology, the number of possibilities is reduced and ground-water conditions can be evaluated more properly. The geologist finds that a knowledge of hydrogeology often enables him to interpret the geologic findings with greater certainty than would otherwise be possible.

Tracers

In principle the tracer method of studying ground-water movement corresponds to placing a float in a river and timing its travel between two points. We have already noted that although the velocity of a float is readily determinable, the relationship between its movement and the mean water velocity is not fixed. A tracer, injected as a slug into a ground-water body, depicts the movement of ground-water threads with accuracy, but is subject to diffusion, dispersion, dilution, and adsorption. In short, it tends to vanish in the aquifer—and an indicator that gets lost is not much good.

The slow speed of ground-water movement under natural conditions— probably 95 percent of all such movement is at the rate of less than 5 ft per day—was noted previously. This means that any experiment designed to study the motion of water over long distances by use of tracers will require considerable time to complete. And this too is unsatisfactory in the evaluation of an aquifer as a source of water supply.

The ideal tracer: (1) is detectable at low concentration; (2) is absent, or nearly absent, from the water of the aquifer, (3) must not react within the aquifer to form a precipitate, (4) must not be absorbed or adsorbed; and (5) is cheap and readily available. There is no substance that meets these requirements for every aquifer, although reasonably satisfactory tracers may be found for particular sets of circumstances. Tracers may be classified by method of detection: color, chemical determination, electrical conductivity, nuclear radiation, mass spectrography, and flame spectrophotometry.

Organic dyes, the most satisfactory of which is sodium fluorescein, may be detected in very low concentrations. Fluorescein, however, is readily adsorbed by the clay fractions of the geological matrix. The chloride ion in sodium or calcium chloride also has been used successfully as a tracer. Radioactive substances provide convenient and very sensitive tracers since they can be measured by their nuclear radiations at mass concentrations as low as 10^{-17}. They are, however, affected by base-exchange and adsorption phenomena. Certain radio-isotopes, tritium in particular, can be used as tracers without danger of contaminating the aquifer or of being adsorbed.

The basic difficulty with a tracer is that it disperses. Velocities vary across any single pore space in a porous medium, just as in a capillary tube, where the velocity distribution of laminar flow across the diameter of the tube is parabolic. Thus the concentration of tracer will vary in the direction of flow, becoming more widely dispersed the longer and farther that the tracer substance travels. In addition to the longitudinal dispersion there is, simultaneously, a lateral dispersion which occurs because each water thread is continually dividing and reuniting as it flows around and among the grains of the porous medium. For a slug of tracer material the concentration decreases as it moves down gradient and the apparent volume of the slug increases. When pictured in three dimensions, the combined effects of these two types of dispersion, beginning at a point tracer-source, form a cone that opens outward in the direction of flow. The surface of the cone may be sliced at right angles to its axis to find the limits of dispersion at any time, in this dimension. The slug is also attenuated in the direction of flow, there being threads of tracer in advance of the main body and threads lagging behind. Tracer distribution presumably can be expressed by a normal-probability type equation. Of course all of the foregoing discussion assumes a homogeneous medium, isotropic in nature. This simple theoretical picture is undoubtedly modified to the point of caricature in situations where the normal stratification of sediments is encountered.

In some respects the movement of tracers or other contaminating materials through an aquifer resembles the movement of a mixture of chemicals through absorbent paper, as practiced by the analytical chemist when he uses paper chromatography. With this technique a mixture of various dissolved substances can be readily separated for purposes of identification. A strip of absorbent paper is suspended so that one end makes contact with the solution to be analyzed. Capillary and molecular forces act in different measure on each of the dissolved substances, and one of these will concentrate at one point, others at different points. In a similar manner the rapidity of movement of one tracer or contaminant is likely to be substantially different from the movement of a different material, especially if the tracer is placed in a pit above the water table (to study the path of recharge) and moves under conditions of partial saturation part of the way. All of these matters, and many others, serve to complicate the interpretation of experiments with tracers.

To summarize: Tracer methods have their limitations not the least of which is that even after you have detected the arrival of a tracer you don't know much more about the hydrogeology than you did before you started. The properties of a geological matrix are not effectively quantified by studying the results of a successful tracer experiment alone, although when used in conjunction with the other type of aquifer test a picture of the infrastructure of the aquifer may sometimes be discerned.

DEVELOPMENT OF WATER SUPPLIES

Safe Yield

In developing a water supply there is one essential feature: a minimum quantity of water must be provided at all times. But just how large a minimum supply may be expected is not immediately apparent from an inspection of the source. When stream-flow measurements began to accumulate, it soon became evident that the hydrologic data could be made very useful in determining the firm rate of offtake available. It was found that by accumulating the observed daily discharges of a stream and platting the sum against time, a curve could be obtained to show how much storage would be needed to provide any specified minimum flow over the worst period ever experienced. Such curves, called mass curves, are a standard analytical tool of the water-supply engineer. The minimum flow determined in this manner for any specified volume of storage is the regulated yield of the stream, otherwise known as the firm yield, or safe yield, for the particular set of conditions. If the data are hydrologic, then at any given stream site the firm yield is directly based on the volume of storage available and is limited by it. The upper limit, not obtainable in practice, is the mean annual stream flow.

In dealing with aquifers, as we have seen, the quantity of water in storage is vastly greater than the annual replenishment. In 1920, when Oscar Edward Meinzer first introduced the term "safe yield," he defined it as ". . . the practicable rate of withdrawing water from it (the aquifer) perenially for human use" (31). This, a good definition, still makes sense. The trouble with it is that, as applied to ground water, excessive rates of pumping—overdrafts—are not evident until after they have occurred—and even then they may be local or attributable, superficially, to mechanical or hydraulic difficulties. As a qualitative statement the definition is fine. From a quantitative standpoint it leaves something to be desired. Along a parallel line the results of mass-curve analysis, when applied to records of river flow, produce a figure for safe yield for any size of impoundment. Then if a reservoir be built as planned, the probable minimum water supply is reliably known. Geohydrologists, consequently, sought to define the term for ground-water use.

Meinzer's protegees and successors analyzed the problem as applied to geohydrology and concluded that inasmuch as the storage in individual aquifers, generally, could be considered to be so large as to be virtually unlimited, the safe yield would be determined by the average annual recharge to each. In 1945, Stuart said:

The safe yield of a water-bearing formation is the maximum rate at which water may be withdrawn without impairing the quantity or quality of the supply. In an artesian system such as the Pennsylvanian sandstones, the safe yield is limited by the transmissibility of the sandstones, the intake capacity of the sandstones, the amount of water that can be taken from storage, and the danger of chemical contamination by water from formations below. Accurate determination of these limiting conditions requires an extensive study of the entire aquifer which, in this case, covers most of Central Michigan (50).

This definition, while not contradicting Meinzer's served to point out some of the factors to be considered in arriving at a safe figure. It is also suggested that water coming from a lower, mineralized aquifer might contaminate the water-supply aquifer if excessive concentrations of offtake were to take place.

Shortly thereafter, Conkling, from his experience in the West proposed his own definition:

Safe yield is the annual extraction from a ground water unit which will not, or does not (1) exceed the average annual recharge; (2) so lower the water table that the permissible cost of pumping is exceeded; or (3) so lower the water table as to permit intrusion of water of undesirable quality (6).

This definition is pretty flexible: Any time a ground-water hydrologist must determine the permissible cost of pumping, a goodly factor of uncertainty is implied. The hydrologic nature of the concept was also being called into question. But considering the fact that the author of the paper was a consulting engineer, a man who had to take costs into account, the definition served his purpose adequately. But it did not stand for long without challenge.

In 1949, Williams and Lohman of the U.S. Geological Survey said,

The perennial yield of the aquifer underlying an area of ground-water development . . . has been regarded as the maximum rate at which water can be salvaged from the natural discharge, or added to the recharge, or both . . . . In some reports the economical pumping lift has been considered to be a factor in this definition; however the economics of recovery seem to be irrelevant to the determination of the quantity of water which an aquifer will yield and so are not considered here (64, 212).

This was a conscious attempt to put safe yield back as a hydrologic quantity to be determined and, since the reservoir storage was effectively very large, purely on the basis of natural factors.

Two years later the Federal Government issued a circular on the water situation in the United States. This circular was a compilation of information obtained from all of the offices of the Geological Survey, and the approach used might fairly be interpreted to be the official position of the agency at that time. In a special state-by-state summary, under a heading "Deficiencies in Information," there is used, time and again, the phrase "Safe yield of basin not known at present" or a paraphrase of this statement (29).

There can be no question, in this instance, that the assumption had been made that safe yield was just another hydrologic quantity. It was classified merely as a piece of information that might, or might not, be lacking for a specific area. This approach was fully in accord with the Williams-Lohman analysis.

In subsequent years it became evident to all after much discussion that the term was psuedohydrologic, remarkably similar in nature to the concentration-time concept mentioned with reference to surface water. The Geological Survey quietly dropped the term and its synonyms.

In 1961, The Committee on Ground-Water of the American Society of Civil Engineers clearly summarized the new viewpoint:

In any ground-water equation, the safe yield from a designated reservoir would be achieved if the artificial discharge by wells . . . were so patterned as to suppress all other discharge from the reservoir . . . and if storage were utilized only to provide regulation of the fluctuating inflow to meet demand upon the wells. However, a practical difficulty becomes evident . . . . The patterns of distribution and draft from wells in developed ground-water reservoirs commonly differ from the ideal pattern for yielding the maximum perennial supply. The safe yield may then depend upon the practicability of relocating wells *rather than upon any characteristic of the natural resource* (1). (My italics—R. G. K.)

The U.S. Geological Survey recently called for abandonment of the term *safe yield* as a feasible concept in hydrology (53). Recognition of the pseudo-hydrologic character of safe yield has not yet (1964) been reflected in state laws dealing with ground water, some of which still call for the determination of safe yield of ground-water basins.

The Functions of Aquifers

Aquifers possessing primary permeability perform three principal functions: They act as slow-sand filters at their intake areas (outcrops)—this is their filter-plant function, they transmit water from the intake area to the point of withdrawal—this can be termed their pipe-line function, and they store water or function as reservoirs. When isolated from a source of recharge, aquifers can be considered as ore bodies of the water substance and offtake must be evaluated as a mining operation.

The three functions are not equally useful and thus do not have the same economic significance. Probably the least valuable function, or the most readily replaceable, is the pipeline function of an aquifer. There usually are methods for moving water, economically competitive with the creation of artificial gradients in aquifers to induce the flow of water through highly resistant, porous media. Any time an aquifer must be used to convey water from the area of recharge to the area of use, and the distance exceeds one or two miles, the possibility of substituting open-channel flow, or a pipe line, should be carefully examined.

The reservoir function of aquifers is probably most valuable in areas of intermittent stream flow or in areas solely dependent on the direct infiltration of rainfall. Under such circumstances storage is vital, be it above ground or underground. Considered as reservoirs, water-bearing formations possess many advantages: evaporation can be held to a minimum, productive land is not devoted to water storage in lieu of other uses, sedimentation is not a problem, and contamination by injurious substances, particularly radioactive fallout, is minimized. It is estimated that the fresh water stored in the aquifers of continental United States totals more than 5×10^{10} acre-ft, or possibly 150 times as much as all of the surface storage presently in existence there, excluding the Great Lakes. This is equal to about 50 times the average annual runoff from the continental area of the United States.

The filter-plant function of aquifers is most valuable in the humid sections of the country, especially in the East where perennial streams are in hydraulic contact with the outcrop areas of aquifers. As water travels from the stream through the stream bed and into the aquifer in response to hydraulic gradients, it loses all of its suspended matter. The incoming water joins the water already in aquifer storage, free of all silt particles and other substances formerly in suspension. The water is also free from pathogenic bacteria, tastes, and odors which apparently are removed by a sort of biofiltration at the river-aquifer interface. The capacity of a stream bottom to act as a filter plant varies from zero to as much as 10 or 12 ft of water per day. Along the Ohio River at Louisville, for example, Rorabaugh estimated that the rate of flow through the river bottom to the aquifer was slightly more than 2 ft per day (45). In other areas, different figures have resulted. There are good reasons to believe that even at a single location the rate will vary with the water temperature, the quantity and fineness of silt on the river-aquifer interface, the head available to infiltrate water, and other factors.

Numerous well installations along the Ohio and Mississippi Rivers, not to mention smaller streams and the Great Lakes, tap aquifers whose nearby source of replenishment is the body of surface water. In such areas of potential recharge, streams polluted by bacteria or organic materials can be made to furnish clean potable water.

The Aquifer as a Filter Plant

In certain respects, aquifers are unique natural resources. For example, trees must be cut and their timber removed from the forest and processed before it can be used. Coal must be mined and removed from its bed before it can be crushed to size, graded, and used. Renewable or not, our natural resources are brought into production only after the material involved has been transported and processed. Of all natural resources, aquifers alone produce a product ready for most uses at the point of extraction without further processing. As with all generalizations, there are, of course, exceptions but they are relatively unimportant. The services that aquifers perform—filtration, transportation, and storage of water—are accomplished before the water reaches the well. Nor are the capabilities of the geologic matrix of the aquifer injured by use. Although the filter-plant function of an aquifer might, theoretically, be impared by utilizing it, in practice, to the writers knowledge, this has never been conclusively demonstrated. We find that when a stream bed does lose its capacity to allow the infiltration of water, this has been caused by circumstances not connected with the utilization of the aquifer. These circumstances include water diversion, pollution, the pooling of a reach of river, and the mining of the coarse materials of the aquifer in the area of infiltration and their replacement by less permeable, fine grained materials.

From the practical standpoint of evaluating the magnitude of a supply based on the use of an aquifer as a filter plant, matters are extremely complex. There are a number of independent variables to be considered at the same time: geologic conditions, the hydrology of the stream, legal restrictions, the present and probable conditions of stream-bed sedimentation, future plans for stream development, the existence of a permeable interface between aquifer and surface source, the transmissibility of the aquifer, and the type of structure to be used in producing the water—vertical well, infiltration gallery, or horizontal collector.

As with all hydrologic projects, the principal concern is with the extremes: the minimum water supply that any system of structures will produce, the maximum amount, the maximum and minimum temperatures. We would also like to know the probable range in water quality and temperature.

Probably the most effective way to bring out the essence of such a ground-water problem is to examine one in reasonable detail. The Dubuque, Iowa, project that the author undertook in 1954, is well adapted as an illustrative example because it contained a minimum of hydrologic and hydrogeologic complications (20).

The aquifer under consideration at Dubuque is basically a glacial outwash composed of sand and mixed sand and gravel capped by a silty sand. This material had been deposited in the ancient preglacial valley of the Mississippi River that had been carved out of the underlying bedrock by forces of erosion.

The initial portion of the field work consisted in delineating the geology, both across the buried valley and longitudinally, by means of test drilling. A typical cross section of aquifer, and its relationship to the Mississippi River, is shown in Fig. 5.13. This geologic exploration was followed by an aquifer-performance test to determine (1) the transmissibility of the formation and (2) whether a recharge boundary existed nearby.

A test pattern of observation wells was installed, and an offtake rate of 1.5 million gal per day was maintained on a well tapping the aquifer. The effects were measured in the observation wells. Analysis of the data demonstrated conclusively that there was a recharge boundary at an effective distance of some 300 ft from the pumped well under test conditions (this recharge boundary was some 100 ft offshore). The transmissibility of the aquifer was found to be 515,000 gal per day per ft. No value was obtained for storage coefficient inasmuch as the water pumped by the well during the test was effectively replaced in the aquifer by water from the river, and the bulk of the water was not derived from storage in the aquifer.

With the hydrogeology of the aquifer known, consideration was given to the hydrology of the Mississippi River. The river is pooled for navigation purposes by a low dam, near Bellevue, Iowa, some 30 miles downstream from the site of the proposed well field. This implied the possibility of silting at the head of the pool. Fortunately the surface formations of the watershed do not produce much sediment, and the river bottom is relatively free of

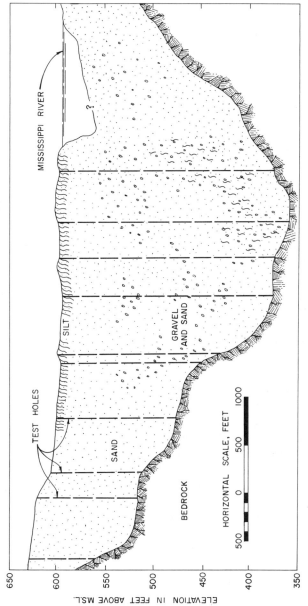

Fig. 5.13. Geologic cross section of preglacial valley at Dubuque, Iowa. The valley fill is a mixture of sand and gravel with occasional traces of silt.

silt. The performance test conclusively demonstrated that the river bottom was not sealed off from the aquifer at the time of test.

A study of the stage-duration curve showed that the median stage opposite the test site was 594 ft msl, the minimum was above 591 ft and that the stage equaled or exceeded 1 percent of the time was 608 ft msl. In view of the fact that discharges of the upper Mississippi River are regulated by natural lakes and ground-water inflows rather than by man-made structures, the gage-height data were considered satisfactory and a minimum river level of 590 ft was used as the basis for computing the induced infiltration of water to a well field.

River temperatures were considered next. Data were obtained from the Moline, Illinois Water Department. It was found that the maximum river temperature usually occurred in July and averaged approximately 79°F. This period of high river temperature usually coincided with the time that the river stage at Dubuque was above pool. The usual period of low temperature in the river extends from December to March. The average water temperature during this period is less than 35°F, with occasional intervals of severe weather that cause ice to form in the river. Water levels in the river during this period range from 592 to 593 ft msl.

Under these circumstances the yield of a well field can be expected to reach its minimum in March or April, when the water temperature and river stage have been low for a long time. The rate of offtake, at least for the first stage of development, was to have been small as compared to the total quantity in storage in the aquifer, so the temperature variations also might be expected to be small. Temperature of the well water during the aquifer test was 52°F.

Although such an aquifer may be developed primarily for use as a filter plant, it still will contain water in storage. It may also receive a little water that originated in precipitation on the land surface. It is therefore, of interest to examine the entire phenomenon of induced infiltration from a qualitative standpoint.

River water, moving downward through the river-bed materials in response to the hydraulic gradients created by the pumping of wells, will replenish the aquifer. As the water passes through the river-bottom sediments, a biofiltration can be expected to occur that will remove all organic materials, tastes, odors, pathogenic organisms, and suspended matter.

As this naturally purified river water travels slowly through the aquifer, it exchanges heat with the surrounding materials and mixes with water of different temperature that had infiltrated earlier. It also mixes with water previously in storage in the aquifer and, possibly, with a small quantity of water originating in the bedrock. Thus the temperature of the ground water produced by infiltration is governed by the seasonal temperature fluctuations of the source, but has a smaller range. There is a time lag between the occurrence of river temperature peaks or lows and the temperature peaks and lows of the pumped water.

With respect to the mineral quality of the water, an analogous phenomenon occurs. After a relatively short period of intensive offtake an important improvement in quality usually occurs. The ultimate quality of water from the well field will approach that of the source, but it will be slightly more mineralized. The additional mineralization will result, in part, from the slow leaching of the aquifer materials by the infiltrated water, from contributions of mineralized water from the bedrock, and from the water precipitated upon the land surface, which picked up minerals during its travel to the well field. The water quality will fluctuate as the river water quality does, but with a time lag. The original water obtained in 1954 from the test well in the alluvium in Dubuque had a total hardness of 310 ppm (expressed as parts per million of $CaCO_3$). Operation of the well field at an average rate of almost 6 million gal per day resulted, by 1962, in an average hardness of about 140 ppm. No record is available concerning the hardness of river water at Dubuque, but spot measurements have shown a range of from 70 to 170 ppm.

In contrast to well fields drawing solely upon water stored in the aquifer, the yield of the well field at Dubuque would vary with the stage of the river, even though each unit were to be operated at a constant, predetermined elevation. For a given drawdown the yield is a minimum after an extended period of low river stages and temperatures, and a maximum at the end of such periods of high river stage that coincide with warm water in the river.

The Aquifer as a Reservoir

The difference between a reservoir and a mine is found in the concept of recharge or replenishment. It is of the same nature as the difference between a rechargeable lead-acid battery and the nonrechargeable dry cell. The ground-water reservoir must be replenished periodically, in quantity approximately equal to the offtake, for the supply to be completely permanent. The ground-water mine is a one-time thing, although its economic life may be 50 years or more. (We will use the term *mine* as a readily comprehensible synonym for *water-substance ore body*.)

WICHITA, KANSAS. The following description of a ground-water reservoir is based on the excellent study of the Wichita area by Williams and Lohman just prior to construction and during the first years of operation of a new well field for the City of Wichita (*64*), and a later study by Petri, Lane, and Furness (*38a*).

The McPherson formation (the equus beds), which outcrop north of Wichita between the Arkansas and Little Arkansas Rivers just south and west of the town of Halstead, is a true ground-water reservoir. Careful studies over a period of many years have proved that precipitation on the area reaches the aquifer—on the average, between 6 and 7 in. a year of water is added.

In Fig. 5.14 the original piezometric surface of the aquifer in the area of the proposed well field is shown as it was three months before offtake began. This map shows the height to which water would have risen at any point of

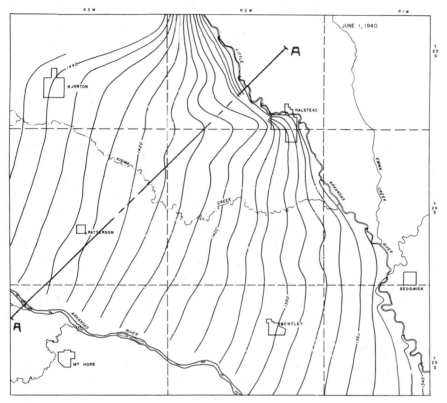

Fig. 5.14. Piezometric surface, area of new Wichita well field, in June, 1940, before start of offtake. Line AA is location of geologic section (see Fig. 5.17). (After C. C. Williams and S. W. Lohman, 1949, *Geology and Ground-Water Resources of a Part of South-Central Kansas*, Bull. 79, Topeka, Geol. Surv. Kansas, Plate 33.)

the area in a tightly cased well that was screened in the total thickness of the McPherson formation. It may be looked upon as if it were a contour map of an actual hard surface. To determine the direction of water movement, imagine that a small ball bearing is placed on this "surface" and permitted to roll under the action of gravity. It will, of course, roll downhill. If we disregard the vertical movement of the ball bearing and indicate on the map the path that it followed, then this line will be the path of the movement of water from the point at which the ball bearing was originally placed. All other things being equal, the steeper the slope of the water table, or pressure surface, the faster the movement of water. This simplification ignores the three-dimensional character of the path of movement of any water particle and the internal gradients within the aquifer itself due to replenishment, stratification, non-homogeneity, and so forth. However for understanding the gross movement of water in aquifers the foregoing explanation should prove adequate

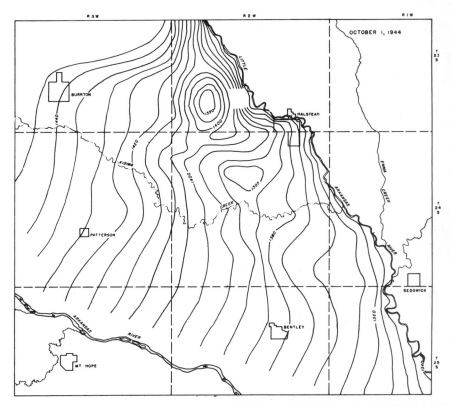

Fig. 5.15. Piezometric surface, area of new Wichita well field, October, 1944, after 49 months of offtake. Contour interval is 5 ft, elevations are in ft above mean sea level. (From C. C. Williams and S. W. Lohman, 1949, *Geology and Ground-Water Resources of a Part of South-Central Kansas*, Bull. 79, Topeka, Geol. Surv. Kans., plate 33.)

and will not be contradicted by any of the later refinements that a more detailed hydrogeological study may suggest.

After 49 months of operation during which a total of over 20 billion gal of water (67,000 acre-ft) was pumped, the piezometric surface had reached the form shown in Fig. 5.15. To facilitate study of the change in water level, Fig. 5.16 was prepared. It shows the net change in water level that occurred during the period. The line of zero drawdown (no change in water level) has

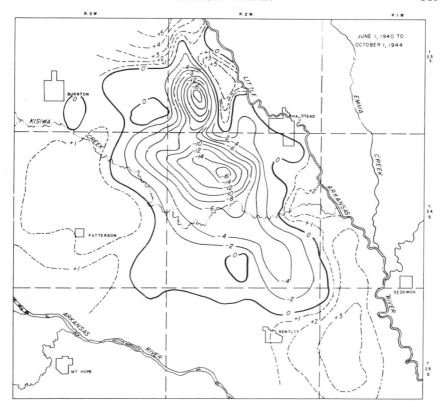

Fig. 5.16. Lines of equal water-level change, Wichita well field after approximately 4 years of offtake. (From C. C. Williams and S. W. Lohman, 1949, *Geology and Ground-Water Resources of a Part of South-Central Kansas*, Bull. 79, Topeka, Geol. Surv. Kans., plate 34.)

been made heavier. A typical geologic cross section along line *A-A* in Fig. 5.14 through the area is shown as Fig. 5.17.

Figure 5.14 shows that the water table originally sloped toward the Little Arkansas River and that the hydraulic gradient of the piezometric surface generally paralleled the slope of the Arkansas River in the area shown. Figure 5.17, however, shows a local hydraulic gradient toward the Arkansas River, so we can infer that a small amount of ground water was also discharging into the Arkansas River.

By October, 1944, much of the 67,000 acre-ft of water that had been pumped had been obtained by a reduction of the quantity of water stored in the ground-water reservoir. By planimetering large-scale piezometric maps similar to Fig. 5.16 and computing the volume of sediments dewatered between specified time intervals, and then using a value for the specific yield, Williams and Lohman arrived at a probable figure of about 45,000 acre-ft

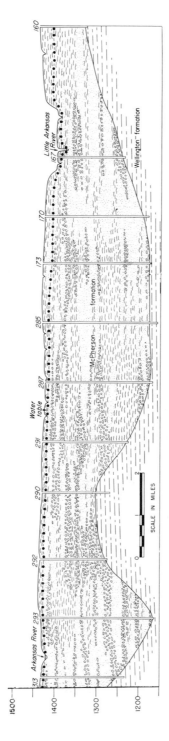

Fig. 5.17. Geologic section AA (see Fig. 5.14) through Wichita well field that shows the position of the piezometric surface (water table) in June, 1940. Elevations refer to mean sea level. The numerical identification of each well is shown. (After C. C. Williams and S. W. Lohman, 1949, *Geology and Ground-Water Resources of a Part of South-Central Kansas*, Bull. 79, Topeka, Geol. Surv. Kans., plate 7.)

as the reduction in storage over the period. By the end of 1944, the natural flow of ground water into the Little Arkansas River was computed to be approximately 10 percent less than the original flow. Williams and Lohman also calculated that an additional quantity of water in the order of magnitude of 200,000 acre-ft would have to be taken from storage before water would infiltrate from the Little Arkansas River and replenish the aquifer.

According to Williams and Lohman:

The conclusion that the safe yield, as determined by recharge during the period of record, had not been reached at the end of 1944 does not in itself define this quantity. An estimate of the safe yield with the present arrangement of wells may be made, however, from data presented above. If the maximum area of influence of the present well field is about 85 square miles, it is believed that the recharge in years of normal precipitation will be about 27,000 acre-ft. When the water table is lowered to a depth sufficient that all natural discharge may be salvaged, percolation into the area will be at least 13,000 acre-feet a year. Thus the potential yield of the present well-field area during a period of normal precipitation is estimated to be about 40,000 acre-feet a year, or about twice the present annual pumpage. Before a quantity of water equal to this yield can be added to the aquifer each year, about 200,000 acre-feet must be removed from storage .... An expansion of the present well field will involve a larger area of influence and the potential safe yield will be correspondingly larger (64, 223).

The continuing study of the Wichita well field resulted in minor changes in the figures presented in the Lohman-Williams report, the most important of which stemmed from a field determination of the specific yield of the aquifer. Instead of the specific yield being 25 percent, as was originally assumed, Stramel produced observational evidence to support a figure of only 20 percent:

As of January, 1955, about 67 percent of the water pumped by the City of Wichita since pumping began in 1940 had been derived from recharge and the other 33 percent had been pumped from storage .... Physical conditions in the well field seem to be excellent for some forms of artificial recharge .... The perennial yield is many times larger than the present use [28,000 acre-ft per year] (49).

In essence, therefore, rainfall on an outcrop area of some 100 sq miles has proved to be more than adequate to support an offtake rate of 28 million gal per day. The aquifer contains all necessary storage to maintain the supply, and this can be increased by the induced infiltration of water from the Little Arkansas River or by the spreading of water in the well-field area. Such water might be pumped from the Arkansas River or Little Arkansas River during periods of high flow and suitable water quality.

CANTON, OHIO. The two previous examples concern relatively simple hydrogeologic and hydrologic relationships—although reference to the publications cited will soon convince the reader that these matters become evident only after an enormous amount of work. The next situation illustrates how modern technology can combine a thin filter-plant aquifer with an

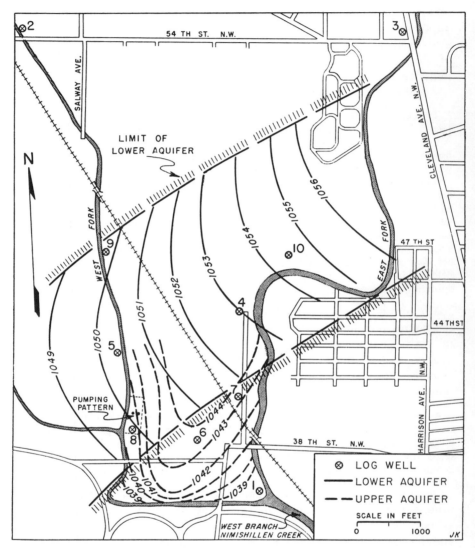

Fig. 5.18. Contour map showing the original piezometric surface in each of the two aquifers found in the Canton, Ohio, area. (From R. G. Kazmann, September–October, 1949, the utilization of induced infiltration and natural aquifer storage at Canton, Ohio, *Economic Geology*, v. 44, no. 6, p. 517.)

independent, deeper, ground-water body to furnish a predictable, firm, ground-water supply.

Canton, Ohio, is situated over and near a number of preglacial valleys. These valleys, due to repeated cycles of glaciation, deposition, ponding, and erosion, are filled with sand and gravel, outwash from the glaciers. Sometimes this material is not continuous to the surface and a layer of tough impermeable blue clay separates the upper stratum of permeable material from the lower. Schaefer, White, and Van Tuyl studied the Canton area in detail in 1945 and called attention to the water potential of the area (47).

Their bulletin set off a chain reaction in Canton, and a search was initiated to find another buried valley similar to the one then being utilized as Canton's northeast well field. In the latter area there exists a more or less continuous deposit of mixed sand and gravel (with an occasional small, discontinuous, lens of clay) extending from land surface to bedrock. Including the output of industrial wells in the area, a total offtake of some 30 million gal per day was being produced from this single aquifer at the time.

Test drilling sites selected on the basis of Schaefer, White, and Van Tuyl's work produced a surprise. Sand and gravel was found at the surface as were two small streams to serve as potential recharge boundaries for aquifer development. But the surficial aquifer had been deposited in an erosion surface of a layer of blue clay and was only from 20 to 40 ft thick. Beneath this surficial aquifer, but separated from it by a continuous layer of impermeable clay, was a clean, permeable deposit of sand and gravel ranging in thickness up to 150 ft (19).

Evidently, after the lower deposit had been laid down, a period of ponding occurred during which a thick layer of clay was deposited on the sand and gravel, covering it completely. This was followed by a period of erosion which removed most of the clay in other areas. Although the surface of the clay in the area under exploration was eroded, it formed a continuous layer throughout the area. Sand and gravel had later been deposited on the clay.

Exploratory drilling indicated that the clay layer might be continuous. Water level measurements made in wells that were completed in the lower aquifer showed one piezometric surface. Similar measurements in the upper aquifer showed a completely independent water table. Figure 5.18, which shows the two independent piezometric surfaces, conclusively proves the existence of two independent aquifers in the area.

After study the situation resolved itself as follows: The upper aquifer was in hydraulic contact with the small streams that join to form the West Branch of Nimishillen Creek. Consequently any water pumped from the upper aquifer would be replaced by infiltration—if the water were there. The maximum, average, and minimum offtake rates of structures built on the assumption of permanent and adequate recharge boundaries were computed.

But the little streams are intermittent and could be expected to be virtually

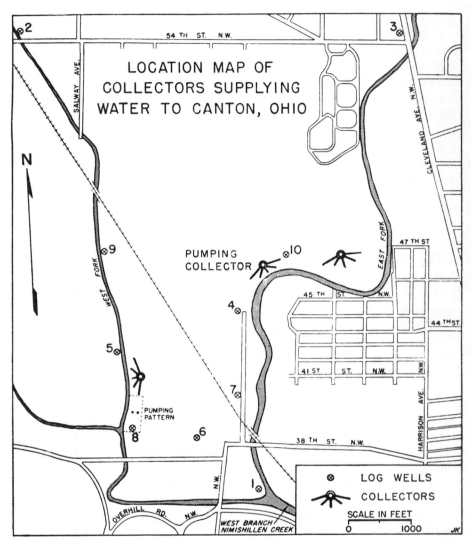

Fig. 5.19. Relationship between outlying, dually screened collectors and the dual-purpose pumping collector. (From R. G. Kazmann, September–October, 1949, The utilization of induced stream infiltration and natural aquifer storage at Canton, Ohio, *Economic Geology*, v. 44, no. 6, p. 522.)

dry during a large fraction of the year. It was found to be necessary to draw on water in storage in the aquifer for an average of six months per year. The upper aquifer being thin, it was found that the usable quantity of water in storage was inadequate to assure the desired firm offtake of 10 million gal per day.

From an engineering viewpoint the deep aquifer, although it contained a tremendous amount of water in storage, had to be treated as a potential water mine rather than as a reservoir. The rate and occurrence of recharge to this aquifer were unknown, and, moreover, the recharge area was certainly not under the control of the city of Canton. The technical problem thus resolved itself into finding a method of utilizing the upper, thin aquifer as a filter plant and connecting it to the lower aquifer, which would then be transformed into a functioning reservoir.

Following many computations of limiting conditions, which included preparation of synthetic flow-duration curves, estimates of the filter-plant capacity of the stream bed under various conditions of head, and calculations of infiltration capacity, well yield, and well interference, a satisfactory solution was reached. It was decided to construct three large-diameter, radial collector wells, to complete each one in both aquifers, and to utilize the lower aquifer as a pipe line to convey the infiltrated water from the exterior units to the central unit, which would be the only one equipped with pumps.

(A collector well consists of a monolithic concrete caisson, approximately 15 ft in diameter, sunk to the bottom of the aquifer, or to a predetermined elevation. After the requisite depth has been reached, a concrete plug is poured to seal the bottom. Then slotted steel pipes are jacked out of the caisson, horizontally into the aquifer, to produce the equivalent of a very large diameter well. Pipes may be projected at more than one elevation. Each tier of pipes, in plan, resembles the spokes of a wagon wheel. This is the type of well built at Canton with one tier of pipes in the upper aquifer and the other tier in the lower aquifer.)

The final locations of the three dually completed horizontal collectors are shown in Fig. 5.19. The method of recharge is shown schematically in Fig. 5.20.

The Canton water-supply development was placed in operation in 1948, and an average offtake of approximately 6 million gal per day has been maintained for the past 15 years with only an occasional shutdown for purposes of cleaning or maintenance. The peak monthly output has averaged 10 million gal per day. According to data contained in the annual reports of the Canton Water Department, between January 1, 1951, and December 31, 1961, a total of 26 billion gal of water were pumped from the dual-purpose collector. There has been no substantial change in ground-water levels in the area since 1949, according to the Superintendent of the Canton Water Department (43).

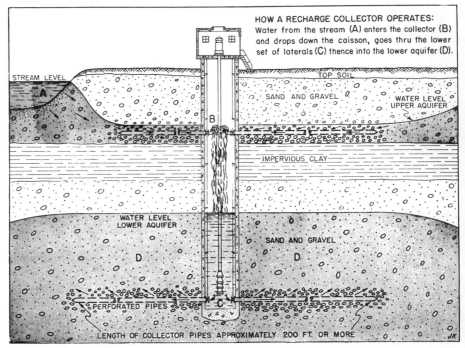

HOW A RECHARGE COLLECTOR OPERATES:
Water from the stream (A) enters the collector (B) and drops down the caisson, goes thru the lower set of laterals (C) thence into the lower aquifer (D).

Fig. 5.20. Schematic cross section through Canton's dual-purpose, pump-equipped, horizontal collector. (From R. G. Kazmann, September–October, 1949, The utilization of induced stream infiltration and natural aquifer storage at Canton, Ohio, *Economic Geology*, v. 44, no. 6, p. 521.)

The Aquifer as a Water Mine

Water mining may be defined as the process of decreasing the quantity of water stored in an aquifer. When the process is halted because over a long period the input into the aquifer equals the offtake, there is no year-to-year drop in water levels. There are instances, however, where the replenishment of the aquifer is either nonexistent or so small as to be trivial in comparison with either the annual offtake from the aquifer or the total quantity stored.

The most straightforward set of circumstances is found in the mining of ground water in an arid or semiarid region. In such an instance the basic hydrology of the area makes a firm, perennial ground-water supply impossible without the large-scale importation of water and artificial recharge. Under such circumstances there is an economic governor on the use of underground water: cost. When the offtake from a well becomes so small that it will not support an economic rate of commodity production, the offtake ceases and the production is moved elsewhere. Within a major area of ground-water mining there will usually be found small subareas where the aquifer is locally thicker or at a lower elevation. Offtake will continue in such areas for a longer period. The end result will be a constantly diminishing rate of economic activity reflecting and affecting the rate of water withdrawal. Sooner or later a rate of offtake will be reached that will decrease very slowly and be virtually constant, year after year for a very long time. Note that in the foregoing discussion one basic assumption has been made: that the aquifer is isolated from any other water-bearing formation, that as the fresh water is pumped out brackish, or salty, water will not replace it.

This assumption, however, often is not valid. An aquifer may have a geohydrologic boundary with the sea or with a brackish river, and sometimes the fresh water may constitute a lens of limited extent that is in hydraulic contact with salty water in another section of the same water-bearing formation. The hydrogeology of these circumstance is not straightforward. The hydraulic, hydrogeologic, mineral, political, and economic factors in all their ramifications present a three-dimensional lattice of problems.

The case histories summarized below exemplify these basic situations: The High Plains region of Texas is an area of water mining in an arid zone where the depletion of water, alone, constitutes the problem. The Los Angeles Basin is also in an arid zone, but the mining of ground water has caused sea water to infiltrate the aquifer. This recharge threatens to destroy the usefulness of the entire ground-water supply long before the fresh water runs out. In this instance imported water is available for recharge purposes, and the steps undertaken to combat the intrusion of sea water form a significant chapter in resource development. The third situation is found in the humid, well-watered area of the Vermilion River Basin of Louisiana. This area contains an aquifer fresh in its upper sections and salty in the deeper sections. It is a single aquifer containing two distinct types of water separated by an intermediate zone of mixing. The land surface is crossed by a perennial stream that is intermittently brackish and that may be in hydraulic contact with the fresh-water aquifer. All of these situations are still under active study at this time, and in none of the instances has the final chapter of the story been written. The case histories were selected for summary and analysis inasmuch as they present progressively more complicated situations. Other situations, even more complex, are being studied in other parts of the world.

THE HIGH PLAINS REGION OF TEXAS. The High Plains region of Texas is located in the north western part of the state; its best-known cities are Amarillo and Lubbock. Most of the usable ground water in the High Plains is found in the Ogallala formation, a sandy deposit, in many places 200 to 300 ft thick, lying at or near the surface throughout almost the entire region. This formation is composed of silt and fine sand, with some coarse sand and gravel. The area in which the aquifer is present is bounded by the escarpments of the High Plains on the east and west. In Texas the area is divided by the Canadian River. It has been proven that the source of water to the aquifer must be entirely within the High Plains area. The water now being utilized undoubtedly originated in the rain or snow that fell on the land surface during ages past.

Although ground water has been used for irrigation purposes since 1911, there were only about 300 wells in operation before 1935 (63). The number of irrigation wells increased rapidly to 1700 in 1939, 3500 in 1944, and 44,000 in 1960. The acreage irrigated rose from an estimated 40,000 acres in 1935, to 450,000 in 1944, and to more than 4,000,000 in 1960 (7).

Almost all of the water used was taken from storage in the aquifer. As a result water levels have been lowered at an increasing rate throughout the area. This trend in water level caused concern among the residents. In 1951, the farmers in a part of the area organized High Plains Underground Water Conservation District No. 1, which now includes most of the area south of the Canadian River except for Swisher, Hale, Crosby, and Briscoe counties and small parts of other counties. Figure 5.21 is a graphic history of precipitation, ground-water production, and water utilization in the High Plains of Texas. Figure 5.22 depicts the water-level declines throughout the area that occurred between 1938 and 1962.

By January, 1962, Broadhurst, the Chief Hydrologist of the District, was able to compute the net percentage of water that had been mined from each county in the District (3).

Table 5.1. Percentage of Original Aquifer Storage That Was Pumped Out by January, 1962

County	Percent	County	Percent
Armstrong	32	Lamb	15
Bailey	13	Lubbock	44
Castro	19	Lynn	38
Cochran	20	Parmer	12
Deaf Smith	18	Potter	33
Floyd	22	Randall	20
Hockley	30		

The conservation district has undertaken a vigorous campaign to reduce waste in the use of irrigation water. In 1959, it helped a district farmer in the preparation of an action before the U.S. Internal Revenue Service to allow a depletion deduction to compensate for the exhaustion of the underground water supply (35). Underground water is a substantial factor in determining the value of the overlying land, and when this deduction was disallowed, the District aided in preparing the case presented to a Federal District Court. In January, 1962, the case came for trial and in May, 1963, a decision favorable to the plaintiff and against the Internal Revenue Service was handed down (57). The District has sponsored experiments in recharging the aquifer by use of the water that accumulates in the shallow lakes, or playas, that appear throughout the area during wet weather. And it has stopped the contamination of the aquifer that resulted from the surface ponding of the oil-field brines.

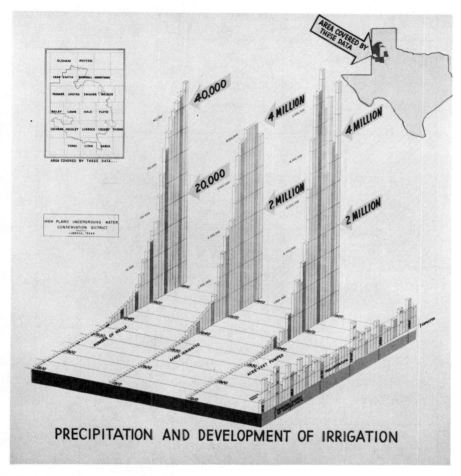

Fig. 5.21. History of water production, High Plains of Texas, 1910–1961. (Courtesy of High Plains Water Conservation District Number 1, Lubbock, Texas.)

Admittedly these actions will not restore the water levels in the aquifer. The total offtake is far greater than the quantity of surface runoff or rejected recharge. The best that can be hoped for is a prolongation of the economic life of the region.

At this time it is estimated that overall about 20 percent of the 200,000,000 acre-ft originally in storage have been withdrawn and that the recharge, originating in rainfall, averages something more than 50,000 acre-ft per yr

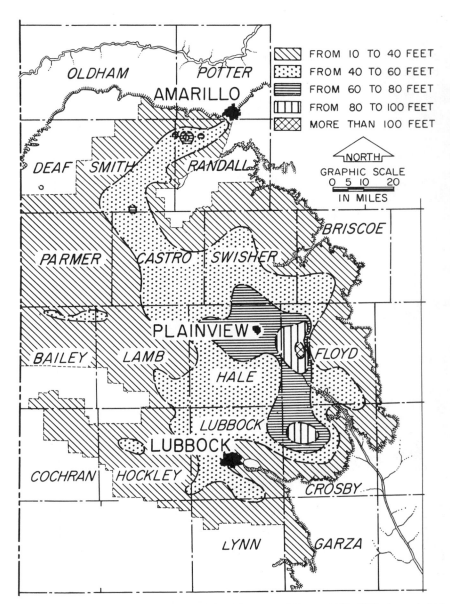

Fig. 5.22. Water-level declines in the High Plains area of Texas, 1938–1962, that resulted from the removal of approximately 50 million acre-ft of water from the aquifer. (Based on data from High Plains Underground Water Conservation District Number 1, Lubbock, Texas.)

and less than 100,000 acre-ft per yr. This is, of course, only a small fraction of the 5 million acre-ft per yr being pumped at present (1964).

In this instance the ground-water deposit must be considered exhaustible, like oil or gas, and the final outcome of the mining operation can be anticipated and proper provisions must be made by each individual who is affected.

WEST COAST BASIN, LOS ANGELES COUNTY. The West Coast Basin of Los Angeles County extends from the ocean inland to the Inglewood Fault (a distance of from six to eight miles) and about eleven miles along the coast

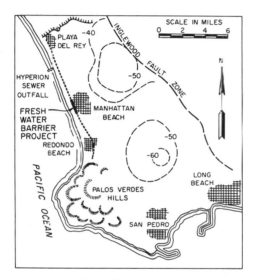

Fig. 5.23. Piezometric surface of the West Coast Basin, Los Angeles County, 1951 (sea-level datum), showing fresh-water barrier recharge project. Solid section of line is site of original experiments. (After F. B. Laverty and H. A. van der Goot, September, 1955, Development of a fresh-water barrier in Southern California for the prevention of sea-water intrusion, © *J. Am. Water Works Assoc.*, v. 47, no. 9. p. 887.)

from the Palos Verdes Hills to Ballona Creek. Figure 5.23, a map of the area, also shows ground-water level elevations and the location of the fresh water recharge project previously mentioned (27).

Initially the ground water in the area was used for domestic and agricultural purposes. During the past 30 years, however, the agricultural use has decreased and industrial and municipal pumpage has increased. By 1953, the total ground-water offtake was at the rate of 90,000 acre-ft a year. The decrease in the ground-water levels of the basin necessitated the importation of water from the Owens Aqueduct System in 1935 and later, in 1949, Colorado River water. By 1957, the annual ground-water offtake had been reduced to 70,000 acre-ft as a result of the increased use of imported water

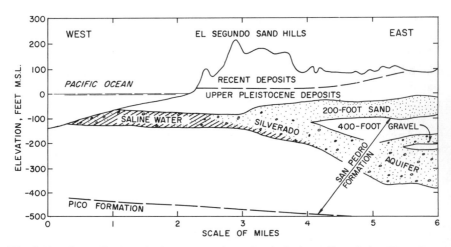

Fig. 5.24. Generalized geologic cross section of principal aquifer of the West Coast Basin, Los Angeles, on a line perpendicular to the coast. The extent of saline water intrusion before the start of recharge is shown. (After November, 1958, *Sea-Water Intrusion in California*, Bull. 63, Sacramento, California Dept. of Water Resources, plate 17.)

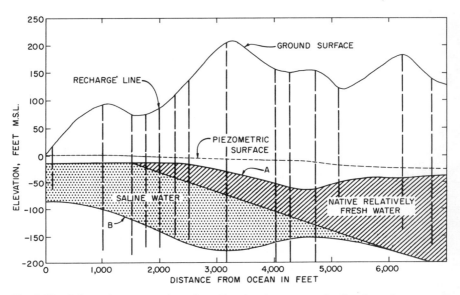

Fig. 5.25. Schematic cross section of aquifer showing extent of saline intrusion normal to recharge line prior to start of recharge experiment. (A) Upper boundary of aquifer; (B) approximate lower boundary of aquifer. The dashed vertical lines indicate test wells. (After F. B. Laverty and H. A. van der Goot, September, 1955, Development of a fresh-water barrier in Southern California for the prevention of sea-water intrusion, © *J. Am. Water Works Assoc.*, v. 47, no. 9, p. 889.)

together with the voluntary curtailment of offtake by the major producers in the basin.

The principal aquifer in the area, the Silverado zone of the San Pedro formation, is of Pleistocene age. It is a distinct, confined body of sand and gravel, with more or less discontinuous layers of relatively impermeable sandy silt, silt, and clay. Figure 5.24 is a generalized geologic cross section of the principal aquifer, showing sea-water intrusion. Overlying the aquifer is a capping clay layer and, on the west end of the area, sand overlies the clay. The entire hydrologic and hydrogeologic situation has been discussed in detail in official publications issued in 1957, 1958, and 1960 (5). Although the matter is remarkably complex, basically the situation is this:

Water mining in the area has resulted in the induced infiltration of sea water to the aquifer. Because of this, although ground-water levels may become stabilized, the water quality must inevitably deteriorate as the sea water moves farther and farther inland. Conditions directly east of the coast line are depicted in Fig. 5.25. The underlying wedge of salt water, the position of which was identified by sampling water from wells and determining the chloride content, has moved progressively inland.

Studies were made by the Los Angeles County Flood Control District (admittedly an unusual organization for the study of ground water) in an effort to find a method of stopping the advance of salt water. Many solutions were considered, including injection of substances that would reduce aquifer permeability in the critical zone and thus reduce the flow of salt water in a landward direction. The most promising experiment was that which utilized artificial recharge by means of wells to create a ground-water ridge, or pressure ridge, of fresh water between the area of pumpage and the sea. These experiments have been under way since 1952. The injection of fresh water was finally found to be effective and feasible, and, in 1962, a full-scale project was authorized. The efficacy of the recharge experiment in stopping the landward movement of sea water is shown in Fig. 5.26. It must be admitted, however, that the injection of fresh water accelerated the landward movement of the salt water that had been trapped east of the ridge. This body of salty water acted much like a slug of tracer material, and the temporary increase in chlorides landward was soon reduced by dispersion and dilution. Had it been economically justified, much of this salt water could have been pumped out by the operation of wells constructed for the purpose and properly located in the area.

Inasmuch as it is a pioneering project, the calculations of costs and benefits for the construction needed to stop the intrusion of salt water are indefinite and subject to criticism. It is estimated that an annual input of 75,000 acre-ft will be required to protect the fresh-water aquifer. In addition to the cost of purchasing water, the annual operating costs of the recharge project will total $516,000. Thus the bare operating cost will be equal to 7.5 dollars per

acre-ft of water recharged. To this figure must be added the price of Colorado
River water that would be purchased from the Metropolitan Water District
(estimated at 20 dollars per acre-ft). Incidentally, the net incremental cost
of the water to the Metropolitan Water District is estimated by Hirshleifer
and his colleagues as being in the neighborhood of 28 dollars per acre-ft
(*14*, 306) so the total unsubsidized cost of recharge might well total as much

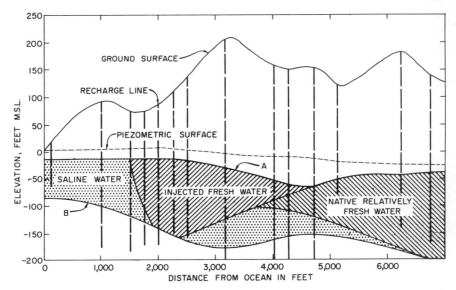

Fig. 5.26. Schematic cross section of aquifer normal to recharge-line showing injected
fresh-water wedge two years after start of water injection. (A) Upper boundary of aquifer;
(B) approximate lower boundary of aquifer. The dashed vertical lines indicate test wells.
(After F. B. Laverty and H. A. van der Goot, September, 1955, Development of a fresh-
water barrier in Southern California for the prevention of sea-water intrusion, © *J. Am.
Water Works Assoc.*, v. 47, no. 9, p. 901.)

as 40 dollars per acre-ft. [This figure may be compared to the cost of desalinization of sea water at an as yet (1964) unattained figure of 320 dollars
per acre-ft.]

On the other hand the project would, of course, preserve the aquifer from
destruction by contamination, and ultimately be beneficial to the quality
of water previously conserved by the Flood Control District through its
water-spreading operations.

There is, in addition, the distinct possibility that the effluent from the
nearby Hyperion sewage treatment plant could be used for recharge purposes
and thus eliminate the cost of purchased Colorado River water. The effluent
of this plant, consisting of previously softened but once-used water, is superior
in mineralogical characteristics to the raw water imported from the Colorado

River by the Metropolitan Water District. Studies of this possibility, and pilot-plant operations for the treatment of effluent, have been underway for several years (*35a*).

In short, the technical problem caused by salt water intrusion into the West Coast Basin of Los Angeles is evidently being solved successfully at this time.

THE VERMILION RIVER BASIN, LOUISIANA. There exist in southwestern Louisiana a series of aquifers of Pleistocene age known together as the Chicot Reservoir. The principal identifying geologic characteristic of these aquifers is their gravelly texture. The coarseness of texture and the composition of the gravel pebbles are the principal criteria for differentiating these deposits from those beneath, and for assigning them to the Pleistocene age. It can be said that some of the sand and gravel aquifers of the Chicot reservoir are among the thickest uniformly permeable granular water-bearing beds in the United States. The aquifers of the reservoir are continuous for more than 100 miles from west to east and equally as far from north to south (*16, 17*).

The Vermilion River Basin, the principal city of which is Abbeville, overlies a portion of the Chicot reservoir. One of the more important rice farming sections of the country is neighbor to Abbeville, there being some 70,000 acres of rice under cultivation within a short distance. The rice is irrigated, primarily, by water from the Vermilion River. The natural flow of this river is supplemented by water from Teche Bayou through Ruth Canal and, to a very minor extent, by water from Bayou Fusilier. Possibly as much as 40 percent of the rice in the basin is irrigated from wells—either completely or now and then, as a replacement for the river water when it gets too salty.

The aquifers of the Chicot reservoir outcrop at some distance from the area, in Beauregard, Allen, and Evangeline Parishes, a minimum of 30 miles from the head of the Vermilion River, and 45 miles from Abbeville. Figure 5.27 shows the piezometric surface of the Chicot reservoir based on a study made in 1903. The contours show that the ground-water flow in the vicinity of Abbeville was southwardly, parallel to the Vermilion River. Moreover, the aquifer was under artesian pressure, the piezometric surface at Abbeville being about 5 ft msl, or about 5 ft above the level of the river. The Chicot reservoir had been barely touched by ground-water withdrawals to the west at that time—only one small cone of depression is shown about 30 miles west of Abbeville. Evidently water was moving down-dip to a sea-water contact zone under the Gulf of Mexico.

Underlying the fresh water of the Chicot reservoir is water high in chlorides. In the vicinity of Abbeville, although the base of the Pleistocene deposits is more than 1200 ft below msl, there is a small area in which salt water is encountered only 300 ft below the surface (Fig. 5.28).

Fig. 5.27. Piezometric surface of the Chicot Reservoir, spring, 1903. (After P. H. Jones *et al.*, 1956, *Water Resources of Southwestern Louisiana, U.S. Geol. Surv. Water Supply Paper 1364*, plate 13.)

As we know, when a cone of depression is created in a piezometric surface, flow will be induced toward the center of the cone. In this instance the water replacing the water pumped from the wells could be (1) fresh water from the north, (2) fresh water from the south followed by a fresh-salt-water interface and the usual salt-water intrusion wedge similar to the one encountered in the West Coast Basin of Los Angeles, and (3) salt water through coning (upward movement) from the underlying saline-water aquifer. There is a fourth possibility: water from the Vermilion River might infiltrate the aquifer and, occasionally, salty water from the river might contaminate the aquifer.

As a result of concentrated offtake from the Chicot reservoir it is altogether probable that the aquifer, either as a reservoir or as an ore body, might be damaged before its fresh-water potential had been fully realized. Study of the hydrogeology of the area was undertaken partly to establish a basis for protective measures. This investigatory work has resulted in a number of reports, the most complete of which have already been cited.

The coning of the salt water that underlies the fresh water contained in an aquifer has not yet been encountered in this exposition. For coning to occur, salt water must underlie and be in hydraulic contact with the fresh water of an aquifer. Such a distribution of water types in an aquifer comes about because of incomplete flushing of the salt water trapped as the aquifer sediments were deposited. The trapped water, called *connate*, is found throughout the Chicot reservoir, and Fig. 5.28 can be regarded as a crude map of the connate-water surface. The fact that so much of the area is underlain by fresh water that has overridden the salt water suggests that there must be an outlet for the salt water in the Gulf, else partial flushing would not have been accomplished. The "floating" fresh-water wedge gets thicker in proportion to its nearness to the recharge area. The underlying salt-water wedge gets thicker in the direction of the Gulf.

When two fluids of different density exist in a porous, homogeneous medium, there is a tendency for the interface between the fluids to become a horizontal plane. Of course, in any widespread aquifer that is composed of stratified, nonhomogeneous deposits, the "horizontal" plane may tend to resemble an eroded land surface. The intrusion of salt domes also tends to complicate matters. Southwestern Louisiana does not lack salt domes. Even an interface that is as much as 100 ft per mile off the horizontal, as shown in parts of Fig. 5.28, is not so far from the horizontal to invalidate the approximation.

If the pressure head in the fresh-water zone is reduced by pumping, the salt-water interface rises in response to the density head of the salt water. If the wells are shallow, and the equilibrium level of the interface is below the bottoms of the wells, then fresh water is skimmed off. However, the presence of a salt-water mound beneath the pumped wells poses the constant threat of encroachment in areas of concentrated offtake. One way to counteract this threat is to build wells separated by large distances and to operate them at

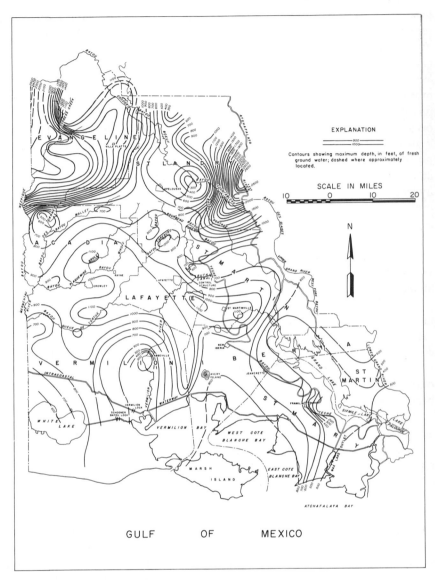

Fig. 5.28. Maximum depth of fresh-water occurrence, Vermilion River Basin. (After P. H. Jones *et al.*, 1956, *Water Resources of Southwestern Louisiana, U.S. Geol. Surv. Water Supply Paper 1364*, plate 15.)

low rates of offtake, as a replacement for small numbers of high-offtake wells that produce for short periods. Unfortunately, this is sometimes impracticable and has not occurred in this area.

Figure 5.29 shows the cone of salt water formed in an aquifer beneath a partially penetrating discharging well and depicts a device used to demonstrate that the salt water was entering only through the bottom of the screen (*37*).

Figure 5.30 shows how the salinity of the Vermilion River compared with the salinity of a well 4000 ft from the river during a period of drought. Well VE-75 is located about a mile south of Perry (see Fig. 5.32), so that the chloride

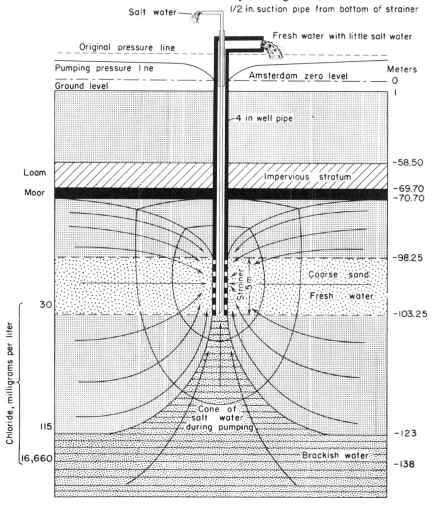

Fig. 5.29. Cone of salt water induced by pumping overlying fresh water. (From J. M. K. Pennink, 1905, Investigations for ground water supplies, *Trans. Am. Soc. Civ. Eng.*, v. 54, pt. D, p. 179.)

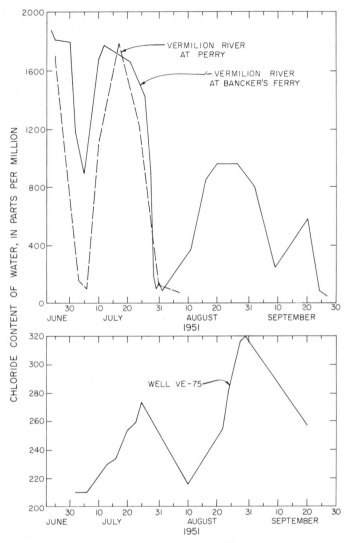

Fig. 5.30. Relationship between salinity of Vermilion River and salinity of water from irrigation well, VE-75, located approximately 4,000 ft from the river. (After P. H. Jones *et al.*, 1954, *Geology and Ground Water Resources of Southwestern Louisiana*, Geol. Bull. 30, Geological Surv., Baton Rouge, Louisiana, p. 229.)

content of the river just opposite the well is approximately that shown for either Perry or Bancker's Ferry. There is both a time lag and an amplitude reduction in the change in chloride content as between the river and the well water. The peak in chloride content in the river preceded the peak chloride content in the well water by a maximum of 15 days in July. In August the low chloride content in the river occurred 10 days before the well water improved, and in late August the river reached a new peak in chloride content about 15 days before the well did. It should be noted that whereas the river water varied in chloride content from less than 100 ppm to a maximum of about 1800 ppm, the well water went from a minimum of 210 ppm, to a maximum in July of about 280 ppm, then down to 210 and back up to about 320 ppm, the second peak being significantly higher than the first.

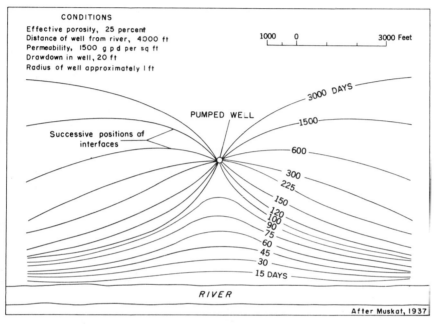

Fig. 5.31. Movement of salt-water and fresh-water interface toward a pumped well near a river, showing position as a function of days after salt water appears in river channel. (From P. H. Jones *et al.*, 1956, *Water Resources of Southwestern Louisiana, U.S. Geol. Surv. Water Supply Paper 1364*, p. 290.)

The Geological Survey conducted aquifer-performance tests in the area north of Abbeville and determined a transmissibility coefficient of approximately 900,000 gal per day per ft and a storage coefficient in the order of 3×10^{-3}. At Abbeville the entire aquifer is about 600 ft thick, so the permeability might be taken to be in the order of 1500 gal per day per sq ft. In computing the movement of a salt-water interface, the porosity is critical, since salt water must physically fill the pore spaces and displace fresh water. Consequently the storage coefficient, while influencing the magnitude of drawdown, is not the determining factor; the porosity is. The Geological Survey assumed that the porosity of the aquifer was 25 percent—a reasonable figure, well in accord with the results obtained in other aquifers composed of similar sediments. Figure 5.31 shows the time of travel of a salt-water fresh-water interface in an aquifer whose characteristics are similar to the one

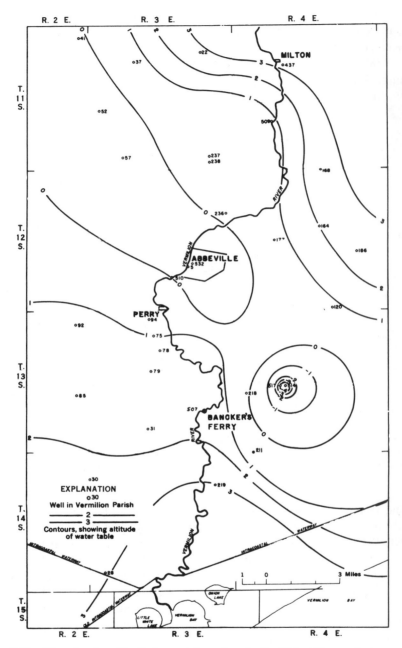

Fig. 5.32. Elevation (m.s.l.) of piezometric surface in the Chicot Reservoir, lower part of the Vermilion River basin, March, 1951. (After P. H. Jones *et al.*, 1956. *Water Resources of Southwestern Louisiana, U.S. Geol. Surv. Water Supply Paper 1364*, p. 237.)

under consideration. A time lag of more than 90 days is indicated—assuming that the river is of constant quality throughout the period of recharge.

Somewhat surprisingly, the Survey report concludes:

The Vermilion River is a very important source of recharge to the Chicot reservoir. Because the water recharged is periodically salty, the Vermilion River is probably the principal source of salt-water encroachment to the Chicot reservoir. To avoid further salt-water encroachment upon the ground-water supply of south-western Louisiana it would be necessary to maintain the Vermilion River as a fresh-water stream to its mouth at all times (*16*, 293).

This implies, of course, surface impoundment in the watershed or additional diversions from other watersheds as well as the construction of a salt-water barrier at the mouth of the river—expensive and complicated engineering construction.

In March, 1951, ground-water conditions in the Vermilion River Basin were found to be those shown on Fig. 5.32. Possibly the most significant feature of this map is the fact that the Vermilion River is crossed twice by the 0-ft contour in the vicinity of Abbeville and, to the south, once each by the 1-ft, 2-ft, and 3-ft contours. The river ranges in elevation plus or minus 1 ft as compared to mean sea level. If the river constituted a hydraulic boundary, say a line of recharge or discharge, we might expect to find that the line of zero elevation (of the piezometric surface) would parallel the river and not cross it. As it is, the map shows that the piezometric surface on both sides of the river, from just south of Abbeville to Vermilion lock, is at or above sea level. Based on hydraulic data alone it would appear that there is no significant quantity of ground-water discharge into the river.

We can next examine the abrupt changes in chloride content shown in Fig. 5.30. The large change in well-water quality that follows the changes in river-water quality in less than 15 days does not corroborate the slow rate of movement of the interface that hydraulic calculations would lead us to expect (Fig. 5.31). All experience with tracers would have lead us to anticipate that the theoretical time of travel of the salt-water front would have been less than that actually observed. This is especially true because of the sluglike character of the salt water: the variation in chloride content of the river would effectively deliver small slugs of salt water to the aquifer, assuming infiltration, and we have already seen what happens to such tracers.

Here, if the chemical changes are interpreted as being due to movement of the interface, the rapidity of movement is more than ten times as fast as that shown in Fig. 5.31. Making due allowance for uncertain hydraulic data, this is so unlikely a possibility that the river-infiltration hypothesis must be rejected.

It must be concluded that coning is most probably the reason for the deterioration of ground-water quality, not the infiltration of saline water from the river. The coincidence of salinity change in the river followed by salinity change in the well water can be explained by the fact that the water is used for the irrigation of rice. Concentrated offtake from a well may be expected after, and only after, the salinity of the river makes the river water unsuitable for irrigation purposes. The river intake is then shut down and the well pump is started. A high rate of well offtake results in coning which is immediately reflected in the deterioration of well-water quality. As soon as the quality of river water improves, the river-water pumps are started. Simultaneously the well is shut down and as a result the apex of the cone of salt water begins to descend and rejoin the salt water body. When the cycle starts again a few weeks later, coning occurs sooner (the salt-water interface is nearer to the bottom of the well, not having returned completely to its original position) and the chloride content rises faster, possibly to a new high.

If the coning interpretation is correct, there is, of course, no need to build a salt-water barrier at the mouth of the river to prevent the entrance of salty water. This interpretation also makes it necessary to reexamine the additional interwatershed diversion of water suggested in another part of the publication. More important than any of these to the student of hydrology and hydrogeology is the lesson taught by this report: even after data have been painstakingly collected and alternate hypotheses proposed and examined, it is by no means certain that the proper interpretation will be selected. There is a considerable margin of error contained in the best study of hydrogeology. It is a tribute to the objectivity and truly scientific attitude of the Geological Survey that the data published are so complete that in this instance they have fully supported an alternate hypothesis.

Side Effects

This portion of the chapter is devoted to side effects and is not particularly concerned with feedback effects. After all, feedback effects are always taken into account from the very start of a ground-water development. For example, if one well in an area produces at the rate of 100 units of water, two wells might produce 180 units, and three wells, 250 units, and the decrease in the average unit-offtake rate is the result of interference, or feedback. This is expected and allowed for.

Side effects, however, are of a different nature. They range from the subsidence of the land surface for one reason or another, to the recovery of a water table due to the curtailment of pumping (to reduce sea-water intrusion) with its consequent threat to the continued placid operation of subways in Brooklyn (which had previously been disturbed by nothing more serious than labor strife). One of the intellectual difficulties about discussing side effects in a book on hydrology is the uncertainty as to whether the material is legitimately included. Yet in a world filled with serious problems the side effects sometimes constitute a sort of an ironic, comic relief, almost slapstick comedy—if considered from a sufficiently detached viewpoint.

And who can claim a more detached, objective viewpoint than the writer of a text on hydrology? Only the readers.

Land subsidence, the most important side effect that accompanies the large-scale removal of water from an artesian aquifer, has many causes. Poland and Davis have summarized most of the possible causes of subsidence as follows: (1) loading at land surface, (2) vibration at or near land surface, (3) compaction due to irrigation and farming, (4) solution due to irrigation, (5) drying out and shrinking of deposits, (6) oxidation of organic material, (7) lowering of water table, (8) decline of pressure head in confined aquifers, (9) decline of pressure in oil zones due to removal of oil and gas, and (10) tectonic movement (*39*). Item 9 could be restated as "removal of hydrocarbons and connate water from oil zones." And the list could be extended to include the removal of any mineral from beneath the land surface.

With respect to ground water: the water confined in an artesian system, being under pressure, tends to support the confining beds. If these are fine-grained materials, when the pressure in the aquifer is reduced, water is also "squeezed" from these materials into the aquifer. Thus the deposits are compacted and this change in volume is ultimately reflected in subsidence at the land surface. In the Houston-Galveston area, Winslow and Wood found that a decline of artesian pressure of 100 ft was reflected by a 1-ft lowering of the elevation of the land surface (*65*). Poland and his colleagues found that a similar change in pressure in part of the San Joaquin Valley resulted in land surface subsidence from 4 to 10 ft (*41*). In the Santa Clara Valley they found a ratio of 1 ft of subsidence for a water-level decline of 12 ft (*40*). The side effects of the lowering of artesian pressures in the area were both unfavorable and favorable. In Texas City, where the pumpage was concentrated in a small area, more than 3.5 ft of subsidence had taken place by 1954. Difficulties have occurred because of the steepness of the "cone of subsidence" which has resulted in protruding well casings, broken pipe lines, reversed flow in sewers and cracked foundations. In the Houston area, where the subsidence is far more uniform, there have been instances where well casings have failed and foundations and highways have cracked. This destruction may have been aided by the lowering of land surface. Another effect of subsidence has been lowering of the land in coastal areas. Part of the Baytown district, once used for grazing, is now tideland. In the Texas City area some of the land formerly believed high enough above sea level to be safe from hurricane tides is now subject to innundation.

On the plus side is the fact that the water made available to wells by the compaction of fine-grained deposits (computed to be from 20 to 25 percent of the total water pumped) has tended to reduce pumping lifts. Finally subsidence has centered in the Houston ship channel area, deepening the channel so that less dredging has been required.

Another notable area of subsidence is the Long Beach area, Los Angeles

County (Fig. 5.23). In this area the lowering of land surface is due primarily to the extractions of oil and gas from deeply lying strata and is only partly due to the withdrawal of ground water. The area has become an often-cited example to illustrate the magnitude of decline of land surface (up to 20 ft, in some parts) and the widespread structural damage both above and below ground that may be caused by such subsidence (*12, 48*).

Another type of subsidence occurs when water is applied for irrigation purposes to certain types of soil. This has happened in about 2000 sq miles of San Joaquin Valley floor. Major trunk canals and local distributaries of surface water for irrigation purposes (to replace the water now being taken from aquifers) have been changed in grade and elevation by subsidence of the irrigated lands. This side effect (or is it a feedback?) has been most disturbing, since open channel flow is predicated on predetermined hydraulic gradients. Consequently, if the designed flow lines of the canals end up above the elevation of the canal banks (due to ground subsidence), either water will be lost or the water-carrying capacity of the canal will be seriously reduced (*28*). This particular side effect has caused a number of modifications in California's water plan and will undoubtedly serve to increase the cost and decrease the economic feasibility to some extent.

Another interesting side effect, this time resulting from the successful attempt to reduce or eliminate sea-water intrusion, has been noted in Brooklyn. The history of ground-water development in that area has covered the whole cycle of growth, overdevelopment, deterioration, and attempted corrective measures—all within a period of less than 50 years.

From only minor offtake in 1903, total net withdrawals for public supply and industrial use increased to approximately 52 million gal per day (mgd) by 1909. In 1917, the municipal use of ground water in Brooklyn began to decline. Contamination of a few well fields by encroaching salt water hastened the reduction in city offtake. Nonetheless net withdrawals in Brooklyn (Kings County) reached an all-time peak of about 75 mgd in 1929 and declined slowly to about 55 mgd in 1946, the last full year of operation by the Flatbush public supply system.

As the realization grew that Brooklyn's ground-water reservoirs were in a critical state of depletion and contamination, state and municipal agencies began to swing into action. In 1933, a law was passed by the New York State Legislature requiring official permission to drill or operate any well having an offtake capacity of 69 gal per minute (gpm); in 1954, this was reduced to 45 gpm. The official agency in charge has required that all water used for cooling purposes above the current minimum (noted above) must be returned to the same waterbearing formation from which it was taken.

The net withdrawals of ground water in Brooklyn declined from 22 mgd in 1948 to 9 mgd in 1961. This decrease in offtake combined with recharge from rainfall and the continued movement of salt water toward the existing cone of depression resulted in a significant rise in water levels throughout the area.

Brashears, former geologist in charge of the U.S. Geological Survey ground water study in Long Island, wrote:

For many years prior to June, 1947, ground-water levels in most parts of Brooklyn were below sea level. This was in sharp contrast to the situation in 1903, when the water table had been everywhere above sea level . . . . Water levels were 30 to 35 ft below sea level and with the water limits of the cone [of depression] along the shoreline in many places . . . .

During the years when ground-water levels were depressed far below normal, many types of sub-surface facilities were constructed in Brooklyn. Several subway lines were built or extended during this period and numerous large buildings with deep basements and sub-basements were erected . . . . Inasmuch as the water table was a considerable distance below basement and subway foundations there appeared to be no good reason for designing walls or floors to withstand hydrostatic pressures . . . .

Damage from underground seepage has already occurred to several man-made structures. *The New York Times*, for example, reported on July 23, 1954, that boiler rooms in two housing projects in the northwestern part of the county had been flooded and that the City Housing Authority was planning to set basement floors in future projects at altitudes above the 1903 high water table level. The same newspaper report referred to damage by flooding at the City's I.R.T. subway station at Newkirk Avenue in Central Brooklyn. The rising water table had cracked the subway floor at the latter site . . . .

The future effects of the water table rise in Brooklyn are difficult to predict. Most ground-water experts conversant with the problem do not anticipate a recovery to the 1903 water table position. For one thing, net industrial pumpage (total pumpage less artificial recharge) in the county is still 12 mgd [as of 1958] and withdrawals are steadily increasing in adjacent parts of Queens County. These withdrawals will tend to prevent a full recovery of water levels. In addition, natural recharge from precipitation in Brooklyn is considerably less than before the turn of the century, because former areas of recharge are now covered by buildings and pavements . . . . However there is a recharging feature (hidden recharge benefit) involving the leakage of water from buried pipe lines and sewers which is not widely appreciated . . . it has been estimated, by assuming typical pipe-leakage factors for underground conduits, that 10 mgd or more may be recharged to the water table in Brooklyn in this manner (2).

In 1963, Perlmutter and Soren stated that seepage at several subway stations in Flatbush had increased from less than 20 gal per min (gpm) in 1947 to as much as 1000 gpm in 1961 (*38*). They stated that the use of recharge wells to return water has been discontinued in places (illegally?) where local recharge mounds on the rising water table have reached basement levels.

The side effects in the development and continued utilization of ground-water resources are so obscure and unpredictable as to seem whimsical. The forecasting of future ground-water conditions would seem to require strict adherence to determinable fact (which would then serve as a solid basis for flights of the imagination), combined with resignation and a wry sense of humor to withstand the impact of unforseen side effects.

LEGAL CONSIDERATIONS

Ground-water hydrology is a term that includes more than hydrogeological conditions. Not only must surface water be appraised and its relationship to the associated ground water evaluated, but man-made limitations, the "rules of the game," must be taken into account. Consequently any reasonably complete discussion of ground-water hydrology must include at least a brief section on legal considerations. The reader should carefully note that the legal situation is presently in a state of change and that legislation affecting the development and utilization of ground water is presently under study by committees of legislators of several states.

Legislation pertaining to ground water is a relatively new development. Until the advent of the deep-well turbine pump, in the last decade of the nineteenth century, ground-water developments were minor. Aquifers, whether potential mines or reservoirs, were full. No legislation was needed or even considered. It is no accident that the first decade of this century saw extensive ground-water studies in Louisiana and New York, the beginnings of irrigation from wells throughout the country, and two landmark court decisions concerning the production and utilization of ground water: Forbell v. The City of New York (11), and Katz v. Walkinshaw (18).

Equally important, if something is to be regulated, the nature of the "something" has to be understood or the regulation will result in a multitude of unwelcome consequences. As we have seen, pseudohydrologic concepts such as safe yield that have been written into law have only recently been discarded by experts in hydrology. The side effects involved in modern hydrology have not yet been completely recognized, and the "something" in this instance, the occurrence and movement of ground water, is imperfectly known. It is partly due to caution born of self-recognized ignorance that lawmakers have generally been reluctant to rush ahead in the field of ground-water control. Nonetheless, in the absence of direct action by legislative bodies, the courts have attempted to extend existing law to decide questions involving ground-water hydrology.

As in the case of surface water there are, basically, two conflicting doctrines: the common-law doctrine of riparian rights (based on ownership of land overlying an aquifer) and the diametrically opposed doctrine of prior appropriation (based on priority of beneficial use, where ownership of contiguous land is not essential). There have been no constitutional interpretations promoting the widespread development of ground-water resources by the Federal Government corresponding to those that have occurred in the field of surface water. The Desert Land Act of 1877 is probably the only exception: and it merely recognizes the appropriation of water for use on Federal land or land that has passed from public to private ownership. Mention should also be made of another, independent, relatively minor doctrine of water control which is based on a state's police power. This generally untested application of police power cannot be classified in either of the two principal categories mentioned above.

Land Ownership or Quasiriparian Rights

According to Thompson and Fiedler, modern doctrine with respect to rights in the use of ground water dates from the decision, by an English court, of Acton v. Blundell in 1843 (55). In this case, the plaintiff was deprived of water from a well on his land through mining operations on the defendant's land about three quarters of a mile distant. The court ruled " . . . that the person who owns the surface may dig therein; and apply all that is there found to his own purposes at his free will and pleasure; and that if, in the exercise of such right, he intercepts or drains off the water collected from underground springs in his neighbor's well, this inconvenience to his neighbor . . . cannot become the ground of an action." This is the essence of what is called the English doctrine. It might narrowly be interpreted as permitting each man to deal with his own natural, nonhuman enemy even if his neighbor is injured as a by-product. This is akin to a man's being allowed to improve the surface drainage of his property even if the runoff causes inconvenience to his downstream neighbor. Although the court dealt with water as a nuisance, the decision was soon extended to cover water, the commodity. The English rule was followed in some states as recently as 1930.

However another doctrine, now known as the American doctrine, or doctrine of reasonable use, began to take form as early as 1862. This approach did not become firmly established until 1900, when the decision in the case of Forbell v. The City of New York held that it was *not* a reasonable use to take ground water from beneath land and sell it for use on land distant from that from which it was obtained (11). This, of course, is quite a novel idea and, if applied uniformly to all minerals extracted from beneath the land surface, would produce some astonishing results. It is another of a long line of instances wherein water is treated as a special commodity instead of being included as private property under the normal doctrines of economic decision.

Shortly thereafter, in 1903, the decision in Katz v. Walkinshaw in California held that the landowner is not authorized to take percolating water from wells and sell it for the irrigation of distant lands, to the detriment of adjoining land overlying the water-bearing beds and whose owners (by benefit of special location with respect to the water-bearing beds) might be considered to possess quasiriparian rights (18). Thus, the California court produced a modification of the doctrine of reasonable use, which is now termed "the doctrine of correlative rights." Among other things it said: "Disputes between overlying land owners concerning water for use on the land, to which they have equal right, in cases where the supply is insufficient for all, are to be settled by giving to each a just and fair proportion." Just how this was to be determined was not set forth.

Hutchins, probably the foremost American authority on water law, said:

The practical arguments for acceptance of the English rule were: (1) the source and flow of these waters are so unknown that it is impossible to formulate any legal rules governing them; and (2) the recognition of correlative rights would substantially interfere with many important projects, such as the drainage of lands, etc. (*15*).

Possibly the first determination of the correlative rights of all users of ground water from a single aquifer, or basin, was handed down in California in 1949 in Pasadena v. Alhambra, popularly termed the "Raymond Basin Case" (*36*). The court concluded that each water user, where the period of use exceeded five years, had gained a prescriptive right against all other users equal to his average offtake. But because the total of all the rights exceeded the safe yield of the basin, each user was enjoined from pumping more than his proportionate share of the safe yield. Robert Thomas recently published a rather comprehensive paper on the water-rights question, in which the Raymond Basin Case is discussed at some length (*54*).

We find that there is one tacit assumption invariably made concerning water: Water is assumed to be a renewable, naturally replenished resource that will be available in perpetuity, like the overlying land. This, in addition to its life-giving qualities, makes water a special case in the field of natural resources. As we have seen, this assumption is rarely if ever completely true and it may be almost completely false. The discrepancy between the legal assumption and the physical fact has been the cause of great dissatisfaction with certain legal doctrines. It has lead to modifications, and changes in the modifications. Even as early as 1938 Thompson and Fiedler said:

In summarizing the results of actual practice in ground-water utilization where the doctrines of reasonable use or correlative rights have been judicially recognized, it may be said that the usefulness of these doctrines has been essentially nullified by difficulties which would attend their application (*55*).

No evidence has accumulated in the past 25 years to support a modification of this statement.

Prior Appropriation

The basic concept of the doctrine of appropriation is that the landowner has no inherent right to use water from sources underlying his lands but that the right to use these sources is based on priority in time of beneficial use, as compared to others using the same source, and may be lost after the use ceases.

The appropriative principle was recognized by the United States Supreme Court in 1874 in the case of Atchison v. Peterson (*59*). In the same year, denying the claims of mining interests that a valid appropriation could be made only for mining purposes, the court extended the principle of appropriation to irrigation uses in the case of Basey v. Gallagher (60).

Harold Thomas contends that either the appropriation doctrine or the land-ownership (riparian) doctrine is a workable legal concept, depending on whether the area involved is arid or humid: "The fundamental differences between the doctrines of water rights based on land-ownership and on appropriation reflect the contrasts in climate in the broad regions where they have been developed and applied" (52).

In other words, legal doctrines follow the climate. In regions of water deficiency (drought) such as the arid lands of the West appropriation doctrine has become established. In the areas of net runoff such as the humid East the land-ownership (or riparian) doctrine controls. In states where both humid and dry climates are found the doctrines coexist. Figure 5.33 shows water-rights doctrines by states as compared to areas of normal water surplus and deficiency. In view of this map, the recent statement of Wells, also a member of the Geological Survey, may be of great significance in foretelling the future direction of water legislation:

Droughts may be classified broadly as (1) water supply droughts and (2) agricultural droughts. Both may be the result of climatic conditions, or the result of the demand outgrowing the supply. Provided that the needs for water in a community are satisfied, no evidence of drought is noticed, however small the supply may be. Conversely, when needs for water exceed the supply, an apparent drought exists even though the deficiency may be no greater than can be expected to recur every few years. However, when deficiencies occur simply because the supply has been overdeveloped, can such deficiencies correctly be termed droughts? (62).

We may reasonably expect, therefore, arguing from the Thomas criterion, that appropriation doctrine will spread into the humid regions of the country as more complete utilization of water resources, both surface and underground, create or accentuate drought conditions.

Appropriation doctrine, however suited it may be to arid regions, is not readily or straightforwardly applicable to all ground-water problems. For one thing the tremendous quantity of water stored in water-bearing formations makes it difficult to balance the perennial replenishment, if any, with the rate of offtake. In some areas, as we have seen, the aquifers essentially are not replenished, and the offtake of water is really water mining.

The extraction process of a mining economy does not constitute a special legal problem when other minerals are considered. No perpetual rights other than those of land ownership are granted to owners of oil or gas wells (and oil or gas are fugitive resources like water). In this field, common pool problems have been handled equitably by means of unitization practices or by limitation agreements. There is no talk about reasonable methods of diversion or about beneficial use or whether one use is of a higher or lower

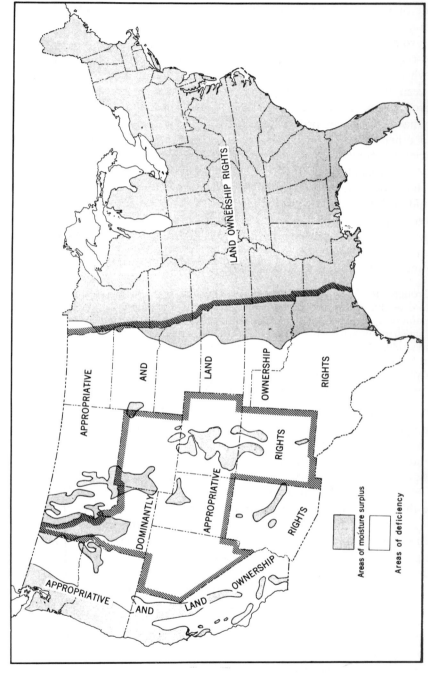

Fig. 5.33. Water-right doctrines by states and areas of normal water surplus and deficiency. (From H. E. Thomas, 1955, *Water Rights in Areas of Ground-Water Mining, U.S. Geol. Surv. Circ. 347*, p. iv.)

order than another. It is assumed that men are not fools and that the resource will be brought into the productive process in the direction of the greatest return to the owner—determined by its utility to others as expressed in a more or less free market.

For another thing, there is usually an enormous timelag between the start of ground-water offtake and the time that deleterious effects on water levels, water quality, or stream flows are noted. This makes any strict application of "prior in time, prior in right" difficult to enforce—the period of unquestioned use may have been so long as to vest title in the appropriator (the Raymond Basin Case illustrates this). A similarly drawn out time scale has been noted by Busby in his discussion of the sedimentation caused by dam construction—the damage upstream occurs many years later, after the statute of limitations has run out (4).

There is, moreover, the problem of priority of rights between surface-water offtake and ground-water offtake, when the ground-water offtake is replenished from the infiltration of water from the stream thus reducing stream flow. Yet the "interfering" ground-water offtakes may be creating additional storage space by dewatering the aquifer, and this may have the desirable result of increasing the salvage of otherwise wasted water during times of high flow.

McGuinness brings up the problem of regulating offtake in an artesian aquifer when this occurs at great distance from the recharge area (30, 10). He correctly points out that the protection of a prior appropriation might require stopping all of the other withdrawals from the aquifer between the senior appropriator and the recharge area. Yet the maximum development of such aquifers requires wells near the recharge area; owners of wells that are distant from the area of recharge might have to depend on artesian storage and to be satisfied with a decreasing yield once the limit of pumping lift has been reached.

The issues that have been touched upon briefly are of formidable hydrogeological complexity. In addition to these physical problems there exists a mixed grille of laws and court decisions that have been conceived by well-meaning, fair-minded men based on their misapprehensions as to the movement of water on land and underground. Added to this is a myth, dating back to Hammurabi, that water, especially in arid regions, must be developed and used in a system of legal priorities not related to the economic evaluation of the marketplace. This makes it difficult, if not impossible, to establish a property right in water that is comparable to that now possible in the ownership of land or other things of value, and tends to develop water supplies under false premises, to the wrong extent, at the wrong time.

McGuinness, who has devoted a great deal of careful study to a system of priorities imposed by some administrative agency, has this to say:

Where prior rights are condemned in favor of a new appropriation for a superior use, there is a difficult question of deciding how much compensation should be paid to the holder of the condemned right. The National Reclamation Association (*Desirable principles of State Water Legislation;* final report of committee appointed October, 1942, 128 pp., October, 1946. p. 31) recommends that "no value, in excess of the actual amount paid to the State in acquiring the right, shall be claimed for either the inchoate appropriative right or the completed appropriative right with respect to the regulation of rates or services to be rendered by the holder of the right or his successors, or with respect to any evaluation for purposes of sale to any government agency or entity or in any eminent domain proceeding . . . ." This means that, under this version of the appropriation doctrine, the water is considered public property and the holder of a right is entitled to its use only so long as his right is not condemned in favor of a superior use; his compensation is to be limited to his cost in acquiring the right, and is not to include the value of the water to him as an essential ingredient in the enterprise he has built up through the use of the water. Such a provision may seem rather harsh, but where the supply is limited it would insure that the highest possible use would be made of the water (*30*, 12).

The writer must confess that the reasoning behind the last sentence seems to be obscure and the conclusion quite indefinite and tending to promote controversy: who determines the "highest possible use," and on what basis? The final paragraph of the McGuinness discussion of preferential uses of water recognizes this, as the following full quotation indicates:

The report of the National Reclamation Association (1946), p. 38) gives the following order of superiority: First, domestic and municipal uses; second, irrigation and stock watering uses; third water power use; fourth, mining use and manufacturing and industrial uses that are not implied in an appropriation for municipal use; and fifth, all other uses without preference as among themselves. The order might be made different in an industrial State where there is little irrigation; indeed, in some states irrigation might be made to rank above industrial use in one part and below it in another.

Significant comment was made by Koenig concerning the use of water, particularly in arid lands:

I submit the proposition that the use of irrigation in the arid lands of the twentieth century is not an appropriate use of that valuable resource, water . . . . Actually, from the stand-point of water use, agriculture is a marginal use of water. In the United States the water that will support one worker in arid land agriculture will support about 60 workers in manufacturing (25).

In 1960 Hirshleifer and his colleagues, in what is probably the best and most adequate contemporary treatment of the economics of water supply, had this to say:

. . . administrators may be inclined to say that competition for water can be ended if decisions or water allocations are only turned over to some bureaucratic agency under their direction. Instead of the ugly picture of competing efforts in the market place to buy up water rights and thus deprive others, a more pleasant image is painted of a committee of experts calmly and rationally dividing up the limited supplies to best meet the needs of all. Now there are indeed problems, which we will discuss later, arising out of market place competition for water supplies—and, of course, there are also problems arising out of political or bureaucratic allocations of water. The point we wish to make here is that the latter procedures cannot eliminate competition for water; the conflict of interest remains whatever the process for making the decision. The only effect is that competition is shifted from the market arena to the political arena, as each contestant attempts to influence the outcome through control of votes and political influence instead of dollars and economic influence (*14, 35–36*).

From the standpoint of the ground-water hydrologist, adoption of the Hirshleifer economic viewpoint as regards water development would remove a number of complications from the study and evaluation of ground-water resources and facilitate the technical work, which is in itself of sufficient complexity.

Police Power

The final legal framework for the control of water is found in the police power of the state. As yet it is only in limited use for the control of ground water. King has this to say about police power:

The term *police power* is but a convenient summarization of the power inherent in the sovereignty to perform adequately all the requisite functions of a civilized government . . . . Any inquiry into an exercise of the police power must fathom and appreciate this approach—the state is performing an essential and basic duty. It is not meddling with economic affairs; the state is furthering the legitimate ends of the public (*21*).

The Model Water Use Act, now being widely circulated, is based squarely on police power. The statement of fundamental policy is best expressed in Section 101f: "The water resources of the State can best be utilized, conserved, and protected if utilization thereof is restricted to beneficial uses and controlled by a state agency responsible for proper development and utilization of the water resources of the State." This statement applies to both surface water and ground water and we have already examined some of the problems encountered in quantitative evaluation of any source. It can be safely predicted that the arbitrary administrative predilection for one water use as against another would simply discourage the development of water supplies by private or public groups. This would be due to general uncertainty, inasmuch as the ground rules could be administratively changed after each change of political power—and probably would be. Moreover the control given to the administration over any form of economic enterprise (beneficial use) would be absolute—everyone drinks water.

One final comment on the Michigan Model Law. In it a "shortage" of water means "the absence of a sufficient quantity of contained water, ground water, or both to supply lawful uses of water" (Section 102f). A good argument can be made that there is always a shortage of water for lawful uses in every inhabited locality, if water to the consumer must be supplied at little or no cost to him for whatever use that he may lawfully apply it.

Fortunately the Michigan Model Law has not yet been adopted by any state. However the fact that such a model law has been proposed should be of interest to every hydrologist, not to mention citizen.

Outlook

Even this brief summary has made it evident that the present legal framework for the development of ground water has a number of shortcomings. These can be attributed to a lack of knowledge of ground-water hydrology, including hydrogeology, the existence of decisions and legislation based on ignorance and, superimposed on these, a general feeling that legal control of the production of water must, somehow, be tied to the end use of the product. This last might be paraphrased as: "The Authority knows better how water shall be utilized in the economic process than you do, and if you won't use it the way we want you to, you won't be allowed to produce it!" They might almost be talking about alcohol!

It seems generally agreed that the appropriation doctrine is a sound basis for long-term water development. Yet the doctrine of correlative rights, as adjudicated in the Raymond Basin Case, contains a valuable lesson—that when the average input to an aquifer can be made to balance the offtake and the aquifer is unitized, all water producers benefit.

Thus, if a water right, under appropriation statutes, could be obtained by some sort of a recharge district (a group of owners of land overlying an aquifer, the waters of which they utilize), then a permanent water supply might be arranged. If, in addition, the individual right of each owner to a share of the total offtake could be treated as any other form of property— rented, transferred, or sold—then the economic basis for water development would be clear-cut. Economic evaluations of proposed water projects in comparison to other investments could more readily be accomplished.

In areas of water mining no permanent rights would be granted and, subject possibly to spacing regulations, the utilization of the stored water would not be restricted. Any restrictions on the transportation of mined water could then be removed. It is not difficult to visualize pipe-line companies acting as common carriers to transport the mined water to areas of use much in the manner of pipe-line companies in the transmission of natural gas.

Where water from streams replenishes aquifers, where what Thomas has termed "water-course" problems exist, we encounter the most difficult of all areas in which to establish proper ground rules. Here too, however, the transfer or sale of water rights from present surface-water appropriators to the owners of ground-water mines or reservoirs might constitute a method of solving the problem. This would enable the orderly conjunctive use of surface water and ground water.

In other areas of hydrogeological development: the drainage of mines, the disposal of wastes underground, and the storage of gas in aquifers, there is much uncertainty both in the technology and legislative rules. These are areas in which research will be very productive, both presently and in the future.

All of these matters are the concern of the ground-water hydrologist in his study of resources, their most efficient production, and their utilization. This section on legal considerations will only serve to outline the problems with a broad brush—the details of individual circumstances must be reserved to the hydrologist and his legal associate, on a case-by-case basis.

NOTES

1. Am. Soc. Civ. Eng., 1961. Ground-water basin management, *Manual of Engineering Practice No. 40*, p. 52. Italics added.
2. Brashears, M. L., December, 1962, personal communication.
3. Broadhurst, W. L., May, 1962, *The Cross Section*, v. 8, no. 12.
4. Busby, C. E., 1962, Some legal aspects of sedimentation, *Trans. Am. Soc. Civ. Eng.*, v. 127, pt. 1, pp. 1107–1044.
5. California Dept. of Water Resources, 1958, Sea-water intrusion in California, *Div. of Resources Planning Bull. 63:* Appendix A, Status of sea-water intrusion 91 pp., 31 plates; Appendix B, March, 1957, Report by Los Angeles County Flood Control Commission on investigational work for prevention and control of sea-water intrusion, West Coast Basin Experimental Project, Los Angeles County, 76 pp., 34 plates, 9 photos 6 appendices; Appendices C, D, E, April, 1960, bound as one volume.
6. Conkling, H., 1946, Utilization of ground-water storage in stream-system development, *Trans. Am. Soc. Civ. Eng.*, v. 111, p. 283.
6a. Cooper, H. H., and Rorabaugh, M. I., 1963, *Ground Water Movements and Bank Storage Due to Flood Stages in Surface Streams, U.S. Geol. Surv. Water Supply Paper 1536J.*
7. Cronin, J. G., September, 1961, A summary of the occurrence and development of ground water in the Southern High Plains of Texas, *Texas Board of Water Engineers, Bull.* 6107, Figure 18.
8. Ferris, J. G. et al., 1962, Theory of aquifer tests, *U.S. Geol. Surv. Water Supply Paper* 1536-E.
9. Fishel, V. C., 1942, in Methods for determining permeability of water-bearing Materials, *U.S. Geol. Surv. Water Supply Paper* 887, pp. 55–68.
10. Fletcher, H. C., and Elmendorf, H. B., 1955, Phreatophytes a serious problem in the West, *Yearbook of Agriculture*, pp. 423–429.
11. Forbell v. The City of New York (164 N.Y. 552).
12. Harris, F. R., and Harlow, E. H., 1948, Subsidence of the Terminal Island-Long Beach area, Calif., *Trans. Am. Soc. Civ. Eng.*, v. 113, pp. 375–403.
13. Hem, J. D., 1959, Study and interpretation of the chemical characteristics of natural water, *U.S. Geol. Surv. Water Supply Paper* 1473.
14. Hirshleifer, J., DeHaven, J. C., and Milliman, J. W., 1960, *Water Supply—Economics, Technology, and Policy*, Chicago, Univ. of Chicago Press, pp. 35–36, 306.
15. Hutchins, W. A., 1942, Selected problems in the law of water rights in the West, *U.S. Dept. of Agr. Misc. Pub. No. 418*, p. 242.

15a. Jacob, C. E., December, 1963, in *Symposium on Transient Ground-Water Hydraulics*, Ft. Collins, Col., Colorado State Univ., pp. 18, 40.

16. Jones, P. H. *et al.* 1956, Water resources of Southwestern Louisiana, *U.S. Geol. Surv. Water Supply Paper* 1364.

17. Jones, P. H., Turcan, A. N., Jr., and Skibitske, H. E., 1954, Geology and ground-water resources of Southwestern Louisiana, *Louisiana Dept. of Cons. Geol. Bull. No.* 30.

18. Katz v. Walkinshaw (141 Cal. 116; 70 Pac. 663; 74 Pac. 776).

19. Kazmann, R. G., September–October, 1949, The utilization of induced stream infiltration and natural aquifer storage at Canton, Ohio, *Economic Geology*, v. 44, no. 6, pp. 514–524.

20. Kazmann, R. G., October, 1954, Report on the present and future ground-water supply of Dubuque, Iowa, multilithed report, 30 pp., 14 figures.

21. King, D. R., 1958, Regulation of water rights under the police power, in *Water Resources and the Law*, Ann Arbor, Univ. of Michigan Law School, pp. 271–353.

22. King, F. H., 1899, Principles and conditions of the movement of ground water, water, *U.S. Geol. Surv. Nineteenth Annual Report*, pt. 2, pp. 71–294.

23. Klaer, F. H., Jr., and Kazmann, R. G., July, 1943, A quantitative study of the well field of the Mill Creek Valley Water Project, Butler County, Ohio, typewritten reproduction of a report prepared by the U.S. Geol. Surv. for the Federal Works Agency.

24. Klaer, F. H., Jr., and Thompson, D. G., 1948, Ground-water resources of the Cincinnati area, Butler and Hamilton Counties, Ohio, *U.S. Geol. Surv. Water Supply Paper* 999.

25. Koenig, L., 1956, The economics of water resources, in The future of arid lands, *Am. Assoc. Ad. Sci. Pub. No.* 43, p. 328.

26. Langbein, W. B., 1954, Water budget, in H. E. Thomas (Ed.), The first fourteen years of Lake Mead, *U.S. Geol. Surv. Circ.* 346, pp. 8–10.

27. Laverty, F. B., and van der Goot, H. A., September, 1955, Development of a fresh-water barrier in Southern California for the prevention of sea-water intrusion, *J. Am. Water Works Assoc.*, v. 47, no. 9, pp. 886–908.

28. Lofgren, B. E., March, 1960, Near-surface land subsidence in western San Joaquin Valley, Calif., *J. Geophys. Res.*, v. 65, no. 3, p. 1053.

29. McGuinness, C. L., June, 1951, The water situation in the United States with special reference to ground water, *U.S. Geol. Surv. Circ.* 114.

30. McGuinness, C. L., 1951, Water law with special reference to ground water, *U.S. Geol. Surv. Circ.* 117, pp. 10, 12.

30a. McGuinness, C. L., 1963, *The Role of Ground Water in the National Water Situation, U.S. Geol. Surv. Water Supply Paper 1800*.

31. Meinzer, O. E., 1920, Quantitative methods of estimating ground-water supplies *Bull. Geol. Soc. Am.*, v. 31, pp. 329–338.

32. Meinzer, O. E., 1923, The occurrence of ground water in the United States, *U.S. Geol. Surv. Water Supply Paper* 489.

33. Meyer, R. R., and Turcan, A. N., Jr., 1955, Geology and ground-water resources of the Baton Rouge area, Louisiana, *U.S. Geol. Surv. Water Supply Paper* 1296.

34. Meyers, J. S., 1962, Evaporation from the 17 western states, *U.S. Geol. Surv. Professional Paper 272-D*, pp. 94–95.

35. Mueller, F. W., 1962, Depletion allowance for ground water? A review of the

Shurbet case, Am. Inst. Min. Met. and Pet. Eng. Annual Meeting, preprint No. 62H118.

35a. Parkhurst, J. D., and Garrison, W. E., September, 1964, Whittier Narrows water reclamation plant, *Civil Engineering*, v. 34, no. 9, pp. 60–63.

36. Pasadena v. Alhambra [33 Calif. (2*d*) 908, 207 Pac. (2*d*) 17 (1949)].

37. Pennink, J. M. K., 1905, Investigations for ground-water supplies, *Trans. Am. Soc. Civ. Eng.*, v. 54, pt. 4, p. 179.

38. Perlmutter, N. M., and Soren, J., 1963, Effects of major water-table changes in the Kings and Queens Counties, New York City, in *U.S. Geol. Surv. Professional Paper* 450, Annual Review of Research Series.

38a. Petri, L. R., Lane, C. W., and Furness, L. W., 1964, *Water Resources of the Wichita Area, Kansas, U.S. Geol. Surv. Water Supply Paper 1499-I*.

39. Poland, J. F., and Davis, G. H., June, 1956, Subsidence of the land surface in the Tulare-Wasco (Delano) and Los Banos-Kettleman city area, San Joaquin Valley, California, *Trans. Am. Geophys. Un.* v. 37, no. 3, p. 295.

40. Poland, J. F., and Green, J. H., 1962, Subsidence in the Santa Clara Valley, California, *U.S. Geol. Surv. Water Supply Paper 1619-C*.

41. Poland, J. F., Lofgren, B. E., and Davis, G. H., 1958, *Progress Reports on Land Subsidence Investigations in the San Joaquin Valley, California, through 1957*, Sacramento, Calif., Integragency Committee on Land Subsidence in the San Joaquin Valley, p. 15, also plate 45.

42. Rainwater, F. H., and Thatcher, L. L., 1960, Methods for collection and Analysis of water samples, *U.S. Geol. Surv. Water Supply Paper* 1454.

43. Ransom, A. E., Mar. 26, 1963, personal communication, graph of water levels enclosed.

44. Robinson, T. W., 1958, Phreatophytes, *U.S. Geol. Surv. Water Supply Paper* 1423, p. 1.

45. Rorabaugh, M. I., 1956, Ground water in Northeastern Louisville, Kentucky, *U.S. Geol. Water Supply Paper 1360-B*.

45a. Rorabaugh, M. I., 1964, Estimating changes in bank storage and ground-water contribution to stream flow, *Symposium on Surface Waters*, Pub. No. 63, Ghent, Bel., Int. Assoc. Scient. Hydrology, pp. 432–441.

46. Rose, H. E., 1945, An investigation into the laws of flow of fluids through beds of granular material, *Proc. Inst. Mech. Engrs.*, v. 153, pp. 154–168.

47. Schaefer, E. J., White, G. W., and Van Tuyl, D. W., June, 1946, The ground-water resources of the glacial deposits in the vicinity of Canton, Ohio, *Ohio Wat. Res. Bd., Bull.* 3.

48. Shoemaker, R. R., and Thorley, T. J., April, 1955, Problems of ground subsidence, *J. Am. Water Works Assoc.*, v. 47, no. 4, pp. 412–418.

49. Stramel, G. J., 1956, Progress report on the ground-water hydrology of the Equus Beds area, Kansas, *Geol. Surv. Kans., Bull.* 119, pt. 1, pp. 50–51.

50. Stuart, W. T., 1945, Ground-water resources of the Lansing area, *Mich. Dept. of Cons., Geol. Surv. Div. Rept. No.* 13, p. 28.

51. Theis, C. V., 1935, Relation between the lowering of the piezometric surface and the rate and duration of discharge of a well using ground-water storage, *Trans. Am. Geophys. Un.*, pt. 2, pp. 519–524.

52. Thomas, H. E., 1955, Water rights in areas of ground-water mining, *U.S. Geol. Surv. Circ.* 347, p. 3.

53. Thomas, H. E., 1962, Water and the Southwest—what is the future? *U.S. Geol. Surv. Circ.* 469, p. 14.

54. Thomas, R. O., 1961, Legal aspects of ground-water utilization, *Trans. Am. Soc. Civ. Eng.*, v. 126, pt. 3, p. 643.
55. Thompson, D. G., and Fiedler, A. G., July, 1938, Some problems relating to legal control of use of ground waters, *J. Am. Water Works Assoc.* v. 30, no. 7, p. 1061.
56. Todd, D. K., 1959, *Ground-Water Hydrology*, New York, Wiley, pp. 23–31, 307–325.
57. U.S. District Court, Northern District of Texas, May, 1963, Civil Action No. 2701.
58. U.S. Senate, Select Committee on National Water Resources, 1960, *Evapotranspiration Reduction*, Committee Print no. 21.
59. U.S. Supreme Court, 1874, Atchison v. Peterson (87 U.S. 507).
60. U.S. Supreme Court, 1874, Basey v. Gallagher (87 U.S. 670).
61. Walton, W. C., 1962, Selected analytical methods for well and aquifer evaluation, *Ill. State Water Survey, Bull.* 49.
62. Wells, J. V. B., 1958, Surface-water resources, *Trans. Am. Soc. Civ. Eng.*, v. 123, p. 1209.
63. White, W. N., Broadhurst, W. L., and Lang, J. W., 1946, Ground water in the High Plains of Texas, *U.S. Geol. Surv. Water Supply Paper* 889F.
64. Williams, C. C., and Lohman, S. W., 1949, Geology and ground-water resources of a part of South Central Kansas, *Geol. Surv. Kans., Bull.* 79, pp. 212, 223.
65. Winslow, A. G., and Wood, L. S., 1959, Relation of land subsidence to ground-water withdrawals in the upper Gulf Coast Region, Texas, *Trans. Am. Inst. Min. Met. and Pet. Eng.*, v. 214.
66. Wyllie, M. R. J., July, 1962, Reservoir mechanics: Stylized myth or potential science? *J. Petroleum Tech.*, v. 14, no. 6, p. 587.

6

Water Resource Development

BACKGROUND

In this section a number of projects in the field of water-resource development are appraised from the standpoints of hydrology and desirable public policy. And by "desirable public policy" is meant a policy beneficial to the body-politic: where the broad, overall benefits manifestly outweigh the broad overall costs. This is not a simple matter, nor is it one to be decided conclusively in each instance at this time. But the technological framework of hydrology has been discussed, with its effects and side effects, and if the following evaluation is incomplete, at least the essence of the approach will have been presented: the forest, not only the individual trees. Are we to gain a perennial supply of merchantable timber, or are we merely lighting a forest fire: warming in its early stage, but an annihilating terror later on? At the onset let me suggest to the reader that neither image is wholly right—nor wholly wrong.

There has been much talk of the need for a National Water Policy that would be uniformly applicable to conditions throughout the country, prevent waste, reduce pollution, control floods, recharge aquifers, make deserts bloom, promote water skiing and fishing and so forth. This kind of talk is for politicians and journalists; qualified hydrologists know better. The range in climate and the difference in geologic conditions in a land mass of continental size precludes anything but valueless generalizations when a National Water Policy is to be translated into hard and fast laws and rules. A shortage of water in Ohio is not to be cured by restricting the washing of cars in Los Angeles. Nor is the cost of producing water in New York to be equated with the cost of producing water in Los Alamos. And what has the cost of flood control at Chattanooga to do with flood protection at Albuquerque? We have seen how little even the most complete control of floods on the Tennessee River affects the level of the Ohio River at Cairo, not far from the mouth of the Tennessee. Be it friend or foe, water is local.

From the standpoint of mankind there is a crude balance in nature as regards water resources: the upstream areas may have inadequate water supplies, but flood protection is not a problem. Conversely floods may be a problem downstream, but the water supply is reliable and inexpensive. Men have taken these factors into account in appraising the worth of property and when planning settlements.

In evaluating water projects the time scale used is of critical importance— the benefits and costs of any extensive project are not completely predictable or subject to evaluation because the time involved can never be known with precision. And whereas the out-of-pocket cost of a project may be returned in 40 or 50 years (it has recently been proposed that Federal projects be evaluated on the basis of a 100-year payout period), the long-term side effects directly attributable to the project may far outweigh the direct construction costs. Moreover these side effects—sedimentation, river-bank erosion, land subsidence, and so on—while certain to occur sooner or later, cannot be placed on a time table, inasmuch as their occurrence results from factors not to be precisely quantified. And what of the future cost to society of displaced populations in arid regions, populations that have settled, confidently expecting a perennial water supply, when this is beyond our power to insure?

We find that many water projects have been set athwart the irrestible forces of geomorphology. To complicate proper evaluation, the time scales involved are not the same. For certain projects the time is measured in decades, for others, centuries. When benefits and costs occur at markedly different times, how does this effect the desirability of the project? What of water mining, sedimentation, gradually reducing flood-control capability in evaluating the merit of projects? Are the form of development and method of development of any significant importance? Or does one method have a distinct advantage over another? These are all legitimate questions for a hydrologist to ponder. It may not be too much to say that the future of the United States may depend on the right answers. In nature, let it be noted, there are neither rewards nor punishments—there are only consequences. We must base ourselves on truth and observed fact as we adapt ourselves, as best we may, to powers beyond our complete control.

For a point of departure we need an idea of the order of magnitude of the relative sizes of artificial impoundments used for various purposes. This will enable us to form an orderly picture of the allocation of resources to the various phases of water development and the probable magnitude of desired and undesired results. According to Thomas and Harbeck of the U.S. Geological Survey:

Most of the multiple-use reservoirs have had their inception since 1930, and since then there has been a major change in size. The average capacity of all reservoirs exceeding 5000 acre-feet was about 68,000 acre-feet at the end of 1929, and by the end of 1949 it had increased to about 150,000 acre-feet . . . . Since 1950, the trend toward larger reservoirs has been even more pronounced; the 158 reservoirs of more than 5,000 acre-feet capacity completed . . . or under construction on January 1, 1954, have an average capacity of about 680,000 acre-feet (*15*).

In the same publication there are listed, by name, all reservoirs that have a usable capacity of 2 million acre-ft or more: 21 reservoirs in all. Not one of the reservoirs is primarily for municipal or industrial water supply, although, as a distinctly minor use, some of the water may be so utilized. The largest reservoir used primarily for municipal purposes is the Quabbin Reservoir in Massachusetts (on the Swift River) which was completed in 1939 and has a usable capacity of almost 1.3 million acre-ft. By way of comparison, the total of all large reservoirs storing water for New York City is only 843,000 acre-ft.

The following table gives the total storage capacity, the "dead" storage, and the maximum usable storage capacity of the ten largest reservoirs in the United States (all of these are now in operation).

Table 6.I. Ten Largest Reservoirs in the United States (1954) (Capacity in Thousands of Acre-Feet)

	Total Storage	Dead Storage[a]	Usable Storage	Use[b]
Lake Mead, Ariz. and Nev.	29,827	2,620[c]	27,207	FIMPR
Garrison, N. Dak.	23,000	4,900	18,100	FINPR
Oahe, S. Dak.	22,500	5,500	17,000	FINPR
Ft. Peck, Mont.	19,400	4,500	14,900	FNPR
Franklin D. Roosevelt, Wash.	9,402	4,330	5,072	IP
Ft. Randall, S. Dak.	6,300	1,400	4,900	FINPR
Lake Texoma, Okla. and Tex.	5,659	1,163	4,496	FNPR
Bull Shoals, Ark.	5,408	964	4,444	FPR
Shasta, Calif.	4,493	116	4,377	FINP
Wolf Creek, Ken.	6,089	1,853	4,236	FP

[a] Dead storage is the volume below the lowest controllable level. Although many power dams have sluiceways for power production well below the lower limit of drawdown, dead storage is usually allocated for sediment. However, much sedimentation occurs at higher elevations than the level of the dead storage pool, although ultimately the lower levels may fill with sediment. Generally, in the humid sections of the country, where sedimentation is minor, navigation, recreation, or conservation requirements govern the elevation of the dead-storage pool. In the arid sections, sediment-storage is a major addition to these considerations.

[b] F = Flood Control; I = Irrigation; M = Municipal; N = Navigation; P = Power; R = Recreation.

[c] U.S. Geological Survey Circ. 346 shows that in 1935 the total storage below the spillway gates (raised for maximum water impoundment) was 31.25 million acre-ft; dead storage was 3.22 million acre-ft for a usable storage of 28.03 million acre-ft. By 1948, the total storage (gates raised) was 29.83 million acre-ft, dead storage was 2.62 million acre-ft, or a net usable storage of 27.2 million acre-ft. Thus, overall, some 4.2 percent of the gross storage was lost by sedimentation in 13 years. On a net basis, however, only 3 percent of the usable storage was lost because much sediment was deposited in the dead storage pool. The indicated rate of sediment accumulation is approximately 0.35 percent a year. By law, there has been established a flood-control reserve as of April 1 of each year: There must be at least 9.5 million acre-ft of storage available. Thus, all loss in capacity is charged to the other functions—in this instance, irrigation, municipal, power and recreational uses. The capacity for these uses went from 18.53 million acre-ft to 17.7 million acre-ft in 13 years; a loss of 4.6 percent. At some future date, there will be a direct, sharp conflict between a possible water shortage due to lack of space for the storage of water, and the legal requirement of not-to-be-encroached-upon space for the control of a possible flood. As between the immediate, real threat of water shortage and the remote threat of a super flood we may confidently expect that the rule will be changed to meet the most pressing situation. The construction of Glen Canyon Dam will serve to delay the conflict in use for some time—the reservoir found there may be the scene of the first such fight on the Colorado River.

It should be noted that the oldest of the reservoirs listed in the table is Lake Mead, which started to fill in 1936. Thus, sedimentation has only just begun in most reservoirs. The information regarding Lake Mead was obtained during an extensive resurvey in 1948 and is already 15 years old. Such extensive surveys are both laborious and expensive and are undertaken at infrequent intervals.

PRINCIPLES

As we have seen, existing water projects have been predicated on a number of different legislative and legal doctrines. Any, or all, of these may be workable under certain circumstances. As a rule, therefore, projects will be evaluated without reference to the particular doctrines under which they were developed.

Nor are any of the following comments to be interpreted as casting doubt on the legality or constitutionality of any of the laws or projects. The rules under which a nation operates may be moral or immoral, beneficial or detrimental, wise or foolish, but within their sphere they govern until changed. The writer may call attention to certain discrepancies between the assumptions behind the laws, or court decisions, and the physical facts—but this does not alter the law. He can only hope that, when the physical facts and law are in disharmony, the laws will be changed by the proper authorities.

The evaluation of water-development projects will consist, first, of a hydrologic summation of the effects and principal side effects. After these have been set forth, the projects will be reviewed from the standpoint of governmental principles and of economic principles. If there is any obvious contradiction between the hydrologic facts and these principles, a possible suggestion for remedying matters will be proposed.

With regard to governmental principles, the basic assumption made is in three parts. The first is that the people of the United States will continue to maintain a Federal Government for as far into the future as can be imagined. The second is that the Federal Government is committed to bring to a successful conclusion any water-development project that it, after study, undertakes, physical circumstances permitting. The third is that the Federal Government will not knowingly mislead its citizens. Should this be done unwittingly, the nation, acting through its Government, will make necessary amends. In other words the Federal Government, representing the people of the United States, will act honorably and equitably toward its citizens. The states and other local governmental units are also assumed to act similarly in the areas of their authority and responsibility.

The economic principle is that the benefits to be derived from any project, or collection of projects, must be greater than the cost—costs and benefits to be evaluated on the incremental principle.

The value-judgment is based on this premise: When the physical outcome of any hydrologic project is not in harmony with the operation of either or both of the stated principles, the governmental unit involved will liquidate its connection with the project promptly. This does not mean that the project must be completely abandoned—it is possible that, after all risks are evaluated, private or public corporations may find short-term values that can be salvaged, and this may be permitted under conditions of full disclosure.

It may seem superfluous to list basic principles so baldly and unequivocally. But the development of natural resources by public (governmental) investment involves a value-judgment, and we must assume that the systematic waste of public funds is hurtful to the body politic (although it may be a fine "pork barrel" for the few); that projects must not be falsely premissed and "sold" on that basis; that, if this should happen inadvertently, as soon as this is understood the action will cease and amends will be made as far as this is possible.

There will, of course, be borderline cases in which physical circumstances are so complex that they may be interpreted in one way rather than another. Under such circumstances final evaluation must await more complete information. Fortunately, for major projects, this borderline condition may be cured by subdividing the project and evaluating each of the parts and then combining and recombining the various segments and studying the results. Such a procedure will usually spotlight the strengths and weaknesses and enable the proper decision to be made.

There is probably one, broad, inclusive positional statement regarding water that must be made. All mechanisms for the storage of water (the displacement in time of the availability of surface water) must sooner or later affect the occurrence and rate of surface runoff. As a consequence every water-storage project decreases to some extent the hydrologic (statistically valid) character of the data obtained from the affected watershed. This in turn increases the uncertainty, and thus the cost, of every succeeding downstream project based on hydrologic data. *There is, thus, a pervading implication that storage of water should be accomplished on a minimum basis and only where absolutely necessary*, so that the direct costs inflicted on society as side effects will be held to the practicable minimum.

FLOOD CONTROL

Flood-control structures are magnificent, awe-inspiring products of modern technology. No one can fail to be impressed with the large volumes of earth fill or concrete used for the dams. Nor are the river cut-offs or the channel training works such as timber dikes of negligible size and importance. The hundreds of miles of earthen levees are also impressive structures by any method of measurement, as are the concrete sections of flood walls in cities. Finally the huge blankets of timber or reinforced concrete used to protect river banks from erosion should not be overlooked.

Just what is flood control? The second Hoover Commission included a task force group concerned solely with flood control. This group, headed by an eminent engineer, the late W. W. Horner, reported on the background, objectives, success, and costs of construction undertaken under the designation "flood control":

The term "flood control" is a misnomer. Man does not really "control" floods. He attempts, rather, to prevent the overflow of certain portions of flood plains, with two objectives in mind.

1. Alleviating damage to existing property, i.e., preventing the reduction of existing values.
2. Enhancing the usefulness of flood plain lands, i.e., increasing existing values.

The second objective is clearly identical with that of "reclamation." Moreover many reclamation undertakings also alleviate damage. For example, irrigation projects through which supplemental water is brought to lands already under cultivation to reduce damage by drought. . . .

Flood control is an unfortunate designation from still another standpoint. Floods are not controlled in the sense that they are rendered harmless. Nor are they controlled in the sense that they are eliminated, except, in some instances, immediately below very large and costly storage reservoirs. Generally flood-control works are designed to confine the flood waters to a certain part of the valley bottom by such means as levees, or to store enough of the flood water to reduce rates of flow and thus provide a reasonable degree of protection to certain parts of the flood plain (6, 727).

Firm figures regarding total expenditures for flood-control purposes are not readily obtainable. Based on the Hoover committee report however, as of 1954, the total cost of projects completed or under construction was approximately 5.7 billion dollars (6, 774). White, in 1960, estimated that at least 4 billion dollars had already been spent for that purpose by 1959 (19). The net result of this vast expenditure (most of it after 1936) has been an increase (Corps of Engineers estimate) in the mean annual losses caused by floods (in 1959 dollars) from 212 million dollars in 1936, to 444 million in 1954, and to 700 million dollars in 1959 (16).

This absurd outcome suggests a double drain on the economy: on the one side vast expenditures for improvements, derived mainly from Federal taxation, which in turn cause ever mounting losses to be inflicted upon that part of the population that considers itself the beneficiary of such protection. Seemingly the country would be better off if it could be returned to status quo ante. This, of course, is highly improbable, to say the least.

White points out, quite correctly, that the construction of engineering works is only one of the many possible human adjustments to the flood hazard. Presumably, if men have not been misled into believing that floods were controlled, they would not move into the flood plains. To overcome this entrapment he proposes that maps and reports concerning the possible flood hazards be made available to "property managers and to public lending and construction agencies." This would be similar to the "truth in advertising" efforts made by the Federal Government with regard to the efficacy of drugs. Then, to reduce flood losses, White suggests additional and more complete flood warning, a flood-insurance program in which the premiums are in proportion to the hazard, technical advice so that structures will be more flood resistant, and finally, state regulation of flood-plain occupancy. Of course all of this would result in the people not being able to utilize that for which they believe the Federal Government has paid. The Technical Library of TVA has prepared an indexed bibliography of papers on flood-damage prevention; fifteen references of the 259 items listed are prior to 1952 (*14a*).

From the standpoint of hydrology and, more particularly, geomorphology, the life of a flood-control project is controlled by geologic and climatic circumstances. In the East the rate of sedimentation of reservoirs is relatively low. Not only does vegetation armor the land surface against the erosive power of rain and runoff, but the underlying formations are resistant rock, the alluvial plains are narrow and shallow, and sedimentation is at a minimum. For example, the rate of sediment accumulation in Pickwick Landing reservoir (TVA) has been found to be approximately 0.143 percent of its capacity a year despite an annual runoff of 33 million acre-ft (*7*). This rate of sedimentation compares favorably to the 0.35 percent per year storage loss at Lake Mead which results from an average annual runoff of 13 million acre-ft. Thus, the efficacy of much construction for flood control, ignoring for the moment the multiple-use aspects of much of the new reservoir construction, is a decaying thing. Assuming a sedimentation rate of 0.25 percent a year of the original design capacity, then in 50 years one eighth of the storage assigned to flood control will have been lost. Just what this does to increase the probability of a damaging flood must be determined in each instance. No papers on this subject have come to the attention of the writer. At a sedimentation rate of 0.50 percent a year, one quarter of the storage is lost in 50 years. By way of comparison, the reservoir in the Rio Grande River formed by Elephant Butte Dam has been silting at the rate of more than 0.5 percent per year.

It is, thus, entirely possible that even if floods are completely controlled on a given date by existing construction, only a few years later damaging floods will become increasingly probable. Ultimately, instead of protection from the 200-year flood the protection afforded will be against effects of the 50-year flood, and the protection shortly thereafter will be reduced still more. Lane, an eminent hydrologist and hydraulician, felt so deeply about this problem recently that from his sickbed he requested Albertson and Simons of Colorado State University to inform the profession of his views. *Civil Engineering* of May, 1962, carried a letter relaying Mr. Lane's thoughts:

1. Engineers have been concerned for many years about the possibility of a reservoir filling in part or entirely with sediment and thereby losing its storage capacity for water supply.

2. Despite this concern, designers have apparently overlooked the fact that such silting could cancel out the reduction in peak flow previously obtained by routing a flood through a reservoir. Spillways have been designed on the assumption that storage capacity is available to considerably reduce the flood flow that enters the reservoir upstream. As a reservoir fills with sediment, spillway discharge will increase and may exceed the design discharge, resulting in failure of spillway or dam or both.

3. Considerable residential and industrial development has taken place in flood plains on the assumption that these plains will not be needed [for flood flows] once the storage reservoir has been built. Levees are also usually built to care only for the reduced flow. The success of such developments is obviously threatened if the initial flood discharge is not greatly reduced in passing through the reservoir.

4. Increasingly, dams are built in series on a stream to control it and take full advantage of hydropower and a regulated water supply. If one of the reservoirs fills with silt and a failure results, all the dams downstream will be endangered by the unanticipated increase in discharge . . . .

Improved practices in upstream soil-erosion control will no doubt help to prolong the life of a reservoir. However they cannot be expected to do more than delay the inevitable (1).

The questions of quantitative geomorphology—sedimentation of reservoirs, erosion of river beds and banks below reservoirs, the gradual build up of delta deposits above reservoirs—are becoming critical for the profession of civil engineering. Hans Einstein, son of the great mathematical physicist, and in his own right a leader in theory and research in the field of sedimentation, recently called attention to need for additional research and concluded: "The large storage reservoir is seen as the most important cause for new sediment problems in our rivers. Sediment transportation research should concentrate on the study of river conditions upstream and downstream from such reservoirs" (2, 6).

In the body of his paper Einstein points out that, although we don't know how to accomplish it now, controlled sedimentation by rivers in the flood plains above reservoirs would tend to prolong the useful lives of these impoundments. The writer readily agrees that research in this field is justified. But we can expect a long period of research before laboratory or small-scale field studies result in new engineering principles. And at the present rate of reservoir construction there may be few occasions in advance of construction on which to utilize this hard-won knowledge. According to the *Engineering News-Record* of Jan. 24, 1963, there were 217 dams under construction in the United States and 581 more were under consideration or being actively planned. In March, 1963, Lt. Gen. W. K. Wilson of the Army Engineers stated that an additional 400 million acre-ft of storage was needed and a total water-resources expenditure by the Corps of Engineers amounting to 28 billion dollars was anticipated by 1980! (20). More immediately to the point are Einstein's comments on sediment problems downstream. The time lag here is much shorter than that encountered in evaluating changes upstream:

The construction of a reservoir will have its greatest benefits in the river valley downstream through flood control and increased all-year water supply .... The river that brings fresh water from the reservoir will also be called on to drain the valley bottom and, depending on its size, may even provide inexpensive transportation. Because the river channel is already provided, the laymen are apt to accept its shape and course as given and stable. When the majority of the high flows are held back by the reservoir, most or all of the flood danger appears to be eliminated.

To the engineer who is familiar with the management of alluvial rivers, the picture looks less rosy. He recognizes that the construction and operation of the reservoir severely reduces the sediment supply and radically changes the hydrograph of the river. These changes are so drastic that in most cases there is very little similarity between the new and the pre-reservoir river. Only the channel is the same. It is a sediment-lined channel that had usually reached at least near-equilibrium shape for the old river condition. It would be an extreme coincidence if the channel were still in equilibrium at the new flow and sediment conditions. The sediment supply is reduced. But also the channel capacity to transport sediment is somewhat reduced by the reduction of flood flows and the increase of medium flow durations. Usually the sediment supply is reduced more than the carrying capacity, causing the channel to erode. Often this development may be reversed in lower reaches after some sediment carrying tributaries have joined the main stream with the reduced sediment capacity. The immediate response of the river will be scour in the upper reaches. It will have acquired a full load when it arrives at the junction with any sediment carrying tributary. It may begin to aggrade at and below that junction. If the river channel is left free to develop at will, the upper reaches will, after a given time, adjust themselves to the new conditions. They will stabilize at a lower sediment rate, and sediment load to the lower reaches will be reduced. It must be expected that during that process of adjustments the sediment supply to all parts of the river system will steadily change and call for continued readjustments.

After a channel section has finally stabilized its profile, for instance by coarsening its bed sediment, it is, unfortunately, not yet completely stable. The banks, that usually consist of a finer material than the bed, also begin to fail. They also seem to be stabilized only as long as finer material is deposited from the stream at about the same rate at which it scours. With the finer sizes missing in the load, the banks retreat steadily and the river channel widens. The flows begin to meander between banks and attack them with increased force where they impinge on them. It is not sufficient to stabilize the bed alone; the same must be done with the banks (2, 4).

And indeed, bank stabilization is an ever-increasing item in the annual Federal appropriations for rivers and harbors. Our stream systems have been placed in a state of increasing nonequilibrium, becoming deeper here, shallower there, responding to "channel improvements" and reservoirs with the time-tested forces of erosion and deposition.

In evaluating flood-control projects, and especially those that rely upon large reservoirs to reduce flood peaks, which are combined with channel improvements and low levees to provide safety from floods, short-lived projects should probably be differentiated from longer-lived ones. Short-lived projects will be found in all sections of the country, although most of them have been built west of the Mississippi River.

Flood control, however, is supposed to be permanent, and the enhancement in the market value of "protected" lands is the first immediate and visible by-product of flood-control projects. Inasmuch as it is not physically possible to achieve this permanence in a majority of instances, the Federal Government, in undertaking to provide permanent flood control, is undertaking the impossible. But, if one promises to achieve the impossible and devotes all resources to this end, the result is ruin. Not only will the direct "beneficiaries" be hurt by the inevitable flooding, but all of the citizens of the United States, whose tax burden will rise as public expenditures are made to achieve the impossible, will be unfavorably affected. We can conclude, and the facts seem to support this conclusion, that the Federal Government is an inappropriate instrumentality for the accomplishment of flood control.

With regard to accomplishment of flood control through reservoir construction on watersheds where sedimentation is not a problem, it may be possible to provide some measure of protection during periods of high flow over a significantly longer period. At least whatever has been purchased will retain its value for a long time. Under these circumstances White's proposals regarding full disclosure of the flood hazard have direct and immediate applicability. Whether people should be permitted to take a known, calculated risk and build whatever they please in areas subject to flood is another matter entirely. Under any circumstances there would seem to be an element of entrapment by the Federal construction of projects that purport to reduce or eliminate floods permanently. There is also an element of secondary liability that all of the people of the United States assume by undertaking such projects. And while hydrologists are no more competent than any other citizens to evaluate this, they are obligated to call the situation to the attention of their elected representatives, who have the final word in the matter.

The facts of the matter may be summarized as follows:

1. Losses due to floods have steadily increased as flood-control projects financed and built by the Federal Government have proliferated. In this connection, sedimentation of flood-control reservoirs has not yet played a major part because most of the reservoirs have only recently been filled with water and the accumulation of sediment has just started.

2. Losses may be attributed to the increased occupancy of flood plains based on the mistaken assumption that the permanent control of floods has been provided by the Federally financed and designed construction.

3. When the major reservoirs fill partly with sediment, this will be accompanied by a large and disproportionate decrease in the flood protection afforded. This situation will be due, in part, to the combined design of levees and reservoir storage, which enables the size of the former to be predicated on the capability of the latter to reduce peak flows. The frequency and magnitude of damaging floods in the "protected" flood plains will increase,

raising the already substantial rate of flood-caused damage. The simultaneous development of upstream drainage projects reduces the effective "concentration time" of the overland runoff so that for the same quantity of total runoff, flood peaks can be expected to be higher and more damaging than indicated by the original studies.

4. In the flood plains immediately below large reservoirs, damage occurs due to enlargement and degradation of the river channel caused by changed sediment burden of the river, even though the land surface is not flooded.

When flood control is evaluated from the economic standpoint, generalizations are not easy to come by. Each project must be considered by itself and be justified either alone or as an incremental part of a larger project. However, it is submitted that the cost-benefit ratios used by the agencies of the Federal Government are insufficient justification in themselves, especially when there is a need to go to indirect or secondary benefits to justify the projects. The theoretical estimates of flood losses prevented are contradicted by the actual losses experienced in connection with completed projects. Admittedly, the theoretical, original estimates of flood losses did not consider the additional damage caused to structures to be built as a result of the "protection" afforded by the project. There is a considerable feedback associated with certain hydrologic projects. White's proposals, noted previously, constitute an attempt—the only major one so far—to deal with this.

Moreover, the destruction of the hydrologic character of data that invariably accompanies every large impoundment results in widespread increases in construction cost throughout the downstream drainage basin that cannot be accurately quantified. These are primary costs even if they are diffuse and general. They make the conduct of any, and all, enterprises more expensive and consequently make it more difficult for the individual citizen to earn a living.

But it should be noted that the objections listed are not to flood control, in itself. Hydrologists, among others, may legitimately object to the widespread, deleterious, largely unjustified transformations of hydrologic data into historical data; to the unlimited commitment of public money for objectives that are known to be ephemeral, if not completely impossible to achieve, without being in favor of floods.

We are, thus, confronted with two problems: (1) what to do with projects already under construction or completed and (2) what, if anything, to do about flood control in the future.

At this writing there is no consensus of opinion among hydrologists or students of the problem. Flood-plain zoning, the effect of reservoirs on floods, sedimentation, flood insurance, levee design, bank stabilization—the list can be continued—are currently live topics, as the dates of the references cited clearly show. Yet if modern hydrology is to justify the efforts expended, its practitioners have an obligation to chart paths and propose new directions.

Hirshleifer and his colleagues, treating the matter as economists, generally take a dim view of all sorts of Federal expenditures on water-resource development: "It is quite possible that huge reclamation projects, large dams and canals, and massive river-basin planning may be taking on many of the characteristics of national 'pyramids' or 'monuments' " (5). Of course, any hydrologist or geomorphologist knows that this statement is qualitatively wrong. There was no upkeep on the pyramids, nor does the building of monuments, no matter how costly, pit an entire society of men against the workings of the most powerful of geologic forces. A more appropriate parallel might be drug addiction—which gives the addict the temporary illusion of power and well-being, requires ever-increasing doses to maintain the feeling, and finally destroys him physically. Yet the fact that use of morphine may cause addiction does not mean that morphine may not be useful under the proper circumstances.

How then, should existing flood-control projects be utilized or terminated? One way might be for the Federal Government, or the agencies in charge, to announce a planned yearly reduction in the maximum water level to be permitted in the flood-control reservoirs together with a construction program to increase the discharge capacity of the spillways or gates. This would result in an ever-decreasing flood-retention capability. Possibly a 15 or 25 year changeover period from reservoir utilization for the impoundment and slow release of the design floods to termination of their operation as detention reservoirs might be adopted. Widespread announcement of such a program and the consequent adjustment of individuals in their use of flood-plain lands would reduce construction in the flood plains and, in itself, tend to reduce future damage due to flooding. We may, however, expect a tremendous outcry from present "beneficiaries" who feel that they have acquired a vested right and are entitled in perpetuity to some sort of flood protection at the expense of the rest of the population, even though this protection is essentially ephemeral and fictitious.

At the same time complete title and physical responsibility for the maintenance and possible reconstruction of levees and channels would be assumed by local organizations. As a matter of equity, because the entrapment of individuals and groups has been caused unwittingly, by mistaken national policy, small payments might be made to assist local property owners during the transition period—or possibly credits on the payment of Federal taxes might be allowed.

There could be no objections if individuals, or organizations, undertook to build and maintain their own protective works. It may be that new forms of organization must be devised to facilitate this. However the authority of the local government involved should closely approximate the scope of the operation, and the costs incurred should fall directly upon the beneficiaries. The phased transition from flood control as a national responsibility to flood control as a responsibility of those directly threatened by flooding will occur in any event, sooner or later. The longer the delay in transition, the greater the probable damage and loss of life.

In an effort to reduce flood losses the adoption of a system of flood-plain zoning has been proposed as a precondition to Federal expenditures on flood control. This is only a temporary expedient that will rarely be fully effective. All it will do will be to encourage a falsely premissed public policy and, as a by-product, increase the uncertainty of land ownership rights in the flood plains. Moreover any system of zoning based on an ever-diminishing flood protection must be progressively changed to allow for reservoir sedimentation. It will thus become transformed into a slow, phased withdrawal from the flood plain—increasingly expensive as time passes. For hydrologic reasons Federal flood control, even when accompanied by zoning of the flood plains, may be considered a blind alley, and it cannot be recommended as a basis for public policy.

As to the future of flood control: Men have a right to band together against their common enemy, flood water; they must not, however, damage others in the process. It is extremely fortunate that our jurisprudence and system of courts are admirably suited to assess damages, so that if over-enthusiastic local authorities unreasonably damage their neighbors as they strive to protect themselves against flood, redress is possible. In any event the direct effects of floods are local and when local people can no longer support flood protection, such protection would lapse and they would move to higher ground without involving the remainder of the nation in an increasingly expensive, futile fight. This procedure is an ancient and adequate defence against our old friendly enemy, water.

It is quite possible that one theory as to the existence of Indian mounds in the flood plains of rivers may be correct. This theory conjectures that these mysterious artificial burial mounds may have been built by the Indians in order to provide points of refuge during periods of high water.

In attempting flood-control projects, man is pitting himself against one of the mightiest and most dynamic forces of nature: flowing water. He may win a battle, but he will surely lose the war—quickly, where the rapid sedimentation of flood-control reservoirs occurs. In this instance it is inevitable that man will adapt himself, not nature. The question is whether he will choose the time or will have the choice made for him. The application of hydrologic principles should facilitate the transition and minimize the losses. But like it or not, the transition will occur.

It is of more than passing historical interest to note that not until 1917 did the Federal Government assume complete responsibility for protecting a group of its citizens from floods—and the earliest legislation required the local people to contribute one dollar for every two Federal dollars. And it was not until 1938 that Congress finally opened the door for assumption by the Federal Government of almost the entire cost of flood control (which was accompanied by a real, if unstated, physical and moral responsibility). Thus, systematic phase-out of Federal flood-control activity would merely be the correction of a shortlived, expensive deviation from well-established public policy.

NAVIGATION

From the standpoint of hydrology, projects for facilitating and maintaining navigation must be evaluated in accordance with the probability of obtaining a permanent, steady-state condition. For navigation, presumably, must be considered as a perennial, permanent activity. This viewpoint is corroborated to some extent by history, inasmuch as the recognized Federal program for improvement and maintenance of waterways for navigational purposes got under way in 1824 and has continued to the present time.

The basic program for navigational improvements has consisted in the canalization of rivers and in a program of snag removal, training works, channel rectification, and dredging. It has lately been supplemented by the release of water from multipurpose reservoirs to augment low flows. In order for the canalization of rivers to be successful, the sediment-load of the canalized river must be small. Otherwise the repeated dredging required to maintain the channel becomes prohibitively expensive. So we find that rivers in the geologically older and more stable areas have been transformed into series of canals or lakes. Among such transformed rivers are the upper Mississippi, the Allegheny, the Monongahela, the Ohio, the Cumberland, and the Tennessee.

Until very recently, prior to the authorized project for navigation on the Arkansas River, the canalization of sediment-laden streams was not attempted. Instead, small, persistent efforts at channel improvement such as training works, dredging of sand bars and cutoffs, and the removal of obstructions were the principal means of providing navigational opportunity.

We have already had occasion to evaluate the long-term effect of these efforts on the nature of hydrologic data. We may anticipate that a long-term side effect will be to progressively increase the difficulty and cost of moving shipments from the canalized section of the waterway to an adjoining noncanalized section. Transhipment at these junctions will become increasingly necessary, as the upper reaches of the uncontrolled river channel cut deeper into the alluvium. The quantitative development of geomorphology has not yet reached the stage where reliable predictions can be made as to when and where the end points will be reached.

Another side effect will be the tendency for the banks of the degrading channel to cave and thus obstruct navigation. For as the channel deepens and carries the same flow of water at a lower elevation, the width is lessened for greater flows. In those areas where the channel wall is composed of soft clay or granular material like silty or clayey sand and gravel, there will be a tendency for sections of the channel to be undercut and slough off. This may easily result in an increasingly meandering river which, in turn, will increase the cost of maintaining a channel.

From a physical standpoint, therefore, where hydrologic and geologic conditions are suitable for river canalization, there can be no objection since it is possible to visualize a state of equilibrium and the operation and maintenance can proceed predictably and indefinitely, as advertised. Under such circumstances, where there is no element of entrapment, it should be possible to levy user-charges that will return to the government the cost of operation and maintenance—possibly even a fraction of the construction cost.

From exactly the same viewpoint the maintenance of facilities on noncanalized streams and rivers is not to be recommended. For the one thing that is certain is that the cost of operation will rise, that side effects will become more far reaching and undesirable, and that, in the long run, use of the waterway will have to be completely subsidized at ever-increasing cost and will finally have to be curtailed.

Table 6.2 shows the capital and maintenance costs of Federal Inland Waterways in 1952. Figure 6.1 shows the types of commodities carried on the

Table 6.2. Commerce and Federal Costs of 15 Major Inland Waterways (Intracoastal Waterways Excluded), 1952[a]

Waterway project	Length (miles)	Tonnage 1952	Percent increase over 1938	Ton-miles 1952	Total Federal cost including fiscal year 1953 (excludes maintenance)	Average annual maintenance and operation cost 1949–53	Maintenance and operation cost per ton-mile
				Thousands			
Lower Mississippi River	736	23,444,708	240	10,745,514	$179,936,000	[b]$7,000,000	$0.0007
Middle Mississippi River	195	13,285,980	335	1,945,806	81,698,955	1,129,683	.0006
Upper Mississippi River	663	12,855,945	395	2,053,389	210,702,197	3,823,903	.0019
Ohio River	981	55,957,367	172	10,362,201	145,173,405	7,549,913	.0007
Monongahela River	131	28,083,188	84	1,345,250	40,871,277	1,283,713	.0010
Allegheny River	72	3,539,045	47	65,960	18,157,860	327,935	.0050
Illinois Waterway	336	17,434,271	290	2,870,241	31,013,307	1,582,833	.0006
Missouri River	762	2,845,534	156	41,158	214,863,773	6,729,440	.1635
Cumberland River	513	2,168,148	205	279,880	33,920,561	710,751	.0025
Ouachita and Black River	417	95,010	(c)	8,929	5,248,619	356,495	.3993
Warrior River System	472	2,553,754	38	500,742	25,903,806	1,057,776	.0021
Columbia River	222	3,173,956	167	275,533	[a] 59,407,500	[e] 600,000	.0022
Sacramento River	245	1,889,466	200	116,390	[f] 15,079,392	229,223	.0020
Kanawha River	91	6,900,378	106	366,482	27,167,230	305,397	.0008
Tennessee River	650	5,837,522	450	797,203	[g] 172,831,668	[h] 1,840,208	.0023
Total	6,486	180,064,272	175	31,774,678	1,261,975,550	34,527,270	.0011

[a] Data from annual reports Chief of Engineers, U.S. Army.
[b] Estimate based on 1949 costs of $7,850,000 (as reported by Corps of Engineers to Appropriations Committee, 1954).
[c] Less.
[d] Data from report of Corps of Engineers to Appropriations Committee, Jan. 4, 1954.
[e] Estimate based on 1953 and 1952 costs of $637,300 and $525,800, respectively (as reported by Corps of Engineers to Appropriations Committee).
[f] Includes $12,000,000 for Shasta Reservoir.
[g] Computed using costs to TVA and Corps of Engineers.
[h] Costs responsible to Corps of Engineers $692,063; TVA costs do not include depreciation and river-development studies.
Source: Commission on Organization of the Executive Branch of the Government, June, 1955, *Task force report on water resources and power*, Washington, D.C., Government Printing Office, v. 2, p. 895.

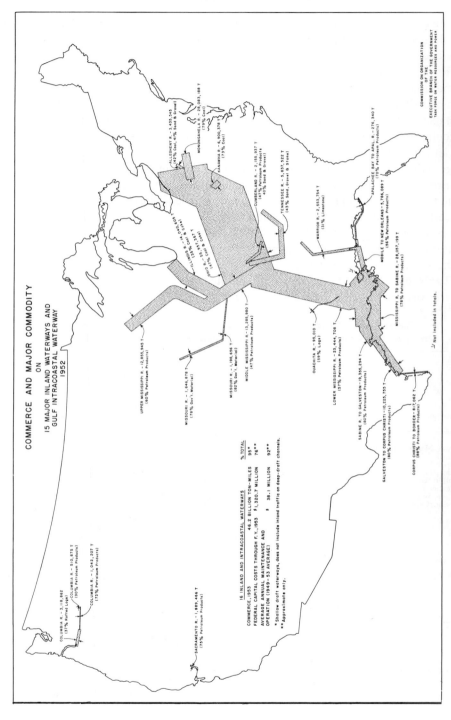

Fig. 6.1. Commerce and major commodity on 15 major inland waterways and Gulf intercoastal waterway, 1952. (From Commission on Organization of the Executive Branch of the Government, 1955, *Report on Water Resources and Power*, Washington, D.C., Government Printing Office, p. 897.)

major inland waterways. If we exclude the canalized waterways, the tonnage carried by rivers consists mostly of petroleum products—and common carrier pipelines might be able to do the job of transportation at a lesser cost to the nation, all things considered.

Brief mention has been made of the project to provide a navigable channel in the Arkansas River. This will extend from the Mississippi River to Weber Falls, thence on the Verdigris River to a point 15 miles east of Tulsa, Oklahoma. This is probably the first navigation project in the United States to attempt the canalization of a heavily sediment-laden stream. And, in fact, the

Table 6.3. Capacity of Upstream Reservoirs, Arkansas River Navigation Project (in Thousands of Acre-Feet)

Dam	River	F	P	D	Total
Pensacola	Grand	523	996	657	2,176
Markham Ferry	Grand	233	30	157	420
Fort Gibson	Grand	922	54	311	1,287
Tenkiller Ferry	Illinois	600	345	285	1,230
Eufaula	Canadian	1,470	1,481	897	3,848
Oologah	Verdigris	963	a	58[b]	1,021
Keystone	Arkansas	1,464	a	415	1,879
	Totals	6,175	2,906	2,780	11,861

[a] Power facilities planned but not included at this time (1963).
[b] Includes 48,700 acre-ft for water-supply use, 9,330 acre-ft for sediment storage and other purposes. F, P, and D mean Flood Control, Power, and Dead Storage respectively. Dead storage is allocated primarily for the storage of sediment.
Source: Based on U.S. Army Engineer District, Little Rock, Ark., February, 1961, Arkansas River and Tributaries, Multiple Purpose Plan, Arkansas and Oklahoma.

sedimentation problem is still under active study. The tentative answer seems to be: intercept the main sources of sediment in the tributary streams. These streams include the Canadian, Grand, and Illinois Rivers. The interception of sediment is to be accomplished by the construction and operation of upstream reservoirs, the vital statistics of which are summarized in Table 6.3.

The presently estimated cost of the entire project is in the magnitude of 1.2 billion dollars. The project devotes almost 25 percent of its total upstream reservoir capacity to the storage of sediment. No storage space is set aside to provide water for navigation, although the sediment storage might be considered as making possible canalization—and thus navigation. Three of the first four reservoirs listed are already in operation (Markham Ferry has not yet been started) and the other three are under construction (1964).

The project is likely to be short-lived despite the provision for sediment storage, for the supply of sediment is large and the reservoir capacity is small. There is here a potential entrapment for municipalities, corporations, and individuals who are counting on permanent flood control and navigation. By any reasonable standard this project should never have been started—and if local interests had been called upon to bear even 20 percent of the cost, it is doubtful that ground would have been broken for it. During the lifetimes of the younger readers of these pages the utter conceptual and physical failure of this type of water-resource development project will have received a convincing field demonstration. There might be some who would cavil at the price tag—there are less expensive ways of acquiring the needed education.

There will be others who will claim that for one reason or another navigable channels *must* be maintained in our major rivers. Considerations of economics, regional development, and national defence will be cited in support of this proposition. It need only be pointed out that the science of economics, like hydrology, should be used to help select the most productive employment of resources. Moreover the alternates made available at each stage of technological development have a great bearing on the final course of action. Possibly there are other methods of transporting the bulky materials that now move on our rivers—methods whose side effects will constitute a smaller burden on society. Such methods might promote commerce and transportation without making it necessary to maintain a channel of specified minimum depth and width and still satisfy the needs of national defense and regional development.

And indeed there are a number of such methods, all of which have become technically feasible in the past quarter century. Among such proven developments are pipe lines that move petroleum, gas, or mixtures of powdered coal and water, conveyer belt systems, and low-draft barges and boats. The most promising of the concepts now being actively investigated are the so-called air-cushion vehicles, or ground-effect vehicles, also known as hovercraft. Hovercraft are vehicles that generate and move on a cushion of air. The surfaces of open rivers, regardless of water depth, could readily be maintained as highways for such craft. There are good reasons for believing that the larger the hovercraft (up to, possibly, 20,000 tons) the more efficient it is, and the higher above water (or land) that it can maintain itself (3). Alternately, with the improvements in power plants, propulsion mechanisms, and similar devices, there is the possibility of using the open rivers only during flood periods and stockpiling the bulky materials for use during low-water periods. The precedent of utilizing a limited shipping season, as on the Great Lakes, might well be followed.

To sum up: the permanent maintenance of conventional navigational facilities in geologically stable areas such as the Ohio Valley, is hydrologically feasible and defensible. Inasmuch as this can be a steady-state, predictable operation, there can be no question but that a valid economic analysis can be prepared and soundly based decisions reached. The canalization of streams that carry vast volumes of sediment is hydrologically unsound, since no steady state that includes canalization can be visualized. The forces of erosion and deposition are beyond our power to control. Seriously to attempt this on a permanent basis is to court physical and economic ruin.

The maintenance of a specified depth of channel in an alluvial river, such as the lower Mississippi, is a systematic attempt to replace the potentially steady-state conditions of water and sediment movement by a condition of hydrologic nonequilibrium. Setting aside considerations of direct cost temporarily, one may legitimately ask whether a desire to swim in running water is sufficient justification for ruining the hydrology of a continent. The fact that this degradation of hydrologic data has already resulted in increased engineering uncertainty, accompanied by increased costs of construction throughout the affected area, should in itself be reason enough to question our policies in the field of Federal maintenance of navigation.

In this connection we may well reread the decision in Gilman v. Philadelphia with regard to the political interference with the use of a national waterway by a state or other political subdivision of the United States:

Commerce includes navigation. The power to regulate commerce comprehends the control for that purpose, and to the extent necessary, of all the navigable waters of the United States which are accessible from a State other than those in which they lie. For this purpose they are the public property of the nation and subject to all the requisite legislation by Congress. This necessarily includes the power to keep them open and free from any obstruction to their navigation, interposed by the States or otherwise; to remove such obstructions when they exist; and to provide, by such sanctions as they may deem proper, against the occurrence of the evil and for the punishment of offenders (*18*).

It is doubtful, the writer submits, whether the power of the United States to eliminate political or man-made obstructions to navigation by sanctions and the punishment of offenders can be effectively applied to the nonhuman agents of geomorphology. For although the United States can unquestionably maintain political control of all of its waterways, it can only *attempt* to establish certain physical criteria of their being. As we have seen, in certain instances, the outcome of the legendary case of King Canute provides the governing precedent. Canute (995–1035), a Dane, ruled England when, to illustrate the limits of his power, he placed his throne at the edge of the sea at low tide and commanded the tide to stay put. It didn't, and the king got wet. Conclusion? Political decisions not in accord with the laws of hydrology and geomorphology are sooner or later subject to final reversal by highest authority and appropriate penalties will be paid.

Yet this sombre outlook as to the feasibility and desirability of maintaining fixed minimum channel depth in alluvial rivers should not be interpreted to mean that the writer advocates the abandonment of rivers for purposes of transportation, communication, and commerce. The existence of ingenuity among men that expresses itself as advances in technology implies that the smooth water surfaces of our rivers may furnish ideal roadways for new types of vehicles. The possibility of using the rivers only during flood periods and indirectly extending the navigable periods by developing vessels of lesser draft should not be overlooked. The only certainty is that the present cycle of artificially degrading the channels of alluvial rivers, then repairing, or armoring the eroded banks, then dredging the channels still deeper, will be broken. From the standpoint of hydrology, and even from the standpoint of the general welfare, this should be done as soon as possible—while we can still choose the starting time and duration of the transition period.

HYDROELECTRIC POWER

Few topics in the field of hydrology have caused as much controversy, public debate, acrimony, and litigation as hydropower. It is submitted that, like many another argument on resource development, advances in technology are rapidly making the entire argument irrelevant, if indeed they have not already done so.

The fundamental reason for publicly owned hydropower developments, rather than the extension and maintenance of private property rights in this field, is that water (as we have previously seen) is always considered a special case and the possibility of monopolistic control has always loomed large in the minds of the duly elected representatives:

Prior to the act of Feb. 15, 1901 . . . water power sites went to patent unmolested either as parts of homesteads or by purchase . . . . Under this procedure a large number of power sites on the public domain were frittered away and have passed into private ownership beyond regulation, beyond control . . . . They are now forever, in part, to be enjoyed by the few who at will may practice extortion and monopoly upon the consuming public . . . . The titles to these sites have forever passed out of the hands of the Federal Government and the people (17).

And indeed, in 1916, when the Congress of the United States heard these bitter words, it required more than 2.5 lb of coal to produce 1 Kw of electricity, and the possibility of using nuclear fission as a source of energy for steam-electric generating plants was not even a concept in science fiction. In the more remote sections of the country, where coal was lacking, the only possible economic development of electrical power was in the harnessing of falling water.

And for the next twenty years, as base loads and peaks continued to grow throughout the country, unheralded, important advances in metallurgy and power technology were made. This resulted in continual improvements in the efficiency of the newer steam-electric generating plants as compared to the older ones. At present it requires approximately 0.7 lb of coal to produce 1 Kw of electricity.

During this period hydropower received more than a fair share of legislative attention: the Federal Water Power Act, in 1920 (amended importantly and restrictively in 1935), the TVA Act in 1935, and the 1939 Reclamation Project Act are representative. This was hydrologically important, for hydropower, with its immediate cash return, was used to finance other phases of integrated, or multipurpose, water-resource developments.

But the amount of power to be generated by harnessing the natural or impounded flow of streams and rivers is limited by the topography of dam sites and the availability of runoff. Even in the combined valleys of the Tennessee and Cumberland Rivers, topographically, geologically, and climatically very favorable for hydropower production, hydropower alone was found to be insufficient to supply the demand less than 15 years after the TVA Act was passed. And this despite impoundments with a capacity totaling approximately 21 million acre-ft and an ultimate planned hydropower capacity of 3.2 million Kw (3200 megawatts) of which 2.9 million had been installed by 1953 (6, 443). By the same date TVA owned and operated steam-electric generating capacity totaling 1.8 million Kw and was then building a number of giant fuel-burning plants to increase the steam-electric generating capacity to almost 7 million Kw. By 1962, it is estimated that its steam plant capacity in operation totaled 10 million Kw and that an additional 2 million Kw of capacity was under construction. Thus 12 million Kw of steam-electric generating capacity may be compared to 3 million Kw of hydropower in one of the areas most favorably located for hydropower development. By comparison the hydropower marketed by the Bonneville Power Administration (produced by the Columbia, Flathead, Pend Orielle, N. Santiam, Yakima, and Middle Fork of the Willamette rivers) was produced by an installed capacity of approximately 6.5 million Kw. Privately owned hydropower capacity in the Northwest totaled more than 5 million Kw.

The inherent characteristics of power-generating systems, moreover, indicate that base loads are most economically satisfied by steam-electric generating plants (be they fossil-fuel burning or nuclear) and that peak loads are most economically handled through the use of hydropower, and this is the trend throughout the United States and in Europe, where hydropower, and especially pumped storage, has a long history (4). It has become evident that for reasons of hydrology the available power for peaking purposes from run-of-river stations or from large impoundments would soon be inadequate, even if every favorable dam site on every river were utilized.

From the standpoint of hydrologic desirability, we must consider factors such as climate and geomorphology in evaluating individual projects. Under the most favorable conditions, such as those found at Niagara Falls, the hydrologic effect of the power project is negligible, and because it is so long the life of the project cannot really be estimated. In the territory of the TVA the power phases of the project are subordinate to flood control, and, again, in themselves, their effect is small. And whether the plants are operated for base-load purposes or peaking purposes would not seem to affect the hydrology of the area noticeably. Even in the arid West, where sedimentation promises to limit the duration of flood control and certain other benefits, the hydropower phases of the projects are not hydrologically important, although power production is used as the major benefit which pays for a disproportionate share of the construction cost. Long after the primary benefits have been exhausted, it is possible that the generation of power may be continued.

In an earlier chapter we noted the projected pumped-storage hydropower of the Consolidated Edison Company of New York to produce power for peak-load purposes. In this instance a single elevated reservoir (capacity, approximately 17,000 acre-ft) is to be built, and the Hudson River will act as the source of water as well as the "lower pool" of the project. The ascertainable hydrologic effect would seem to approach zero for a generating capacity of 1.8 million Kw (1800 megawatts).

A similar project, although smaller, is now in operation in Missouri. This is the famous Taum Sauk project of the Union Electric Company of St. Louis, which is rated as able to produce 8 hr of peaking power daily at 350 megawatts (about one-fifth as large as Con Ed's proposed pumped-storage project). The total water used by this project is 4360 acre-ft, and this is recirculated (12). Thus, the actual consumptive use of a pure pumped-storage hydropower project in a humid zone is within the normal error of hydraulic measurement and is essentially so small as to be undetectable.

The storage required for an installed hydropower capacity of 598 megawatts at Wilson Dam on the main stem of the Tennessee River, by contrast, is 53,000 acre-ft, and at Bull Shoals, in Arkansas, a total projected capacity of 320 megawatts will utilize over 2 million acre-ft. Admittedly the comparison is not on equal terms, but the actual power to be generated at the latter site is only some 70 percent of the potential that could be produced were enough water available. Moreover, admittedly, a part of the 2 million acre-ft of storage is assigned to flood control—possibly 50 percent. Even so there seems something disproportionate between a factor of 200 for relative quantities of stored water and a factor of 2 or 3 as regards power produced!

The impact of advancing technology has not yet been fully recognized either by hydrologists or by legislators. The dual-purpose pump turbine, the feasibility of nuclear power as a source of heat for base-load steam-electric generating plants, the increasing availability of fossil fuels throughout the country, the rapid development in the long-distance alternate-current transmission of electrical energy, the promising experiments of increasing this distance by direct-current transmission, and the ever-increasing fuel-conversion efficiency of the high temperature, higher pressure reactors and generators used to produce electricity have not been fully reckoned with. These new developments have made the assumptions on which public hydropower policy have rested completely obsolete and, essentially, deleterious from the standpoint of hydrology.

Steam-electric generating plants can now be built anywhere. The transportation of fuel, where the economic value of the power is high, is not a problem—this is one result of the atomic energy program. Moreover, the large number of oil and gas pipe lines that crisscross the country make construction of fossil fuel plants for generating electricity feasible in many areas where hydropower is not available. The net condensing-water requirements of a large plant are in the same order of magnitude as that of a 5000-acre irrigated farm—hydrologically small.

Peaking requirements can readily be met in rugged country—potential pumped-storage reservoir sites are many, almost an unlimited number, and the final choice depends on system requirements and economics more than anything else. That anyone could obtain a monopoly on hydropower sites (see the Congressional quotation above) is hardly conceivable if the land is widely held in private hands. In humid mountainous regions all that is necessary to do to provide hydropower for peaking purposes is to purchase or collect X-thousand acre-ft of water in a suitably prepared site, and after that has been done there will be no detectable effect on stream flows. In the West, depending on location, quantities of make-up water for evaporation loss would be needed. And it is possible that chemical monolayers will be found uniquely suited for use on pumped-storage hydroprojects in the arid sections of the world. The reservoir surface would be small, and to preserve water quality there might be good reason to keep the make-up water to a minimum. In any event, under these conditions, fear of monopoly and possible extortion by owners of hydroprojects is a fantasy that should be laid to rest. To correct such an unlikely situation all that is needed is to grant potential competitors permission for the construction of transmission facilities, and the monopoly is eliminated.

The deleterious results of Federal power development, especially on sediment-laden streams, stem from the hydrologic effect of the associated projects "carried" by the power development (discussed later in this section), and the ensuing entrapment of the "beneficiaries." These results have been pointed out previously and will be recognized again under other circumstances. As of 1964 it is more than likely that a complete reexamination of public policy on hydropower development has long been overdue and that a complete recasting of that policy will be deemed essential. It is now becoming apparent that the development of hydropower may now be considered solely on its own merits and without regard to other, hydrologically more significant, water-development projects. Be they Federally owned or privately owned, the peak-power adjuncts of steam-electric generating plants can and should be built without distorting or altering the hydrology and geomorphology of extensive drainage areas.

RECLAMATION—OF LAND

To reclaim land is simply to improve its usefulness to mankind. In the broad sense any procedure that improves the productivity of land can be termed reclamation. These procedures include draining land, protecting it from unwanted flooding, providing it with water, reducing undesirable evaporation, land-forming, and applying fertilizers and pesticides. The reasoning can be carried one step farther to include urbanization of farm land and the more intensive use of urban property.

The reclamation of land is a normal and ancient activity of mankind. Our system of the private ownership of property together with a long history of common law and legislation has concerned itself with the adjudication of disputes in this connection, with the evaluation of damages, and with the delineation of the rights of men, as between themselves and as between individuals and the body politic. Once a man has obtained title to property he is at liberty to clear, drain, build levees around, irrigate, or fertilize it as he thinks best. And indeed these things are being done every day without supervision of public agencies and without the expenditure of public funds. The benefits of the private expenditures are private; the losses are also private. Any program that has been economically or hydrologically miscalculated concerns the persons who made the mistake, but the radius of influence is limited both in time and space.

When we consider public policy in the field of reclamation, we usually have reference to public expenditure only for the drainage or irrigation of land, since the prevention of flooding is not usually considered under this heading.

Drainage

The drainage of land consists of improving hydraulic conditions of the surface and immediate subsurface so that the water will not stand and impede productive work. Or if it does stand, the duration of its stay will be a minimum. Much land has been drained by property owners and by local or state organizations. Of the 100 million acres that have been drained in organized districts and the 50 million acres drained privately, possibly 80 percent was termed improved by 1950 (6, 1186). It is estimated that of the remaining 125 million acres of swampland within the contiguous area of the United States, some 50 million acres are physically suitable for crop and pasture use. Only drainage is needed.

On lands that must be drained in order to bring them into production there is a sufficiency, if not a surplus, of water. This self-evident statement carries with it, overall, the general implication of a humid climate. Otherwise the swamps would be salt water or brackish, since evaporation would progressively have increased the mineralization found in the standing water.

From the standpoint of hydrology and geomorphology, drainage and the subsequent change in land use has two principal results. The concentration times of ever-larger areas of watershed are decreased, thus increasing the likelihood of downstream floods and raising the probable stages. The erosion from the land surface is increased due to the operation of plows and other earth-scratchers which reduce the cohesion of the formerly swampy soils and release fine particles into the stream channel. This last remark does not apply to the cultivation of rice which is usually flooded. It does apply to row crops (and road construction, subdivision development, and other of man's earth-moving activities).

On the one hand channels are improved and the velocity and erosive power of water is locally increased, while on the other hand the tendency of the soil to erode is magnified. Such a sequence of events suggests that the maintenance of drainage systems will inevitably prove to be a major operational expense— and one that is likely to increase as time goes on. As long as the expenditures for operation and maintenance are tied into the increase in productivity that they engender—and there is a net benefit—there would seem to be no question of public policy. That is, why would the general public finance activities that can be undertaken privately and profitably by the property owners themselves? And when, in the course of time, the drainage activity becomes less profitable, or even unprofitable, it can be abandoned without involving the body politic.

As a matter of policy there should be no restriction on citizens or groups of citizens in their efforts against the common enemy, water. It should be understood, however, that in the establishment of improved drainage— especially for agricultural purposes—a constant struggle will ensue against a subtle, powerful, and pervasive geologic force—erosion—and the battle must be refought, time and again. The resources devoted by private individuals or organizations to the establishment of improved conditions of drainage will invariably be diverted from competing economic uses. Thus, drainage activities will wax and wane; emphasis will rise here and fall there in response to costs, the state of technology, and alternate uses for the resources that might have been used for drainage purposes. The side effects are likely, in the long run, to complicate matters only slowly, uncertainly, and in a minor way—to which adjustments are readily made.

As a matter of public policy, Federal funds should not be used to establish and maintain drainage. For here, again, this pits the political power of the state—and the lives and property of all of its citizens, willy nilly—in a widespread, endless conflict with the natural forces of erosion and deposition. This is an unequal struggle that cannot be successfully concluded and it should be avoided. For the government to engage in improving the drainage implies that it will also attempt to stabilize upstream soils and slopes lest the channels deteriorate. And the maintenance of channels in alluvial, or erodable, materials means bank and bed protection against scour and deposition. And so on, ad infinitum, against an adversary that is tireless, knows no pain, and must ultimately prevail to the ruination of the state and its people. The remarks on entrapment made previously under similar hydrologic circumstances are again applicable.

If land must be reclaimed from the swamp, let this be done by individuals and groups within the population in response to the overall demands of the economy. But that money must be expended by many Federal bureaus to reclaim land permanently by means of widespread drainage activities in the face of hydrologic fact, so that the land may be used to produce foods and fibres already in economic surplus, is incomprehensible either economically or hydrologically. The whole matter is another of a long series of consequences resulting from the treatment of water as a special case. The pernicious effects of this approach have already proven to be many and manifest.

Irrigation

A strong case may be made that public policy is created only when public funds are to be disbursed. Elsewhere, under the same physical circumstances save only the expenditure of public money, the principles of common law and equity seem to serve adequately.

The reclamation of land through irrigation has followed two independent paths simultaneously in the United States. One is based on a public policy that seems to assume that making the desert green is one of the principal purposes for which the United States Government was created (although by some inexplicable lack of foresight this was not mentioned in the Constitution). The other is based on an increased understanding of geology and the occurrence of ground water combined with the development of deep well-pumping equipment and small power plants.

The drive for legislation to use the disposal of public lands (later public funds), as an aid to irrigation first produced concrete results when the Desert Land Act was passed in 1877. This was followed by the Carey Act (1894) and then, in 1902, by the Reclamation Act. Between 1903 and 1910, reclamation projects were authorized which were to furnish water to almost 3,070,000 acres (6, 677). Up to June 30, 1952, these projects had cost 304 million dollars and the estimated cost of completion was approximately 64 million dollars more. Of this money, 246 million dollars was the reimbursable charge to irrigation, to be repaid by the water users. The average cost per acre of land receiving a full or supplemental water supply from the first (and presumably the most economically attractive) projects was approximately 80 dollars per acre. This figure, and others quoted in this connection, disregards the change in the price level and equates the value of the dollar in 1910 with its value throughout the entire period. In 1952 dollars the per acre expenditure by the Federal Government would have been higher.

Between 1911 and 1931, another 11 Federal projects were authorized to bring water to almost 1 million acres, with the irrigation cost chargeable to the water users estimated at some 127 million dollars, about 127 dollars per acre. Between 1932 and 1942, 34 new projects to bring water to an additional 4.5 million acres were undertaken (5.2 million acres was the original acreage authorized, but physical circumstances proved unfavorable). Some 1.3 billion dollars was to be spent for this purpose of which 661 million dollars was to be repaid through the sale of power and 565 million dollars by the water users. Average cost per acre of irrigated land was 289 dollars, although the water users were to repay only 126 dollars. Outside of the Missouri River Basin between 1943 and 1953, twenty projects for the irrigation of 360,000 acres were undertaken, to cost approximately 137 million dollars. The water users are expected to pay back 107 million dollars. Cost per irrigated acre: 380 dollars. Simultaneously, Missouri River Basin projects were undertaken to bring water to approximately 1.1 million acres of land at an estimated cost of 320 million dollars of which 255 million dollars would be repaid by the sale of power and 65 million dollars by the water users. Cost per irrigated acre: 290 dollars.

Sears has prepared an estimate on alternate means and costs of land reclamation, and Table 6.4 is taken from his paper. Most of the irrigated

Table 6.4. Comparison of Costs of Alternative Means of Land Reclamation

Purpose of project	Area	Average cost per acre (in dollars)	Year of estimate
Restoration of lands in various stages of productivity.	Average U. S.	30.00	1949
	New England	19.00	1948
		24.50–101.00	1950
	Illinois	14.50–22.63	1947
		24.00	1949
		35.00	1949
	Missouri	36.30	1948
		18.00	1949
Clearing without stumping...	Massachusetts	15.00–30.00	1947
	Southeast	25.00	1946
	Delta States	17.00	1930–40
	Pacific Northwest	18.00–39.00	1944
Complete clearing (after deduction of salable timber).	General	50.00–75.00	1946
	Massachusetts	95.00–160.00	1947
	North and South Carolina	36.00–50.00	1947
	Delta States	30.00–100.00	1945–48
	Pacific Northwest	57.00–200.00	1944
Drainage	General (new areas)	15.00–40.00	1946
	Rhode Island (including clearing).	30.00–125.00	1948
	South Carolina	40.00	1948
	Delta States	8.00–25.00	1945–48
Irrigation[a]	Columbia Basin	233.00	1950
	Central Valley	300.00–690.00	1950
	Missouri Basin	145.00 (supplemental)	1950
		440.00 (new land)	1950
	Rio Grande Fort Summer Project.	380.00	1950
	Colorado:		
	Grande Valley Project	141.00	
	Central Arizona Project	620.00 [b]	1948

[a] Includes only costs allocated to irrigation.
[b] $2200 if new acreage actually benefited is considered.

Source: Paul B. Sears, May, 1952, Comparative costs of restoration and reclamation of land, *Annals of Am. Acad. Pol. and Soc. Sci.*, v. 281, p. 132.

farmlands are in the 17 western states. Table 6.5 shows the irrigated acreage (using surface water) and the acreage of land fully or supplementally irrigated by works constructed by the Federal Government, primarily by the Bureau of Reclamation (after 1903).

From this table it would appear that while the Bureau of Reclamation has brought water to much land, nevertheless non-Federal irrigation works have provided the largest percentage of the surface water used for irrigation. Since 1930, the area of land irrigated by surface water has increased by about

Table 6.5. Areas of Land Irrigated in the 17 Western States by Surface Water, by Surface Water from Federal Projects, and by Private Ground Water

| | Surface Water | | |
Decade	Total	Federal	Ground Water
Prior to 1900	6,514,000	450,000	70,000
1900 to 1909	10,319,000	1,306,000	408,000
1910 to 1919	12,712,000	2,277,000	1,289,000
1920 to 1929	13,365,000	2,703,000	1,935,000
1930 to 1939	14,214,000	3,278,000	2,542,000
1940 to 1949	15,899,000	4,752,000	5,425,000
1950 to 1958	18,274,000	6,366,000	10,560,000

Source: U.S. Senate Select Committee on National Water Resources, Future needs for reclamation in the Western States, Committee Print 14, Washington, 1960, p. 5.

4 million acres. Of this increase 3 million is attributed to expenditures by the Federal Government. By way of contrast, private expansion of ground-water supplies has caused the irrigation of 8 million new acres in the same time interval.

Curiously enough, at the very instant the political moves that resulted in establishment of the Bureau of Reclamation were occurring, ground water began to be recognized as a major source of water supply. By 1887, the first deep water-supply wells were already being drilled in Memphis—and this was simply following the example set 20 years earlier in Chicago. The early wells were either artesian (naturally flowing) or were pumped by air lift. This method of pumping is accomplished by introducing compressed air at the bottom of the well, and the water-air mixture, being of lower specific gravity than water, is forced to the surface by the pressure of the surrounding water. It is, however, an inefficient method of pumping. The deep-well turbine pump, at that time powered by a small steam engine and connected to the pump shaft by a belt, came into widespread use just before 1900. By 1903, maps of the piezometric surface were being prepared in many places (Fig. 5.28), and work had been accomplished by Slichter on the movement of underground water (*13, 14*). Litigation involving the utilization of ground water was underway in New York and California.

No statistical data are on hand to show how irrigation based on ground-water use throughout the entire country has increased, although Table 6.5 shows the use in the West. However, as the efficiency of both the pump and power plant has increased, the use of ground water for all purposes has become less expensive both relatively and absolutely. In Arkansas, for example, ground water has been used for irrigation since 1905. By 1910, some 50,000 acres were being irrigated; by 1943, this area had increased to 145,000 acres; and by 1950, the area had grown to about 300,000 acres. In southwestern Louisiana no early statistics are available, but the early irrigation of an area near Lake Charles, that was based on use of wells, expanded to an estimated 200,000 acres in 1949 and has remained at approximately that figure since that time (9).

There is little doubt that the use of ground water for purposes of irrigation has continued to increase throughout the United States and is now probably in excess of 11 million acres. Curiously enough, the growth of the area irrigated from ground water parallels, at a higher level, the growth of the land area supplied with surface water by the Bureau of Reclamation.

This brief comparison is important: From the standpoint of permanence, there is little to choose as between the life of an agricultural economy based on ground-water mining and one based on the use of a reservoir that is slowly filling with sediment. But from the standpoint of public policy, there is a vast difference. The ground-water development was based on individual decisions based on economics and the current state of technology, with no guarantees of success or permanence. By contrast, in the surface-water development the nation undertook to reclaim desert land permanently and invited—nay, subsidized and actively abetted—settlers to establish themselves. Disregarding, or leaving to others to consider, the investments that are being destroyed by the forces of geomorphology without beneficial effect on the economy, the enticement and entrapment of a generation of men in deserts is not pleasant to contemplate. When the hitherto unconsidered side effects resulting from the local upheavals of earth into dams are evaluated, in view of the principles set forth previously, the Federal connection with such projects should be terminated with all speed. For the wilful entrapment and ultimate destruction of its citizens cannot be the policy of the United States Government and, as has been shown, this is the inevitable result of the present policies. In the light of our present knowledge of hydrology and geomorphology, since the end results are known, the previously unwitting entrapment of the citizens, if continued, will have become their wilful entrapment and those having the power to end it have the responsibility to do so.

It will be pointed out that billions of dollars have been invested and much time, material, and energy have been devoted to the construction of these many projects for the irrigation of desert lands. It would be wasteful to abandon the remaining values that have been created, albeit, at a loss. There is a measure of truth here and it must be considered. Moreover, there are certain contractual obligations that have been undertaken, some with other countries, and these too cannot be cast aside lightly.

Presumably the flood-control features of the multipurpose projects can be handled as previously proposed. In instances where the project is still being built, the work can be stopped and we can consider the previous expenditures as a loss—similar to those occurring in a war—and write it off. With regard to existing projects the government should make every effort to remove from itself the responsibility of insuring a continuing and adequate water supply. This will be difficult and expensive to accomplish and will undoubtedly require many years. It, too, will entail a write-off of investment— this will be worthwhile. It will also require skilled negotiations so that some of the values may be salvaged. But the greatest saving will result from the recasting of public policy and the avoidance of such projects in the future. The projects now authorized but as yet unbuilt are, in their gross cost, greater by many times than those already accomplished. Possibly studies of hydrology and geomorphology will assist in determining how best to rectify our errors and bring our river systems, once again, into some sort of equilibrium.

RECLAMATION—OF WATER

It is becoming increasingly difficult for an educated man to find a serious periodical that does not in the course of a year carry an article concerning measures to combat stream pollution. And indeed we have previously noted the nonhydrologic nature of water-quality data pertaining to our larger streams and rivers. There has been a multitude of proposals for the reduction of pollution. These range from large-scale Federal assistance to communities for the purpose of building waste-treatment plants to the quiet, almost tongue-in-cheek proposal that a law be passed to compel water intakes (private or public) to be built a short distance downstream from the waste-discharge outlet of the particular water user.

From the standpoint of hydrology, all efforts to decrease stream pollution are to be considered as trending in the right direction. The construction and use of dams and reservoirs to store water for dilution of wastes is, of course, subject to criticisms made previously in connection with other projects for dam construction, and will not be repeated again. In any event this a completely impracticable procedure for certain new types of waste materials because of the enormous quantities of water that would be needed. This is especially true with respect to radioactive wastes and certain remarkably stable, nondegradable organic compounds.

The problem of the reclamation of water quality rapidly resolves itself into two interrelated factors: the physical feasibility and the legal framework. Of these the second is more difficult to establish than the first. The trouble seems to be that the right and ability to dispose of waste is so widely separated both in time and space from the damages caused by such action that the victim has little, if any, recourse. If authority and responsibility could be brought closer together so that our present system of law could operate effectively, we would be well on our way to a solution in this area.

The physical problem of water reclamation can be subdivided into the treatment of degradable and nondegradable wastes. In general, degradable wastes can be reduced into their simpler components and rendered harmless by direct oxidation or by aerobic and anaerobic decomposition brought about by microorganisms. There exists a twofold problem: What does it cost? Who pays for it? From studying the literature one gains the distinct impression that the physical problems connected with this type of water reclamation are on their way to economic solution, but that the source of payment is still indefinite.

Nondegradable wastes constitute a far more serious problem. Nor is this problem as potentially amenable of solution as the subproblem of non-degradable detergents (ABS). This latter project has engaged the attention of many capable scientists who are currently employed by soap-manufacturing and chemical and oil companies. They are well on the road to developing a low-cost detergent that will lose its identity after exposure to light, air, and bioorganisms (*11*). The category of nondegradable wastes also includes complex organic compounds, low-level radioactive wastes, residues from the extraction of salt from its parent material, tailings of all sorts resulting from mining operations, and acid waters usually originating in abandoned coal mines.

From the standpoint of hydrology the most formidable of these wastes are undoubtedly the acid wastes discharged from abandoned mine workings. There is nothing to do here except to study the hydrology and hydrogeology on a case-by-case basis and attempt to devise corrective measures. At the same time steps should be taken to prevent this nuisance from occurring in currently unspoiled areas. Nonetheless the situation is vexing and is likely to remain so for the forseeable future.

With respect to other aspects of the nondegradable waste problem the position is far more satisfactory. It is here that application of the principles of hydrology and hydrogeology can make an immediate and very useful contribution. For example, much has been made of how and where to dispose of low-and intermediate-level radioactive wastes. The problem boils down to finding a natural container for a relatively trivial quantity of fluid. At any single waste-producing installation it may be necessary to dispose of 1000 to 10,000 acre-ft a year (450 to 4500 gal per min). In ground-water terms, as we have seen, this is not very much.

The usual procedure is to find an aquifer containing saline water that will accept the waste through an injection well. The idea is to force waste in until the injection pressure becomes too great, usually due to a rise in piezometric surface of the aquifer used for disposal. The details of such a procedure have been presented by Lynn and Arlin, in connection with the disposal of uranium-tailing water in New Mexico (10). The life of the disposal installation in this example was estimated at 10 years, based on the pressure criterion.

In arid regions, where the net evaporation is high, the life of such an installation can be increased by at least a factor of 10 by installing wells for purposes of offtake at suitable distances and direction from the disposal well, setting the total offtake from the output wells as equal to or above the waste-disposal input, and collecting the otherwise harmless saline water of the aquifer in evaporation pits. In an area where the net evaporation approaches 36 in. (see Fig. 3.2, p. 49), as it does near Grants, New Mexico, evaporation pits totaling 300 acres in water surface would solve the problem for several generations.

In humid areas it might be necessary to store the saline water obtained from the formation in a small reservoir until a flood occurred, at which time it would be released. Or, if the salinity were too high, it might be necessary to inject the highly saline wastes from the output wells into an aquifer containing a less saline (but not potable) water and to pump water from *this* aquifer to make room. Such a process, if used properly in conjunction with a membrane stack for electrodialysis of water to concentrate the mineralization, is undoubtedly applicable throughout that part of the country underlain at depth by rocks possessing primary permeability and porosity. But the details must be left to the consultant on a case-by-case basis. The principle is clear and widely applicable.

The proper disposal of calcium chloride tailings such as those produced in the upper reaches of the Muskingum River Basin in Ohio, is only slightly more difficult. This would involve backfilling the mine workings of the parent bed with the presently ponded materials after these had been dried. Admittedly this would constitute a direct, possibly large item of expense to the proprietors, and the cost of the end product would be raised. But the expense inflicted upon all downstream water users by the degradation of water quality is also real, although it is diffuse and not presently calculable with certainty. A study of one aspect of the general problem is currently under way at Stanford University where, under sponsorship of Resources for the Future, Inc., an investigation is being made of the economic aspects of water quality in the pulp and paper industry.

There are, of course, other methods of ridding ourselves of nondegradable wastes. Kaufman has suggested that the highly saline return waters from the west side of the San Joaquin Valley be removed by means of agricultural sewers (8). This suggestion might well be adapted for use by groups of contiguously located industries to convey their more difficult wastes to a central area of favorable hydrogeologic conditions where these wastes could be disposed of satisfactorily.

From a hydrologic viewpoint, there is no technical reason that would prevent a generally satisfactory solution to the stream-pollution problem. It is evident that the most serious obstacle is the difficulty of associating the right to dispose of wastes with the responsibility for damaging consequences. This is just one additional instance in the field of water-resource development where time lags and large distances between causes and effects make it difficult to assess damage and calculate equitable reparation.

It is submitted that the direct intervention of governmental authority to construct, or indirectly force construction, of water reclamation facilities must be considered an unsatisfactory temporary expedient. Although this may be nothing more than a hope, it seems to the writer that a way can surely be found properly to relate acts and responsibilities in the field of water pollution. It is in this area that research and creative thinking would bring great returns to society.

WATER SUPPLY

Public policy in respect to water supply is very narrowly defined. The expenditure of funds for water supply is for a clear, well-understood end; the beneficiaries are recognizable; the benefits and costs are readily calculated by those most concerned. The "public" whose policy it is, is local and relatively well informed.

From the standpoint of hydrology, the construction of dams and impoundments in this connection is undesirable except as a last resort—a "people have to drink and move earth if they must" sort of thing. Yet, as we have seen, the existing impoundments for water-supply purposes are small and the deleterious side effects are limited. One may compare the 1.3 million acre-ft of the Quabbin Reservoir with the 27 million acre-ft of Lake Mead. Yet the capacity of Quabbin reservoir is about three times as large as either Ashokon Reservoir or Pepacton Reservoir, the principal impoundments of the City of New York, and more than three times as large as the largest reservoir of the San Francisco municipal supply. All in all, the damage done by the construction of water-supply reservoirs is minimal and the result of *force majeur*.

In many parts of the United States the life of a water-supply reservoir, or any small reservoir, is limited due to sedimentation. Fortunately geologic conditions in most of the United States are such that aquifers are usually available to serve as reservoirs. Such aquifers can be replenished by capturing, cleaning, and injecting flood waters into them for later use. Should the water originally contained in the aquifer be objectionally mineralized, a systematic, planned program of aquifer preparation can be started to fit the aquifer for its role as a reservoir. In many instances the unit cost of such storage will not prove burdensome even as compared to the cheapest, short-lived alternates.

In the overwhelming majority of cases comparison with an expensive process such as the conversion of saline water will result in the use of aquifer storage. In areas where storage aquifers are absent it will usually be found that the bedrock is old and resistant to erosion, and thus surface reservoirs will be long-lived.

The pressing problems of water supply are not those caused by circumstances of hydrology or geomorphology; nor are they problems of broad public policy on a national level: The expenditures are local, the public is local, and the public policy, if wrong, is rapidly corrected because of the ill-effects on the pocketbooks of that same public. Except in the western states, to some extent, the problem is to establish a legal right to use water; that is, to establish a property right in water that will be comparable in certainty and duration to property rights in land, and that will be subject to the forces of the free market rather than to those of bureaucratic allocation. When water is brought into the economic process in a normal manner, we may expect that all resources will tend to be used in the most efficient manner for the overall purposes of society, and the use of water will not be artificially distorted. There are tested methods for dealing with natural monopolies, including public regulation of companies and, as a final resort, condemnation.

It seems likely that legislation based on the appropriation doctrine will be most suitable for this purpose, both in the humid and in the dry sections of the country. This will not, however, be sufficient in itself. Special forms of organization, or incorporation, will be needed to facilitate the granting of property in aquifers replenished by bodies of surface water. For otherwise, due to time lags, appropriations of surface water and ground water could not be treated in a uniform manner. Naturally, there would be no need to grant a permanent right to a fixed quantity of ground water to property owners in areas of water mining. This would properly place these water-bearing formations in the same category, legally, with petroliferous formations or similarly limited natural deposits.

The object would be to make it possible for individuals, firms, and public agencies to hold property rights in water that are unambiguous in scope and certain in tenure. This would make it feasible to buy, sell, trade, or negotiate in some other manner for water rights. The law should not provide for priorities: let the marketplace decide how the overall water resources are to be used. The compulsory transfer of water rights to public agencies should be carried out only by condemnation proceedings that involve the payment of fair compensation. The legislation should include devices to protect third parties from the side effects of legitimate actions by the owners of water rights. Such devices might include, among others, zoning restrictions, assignment of quota rights on common pools, and the payment of compensation for damages inflicted.

The greatly publicized specter of water shortage is just that: a myth. It is fostered by the attitude that regards water as a special case and assumes that the price, throughout the country, if not abroad, should be kept uniformly low. This is to be accomplished by means of a subsidy derived from the general taxation. Such an attitude ignores the local nature of water supply. It is equivalent to saying that if people wish to live on the Dry Tortugas for reasons of their own, including the economic advantage of the location, then the rest of the citizenry must dig into its own pocketbook to assist these pioneers so that their water costs remain low and that their water use may be as high as the average. This does not make much sense—if the pioneers went there of their own accord without anyone twisting their arms or compelling them to do so for public purposes.

Actually the water available for use greatly exceeds the annual stream flow because, with water reclamation measures, it may be used again and again, many times. In an allied field one may well ask the question: How much annual stream flow do you need to develop a given rate of hydropower production for peaking purposes? We have seen the answer: Due to reuse of water, the net annual water demand may actually approach zero. In the humid sections of the country this answer may well be the ultimate truth. There is no water shortage—there is only the absence of a proper legal framework to bring our water resources fully into the productive process in direct comparison and competition with the other economic factors that satisfy our needs. The production of water is, in its essence, no wit different from the production of food, power, shelter, or any other economic good. The sooner that it is treated in this manner, the more readily will the scientific knowledge of hydrology be properly applicable and the greater the benefits accruing to society.

MISCELLANEOUS

On the preceding pages we have discussed a number of the questions that are now on the daily agenda of the United States and most other countries regarding the development of water resources. No mention has been made of a multitude of problems and projects, both public and private, that are also under study or actually under way. For example, there is the Department of Agriculture soil-conservation program under the Watershed Protection and Flood Prevention Act of 1954, which includes construction of reservoirs up to 5000 acre-ft in capacity, as well as drainage, terracing, and other forms of soil conservation. These are of no great hydrologic significance, if one disregards the increased and unproductive evaporation, and the reduction in runoff resulting from such projects. They are unlikely, in the long run, to do much more than to create small, local, temporary swamps. It should be noted that the Task Force Report on Water Resources and Power estimated that the capital cost of the ultimate headwater engineering program would be roughly 16.8 billion dollars—a substantial sum. However, there is no entrap-ment involved here; the hydrologic effects can be expected to be of minor influence and ephemeral duration inasmuch as the projects will be built over a long period of time, and the earliest will have vanished by the time the last are being built. Consequently, criticism of the public policy involved here must be on other grounds than the criteria set forth previously.

Another topic that has not been discussed at length is the much publicized sea-water conversion program, the effect on hydrology of which is likely to be minor, except as one or more processes developed in the course of the program are applied to reducing the mineralization of potable but undesirably mineralized water or to increasing the concentration of wastes and reducing their volume. The disposal of the concentrated residue will be a problem that has some minor hydrologic aspects as we have seen. Wolman summed up the position in a brilliant article which presented much data, in the course of which he said: "The data presented here make it clear that it would be a grave mistake to hope to find an early economic solution to water problems in the desalinization of sea water, so that desalted water becomes a major competitor of large fresh water supplies." (21).

Local projects, or those confined to a single state, have not been discussed previously because no national water policy (read "expenditure") is involved. For example, an entire volume the size of this one could be devoted to a detailed examination of the famous California water plan, which calls for the conjunctive use of surface reservoirs and aquifer storage to level out the annual fluctuations in the runoff in northern California so that a constant supply of water will be available for use in southern California. The criticisms of similar multipurpose projects found on the preceding pages are applicable to the component parts of the California water plan. Fortunately, half the proposed storage is to be in aquifers, so the entrapment of the beneficiaries is less than might be otherwise anticipated. On the debit side of the ledger is the fact that the legal framework for the large-scale operation of aquifers as reservoirs is not yet in existence. From a purely technical standpoint, the economical recharge of water through injection wells at the required rates has not yet been achieved. The ultimate success of the project as it is presently contemplated is dubious. The saving feature is to be found in the elasticity of water demand which undoubtedly will be responsive to the delivered price of water and the tremendous potential for water reclamation, especially in the Los Angeles area.

The hydrologic implications of our foreign-aid program, which stem from our sponsorship of multipurpose projects, are beyond the scope of this book. But these should not be overlooked by hydrologists. The principles explained previously will serve adequately as criteria for the evaluation of such projects. Neither has much been said concerning the long-term obligations we have assumed vis-à-vis Canada and Mexico with regard to water. Again, the principles are fully applicable on a case-by-case basis and renegotiation of our treaties may be in order.

Another minor omission is a discussion of the role of interstate compacts in the development of water resources. Here, too, the principles of hydrology and geomorphology hold, and these compacts will remain firm only as long as the signatories do not place their might in permanent opposition to the forces of water, frost, erosion, and sedimentation.

No mention has been made of such lesser, though important, problems such as the salt-water balance in aquifers recharged through the overirrigation of agricultural land, the possible reclamation of water-logged lands by the operation of well fields, or even such a problem as the future of New Orleans in view of the possible breakaway of the Mississippi River through the Atachafalaya River as a result of flood-control projects and the decrease in concentration time in the upstream drainage basin. Discussion of these and a multitude of other problems is left to others.

NOTES

1. Albertson, M. L., and Simons, D. B., May, 1962, letter outlining views of E. W. Lane, *Civ. Eng.*, v. 32, no. 8, p. 69.
2. Einstein, H. A., March, 1961, Needs in sedimentation, *Proc. Am. Soc. Civ. Eng.*, *J. Hyd. Div.*, v. 87, no. HY 2, pp. 4, 6.
3. Hammer, R., December, 1962, The new lift for transport: earth skimmers, *Fortune*, v. 46, no. 6, p. 155.
4. Harza, R. D., December, 1962, *Proc. Am. Soc. Civ. Eng.*, v. 88, no. PO 4, pp. 107–133.
5. Hirshleifer, J., DeHaven, J. C., and Milliman, J. W., 1960, *Water Supply— Economics, Technology and Policy*, Chicago, Univ. of Chicago Press, p. 252.
6. The Hoover Commission on Organization of the Executive Branch of the Government, 1955, Report by Task Force on Water Resources and Power, v. 2, pp. 443, 677, 719–831, 895; v. 3, p. 1186.
7. Jenkins, J. E., Moak, C. E., and Okun, D. A., 1961, Sedimentation of reservoirs in the Southeast, *Trans. Am. Soc. Civ. Eng.*, v. 126, pt. 3, p. 70.
8. Kaufman, W. J., 1961, Inorganic chemical contamination of ground water, *Technical Report W*61-5, Cincinnati, Robert A. Taft Sanitary Engineering Center, p. 49.
9. Kilburn, C., and Whitman, H. M., December, 1962, Water levels in southwestern Louisiana, April 1960 to April 1961, *Water Resources Pamphlet No.* 11, Louisiana Dept. of Cons. Geol. Surv. and Dept. of Pub. Wks., p. 10.
10. Lynn, R. D., and Arlin, Z. E., September, 1962, Deep well construction for the disposal of uranium mill tailing water by the Anaconda Company at Grants, N.M., *Trans. Soc. Mining Eng.*, *A.I.M.E.*, v. 223, pp. 230–237.
11. *Oil and Gas. J.*, June 17, 1963, Soft detergents are almost here, p. 41.
12. Rudulph, E. A., January, 1963, Taum Sauk pumped-storage power project, *Civ. Eng.*, v. 33, no. 1, pp. 40–43.
13. Slichter, C. S., 1902, The motions of underground waters, *U.S. Geol. Surv. Water Supply Paper 67.*

14. Slichter, C. S., 1905, Field measurements of the rate of movement of underground waters, *U.S. Geol. Surv. Water Supply Paper* 140.
14a. Technical Library, Tennessee Valley Authority, May 1964, *Flood Damage Prevention*, Knoxville, Tenn.
15. Thomas, N. O., and Harbeck, G. E., 1956, Reservoirs in the United States, *U.S. Geol. Surv. Water Supply Paper* 1360-*A*, p. 9.
16. U.S. Congress, House Appropriations Committee, 1959, Hearings on Civil Works Appropriations Bill, pt. 1, p. 18.
17. U.S. House of Rep., 1916, No. 16, 64th Congress, 1st session, p. 8.
18. U.S. Supreme Court, 1865 (3 Wall, 713, 724–725).
19. White J. F., 1961, Strategic aspects of urban flood-plain occupance, *Trans. Am. Soc. Civ. Eng.*, v. 126, pt. 1, pp. 63–75.
20. Wilson, W. K., Lt. Gen., April, 1963, *Civ. Eng.*, v. 33, no. 4, p. 78.
21. Wolman, A., February, 1961, Inpact of desalinization on the water economy, *J. Am. Water Works Assoc.*, v. 53, no. 2, pp. 119–124.

7

Summation and Outlook

THE HYDROLOGIC CYCLE

This volume has been oriented to the hydrologic cycle as it relates to man's activities. The hydrologic cycle describes the endless flow of water: from the atmosphere onto the land surface and thence into the ocean from where it is again evaporated into the atmosphere, thus completing the cycle.

The techniques of measurement and the equipment used in tracing the progress of water in the various phases of the cycle are simple and effective. The instruments used range from a bucket in which rain may be caught, through a pan from which water may evaporate, to a tape for measuring the water levels in wells, to a small propeller that turns in proportion to the velocity of flowing water in a river.

The systematic observation and recording of the physical data provides a sound basis for visualizing and planning projects for the utilization of water. Improvement in analyzing observational data includes better statistical techniques and the numerical methods that have been facilitated by the new electronic computers. Synthetic hydrology, a new approach to hydrology has been used to "create" hydrologic data that are statistically compatible with available short-term records, so that flow frequency, recurrence intervals, duration curves of one sort or another, and probable extremes may be computed.

Hydrology is concerned primarily with the liquid form of water that is essentially pure. Water that contains more than 0.1 percent of dissolved solids is encountered only occasionally in studies of hydrology. When the impurities are as high as 0.4 percent, the water is considered very mineralized. Some constituents, such as phenols, are obnoxious when concentration exceeds 0.0000001 percent (1 part per billion), and radioactive contaminants are detectable at even smaller concentrations.

Snow and ice, the solid forms of precipitation, have been considered as falling within the realm of hydrology, but only because they melt. The permanently frozen masses of fresh water found in the arctic or antarctic regions are not of particular hydrologic interest. The annual accretion of snow and its annual transformation into liquid water are, however, of concern to hydrologists. By trial-and-error methods, relatively reliable procedures have been developed on an area-by-area basis to convert the depths of fallen snow into possible totals of runoff. In certain parts of the United States, the melting of glaciers contributes a measurable fraction of stream runoff, and thus glaciology is sometimes included as a subdivision of hydrology.

Extensive studies of precipitation show that it is not uniform and differs widely as between places that are not far apart. The variability is most pronounced with respect to depth of rainfall caused by single storms, but even the annual depths of rainfall on closely spaced points exhibit important differences. Our conclusion as to how much rainfall actually falls in an area is influenced by the number of rain gages—the greater the number, the less uniform we believe the distribution to be.

Hydrologists are concerned with the movement of water on the land surface and underground. The quantity that moves is the residual of the rainfall after the evaporation (or evapotranspiration) is subtracted, and after the moisture bound by capillary forces and by molecular attraction of the soil complex, and thus prevented from moving, is also subtracted. Even if we knew the exact distribution of rainfall, there would be no less uncertainty as to the quantity of residual water to be expected. It would depend on the same natural factors of evaporation and soil moisture that vary unpredictably and are not exactly determinable. An accurate knowledge of rainfall distribution would, however, enable us to reduce the errors in our determination of these other factors.

Measurements of rainfall have also been useful in the study of dry periods. The occurrence and duration of droughts are of great importance to farmers and to concentrations of population that require a minimum quantity of water each and every day. In these instances, the time distribution of rain is important, not merely the average annual rainfall. It is in this area that the network of precipitation gages has yielded the most reliable information, for the lack of rain will be apparent over far wider areas than will the individual rainstorms. The duration of a drought directly affects plant growth—and the storage required for municipal and domestic water supply.

The change of state of the water substance from the liquid to gas is called evaporation. In the laboratory or in a wind tunnel this is not difficult to measure. In nature, however, things are vastly more complicated. It has been found most satisfactory to measure the water loss from an evaporation pan and to use the figures so obtained as the basis for estimates and comparisons. Attempts have been made, with varying degrees of success, to measure the factors that affect evaporation (wind velocity, incident solar energy, relative humidity, and so forth) and to manipulate mathematically the figures so that an estimate of evaporation will result. A number of experiments have been made to relate the evaporation from a free-water surface to the evaporation from a standardized pan. No fixed relationship has been found, although yearly averages seem rather consistent.

The evaporation of water from the soil is notably affected by the action of vegetation, and it is also a function of the dryness of the soil: The thinner the layer of water held to each soil particle, the more energy is evidently needed to remove it. Not surprisingly, it is now more or less agreed that the evaporation from a free-water surface is the maximum that can be expected for any given set of meteorological circumstances. This apparently woolly statement is merely the inadequate recognition that evaporation and its effects are best observed rather than computed, and that the prediction of evaporation over short periods is an uncertain business.

The flow of a stream is usually determined by means of measurement of its channel cross section combined with current-meter measurements of velocity at a number of selected points in its channel. To obtain a continuous record of the discharge of rivers, the stream is rated at various stages by means of current-meter measurements, and then a device is installed to record the stage and its variation with time. The rating curve of a station is seldom constant over a long period of time, but frequent reratings enable an adequate estimate to be made of the discharge between gagings.

The measurements of discharge and river stage are the raw material for a variety of purposes. During the last twenty or thirty years many statistical methods for analyzing the accumulated data have been devised. Additional kinds of analysis are still being invented which utilize the immense capabilities of digital and analog computers. The recurrence interval of flood discharges and the maximum probable discharge, the frequency and duration of low flows, the "firm yield" of various sizes of impoundment, the maximum flood stage and minimum stage of a river, the duration and frequency of occurrence of a given depth of water in the river—answers to all of these questions, and many more, are based on the measurement of discharges and stages of streams.

As the use of water, the industrial raw material, has become increasingly important, the measurements of flow and stage have been supplemented by systematic sampling and analysis of water bodies both for dissolved and suspended matter. Periodic measurements of water temperature have also been made to determine the utility of the water source as a cooling medium. To this data the statistical techniques developed elsewhere have been applied with good results.

Much of the data have been summarized in maps, much in graphs (with the time as the abscissa), and a substantial fraction of the total analysis has consisted of duration curves, probability curves, frequency curves, and other forms of statistical presentation. In some instances, the complexity of the interrelationships of the variables that produced the observed data has necessitated the use of such analogs as laboratory hydraulic models of stream systems to enable predictions to be made. Such a model is brought into line with the observed data by trial-and-error modifications until it satisfactorily reproduces past experience. It is then believed to be capable of predicting the operation of the system under critical patterns of runoff resulting from assumed storms and the modifications resulting from reservoir construction and operation. The analysis of hydrologic data has advanced to a high state of sophistication and potential applicability.

The study of hydrogeologic systems as part of the hydrologic cycle is less than 100 years old. Techniques have been developed to determine the characteristics of water-bearing formations as they exist in place. The abilities of aquifers to act as filter plants, pipe lines, and reservoirs can be determined with a precision that is satisfactory for all practical purposes. This advance in field technique has supplemented the laboratory techniques that subject the cores of water-bearing materials to tests.

Ground-water developments have always had to contend with feedback effects; these were early recognized in the phenomenon of well interference. Later on, on a larger scale, the development of well fields in aquifers that were in hydraulic contact with streams, or other bodies of surface water, caused measurable changes in stream flow. It was then recognized that in developing an aquifer for its maximum offtake, this maximum was not a fixed, determinable quantity. Rather it was found to be a variable, intimately associated with the quantity of water stored in the aquifer and the conditions of natural or artificial replenishment. Slowly, as experience accumulated, the importance of well spacing and hydrogeologic boundaries in the proper development of ground-water supplies has been evaluated. The concept of overdevelopment has been better understood: overdevelopment is simply the concentration of well offtake to the point that the pumping lifts are increased until the aquifer itself is either locally dewatered or until deleterious side effects occur. When this happens, the offtake of individual wells must decrease even though a large quantity of fresh water may remain in the aquifer.

The quantity of water stored in aquifers of the continental United States is very large: It is in the order of 50 billion acre-ft. Single regional aquifers, now in a partially depleted condition, still contain approximately as much water as the maximum storage capacity of all of the man-made impoundments in the country combined. One such aquifer is the one now being mined in the High Plains of Texas and New Mexico. Aquifers of even greater storage capacity underlie the mid-South area (upper Mississippi Embayment) north of the latitude of the south boundary of Arkansas. The Chicot reservoir of southwestern Louisiana is another aquifer containing vast quantities of potable water in storage.

We have examined precipitation—its distribution and significance. We have seen that most of the water that reaches the land surface evaporates. However, a small fraction of the water does penetrate the land surface where it adds to the water already in storage underground. In some aquifers there is a small incremental displacement of the original connate water in a seaward direction. In other aquifers the increment due to rainfall is balanced by flow from the aquifers into rivers or lakes (the so-called sustained flow) and by the flow of springs. In still other aquifers no annual increment is registered: the aquifer is full, no adequate outlet exists, and the recharge is immediately "rejected," much as when we add water to a bucket that is already full.

The remaining water supports the flow of streams and the changes in water level in lakes and swamps. On the average all of this "surplus" water is approximately equal to an 8-in. or 9-in. water depth annually over the entire United States: possibly in the order of 1 billion acre-ft a year.

This billion or so acre-ft of water that finds its way into stream channels on its way to the sea contains enormous energy. This energy has been harnessed, to some small extent, by hydroelectric power projects. The remaining energy of the descending water is dissipated in internal friction, in the transportation of sediment of all sizes, shapes, and forms, and in the erosion and filling of the channels of rivers. The sediment is produced through the normal process of slow erosion of material due to the impact of rain on the land combined with the action of frost and wind. This a cumulative, slow, geologic process that is beyond the power of mankind to stop.

WATER AND MAN

There has been a tendency, in recent years, for man to change the environment to suit himself rather than change his practices in order to better adapt himself to the environment. When these efforts have for their goal the large-scale control of geologic forces, they have created side effects and feedbacks that have usually been unpleasant and that rarely have been forseen.

One of the more publicized attempts at environmental control goes under the name *weather modification*. Although as of this writing such attempts have met with only limited success, yet so attractive are the possible modifications of weather, even when confined to considerations of military advantage, that the studies command substantial financial backing and proceed despite many failures and only limited and uncertain successes.

Indeed, the need to evaluate the efficacy of rain making has stimulated a good deal of research into meteorological phenomena, including the intensive measurement of rainfall not only upon the land surface, but also on the water surfaces of inland lakes. The results obtained by increasing the density of rain-gage networks have been edifying and important. The object of all of this work has been to permit comparison of the effect of rain making with what might have happened in its absence. There have also been studies of other condensation phenomena such as fog and mist, all with the ultimate goal of being to produce, stimulate, inhibit, or terminate the particular phenomenon being studied.

Considered from a hydrologic viewpoint—the viewpoint of establishing a sound statistical quantitative basis for understanding and evaluating the occurrence and recurrence of natural phenomena—weather modification, if achieved, will be deleterious. For if natural events are to be routinely and significantly changed by purposeful human efforts, then there is no way of knowing whether an event is hydrologic (amenable to the statistical analysis of natural forces) or historical (the result of human activities or of a mixture of human and natural events). It is easy to see that the human portion of the equation is subject to modification by political forces and that these are not predictable and surely not repeatable, except in the sense that history repeats itself—and as everyone is well aware, it really doesn't in the sense that natural events do.

Yet we may expect that the experiments will continue and that, if successful, weather modification will be undertaken until the unforeseen and undesired effects on existing structures, and projected construction, force its abandonment. The net result of the effort will probably be an improvement in military technology, something that many people will greet with mixed emotions.

The measurement of evaporation has also received much attention in recent years. There is a net annual excess of potential evaporation over rainfall (see Fig. 3.2, p. 49) in a large portion of the country. When reservoirs are built in these arid zones, some of the benefit gained through the storage of water is lost due to increased evaporation. There is a twofold loss here: Not only is the actual quantity of available water reduced, but the remaining water is degraded in quality because the dissolved solids increase in concentration as water evaporates.

Not only do the evaporation losses from the new reservoirs subtract from the usable water supply, but water-loving vegetation establishes itself in the deltas and swampy areas that form just upstream from the reservoir areas, and these disproportionately increase the evaporation loss. Up to now man's activities in storing water for later use have increased the evaporation, whether it be in the building of farm ponds, terracing and contour plowing to reduce runoff or the establishment of impoundments like Lake Mead. Recently, however, certain hydrologists have been intrigued by the potential benefits to be gained by reducing the evaporation and have turned to chemistry for assistance. This, in addition to the war against the phreatophyte that is being waged by agricultural experiment stations, universities, and the manufacturers of herbicides and weed killers.

Progress in chemical technology has drawn attention to the evaporation-inhibiting properties of monomolecular layers (monolayers) of certain waxy films such as cetyl alcohol (hexadecanol). Laboratory experiments have demonstrated the potential efficacy of the films in reducing evaporation from a free-water surface: instead of losing water, the water body would be raised in temperature during the day and, presumably, radiate at night losing its excess heat.

In demonstrating the practicability of monolayers in the field, however, it has been found necessary either to accomplish large-scale experiments in replicate (and this has been usually impracticable) or, for purposes of comparison, to be able to compute the evaporation on the basis of meteorological data that are unaffected by the monolayers. This latter has not proved easy to do. As might be expected, research has taken two distinct approaches: field experiments with large tanks side by side and studies of mass-energy transfer with very elaborate instrumentation. When it is remembered that the subject under study is, actually, the stability (or instability) of a two-phase (liquid-gas) system under constantly varying circumstances, then it is not surprising that the results thus far have not been conclusive. It is one thing to measure evaporation in the laboratory, where conditions can be measured and controlled with precision. It is something quite different to compute the effects of varying insolation, winds of differing velocities and temperatures, changes in relative humidity, varying contributions of heat from the neighboring and adjoining masses of rock, and the influence of phreatophytes on the rim of the reservoir on the total evaporation from a free water surface (even when the precipitation thereto and the surface and ground-water inflows and outflows are determinable).

Whereas a possible plus or minus of 25 percent in the correlation between the short-term evaporation from a pan and evaporation from a nearby lake was tolerable from a hydrologic viewpoint, it has not been acceptable in measuring a reduction of evaporation of, possibly, from 20 to 40 percent resulting from use of a monolayer.

Another experiment in evaporation control has been the application of cetyl alcohol as part of plant food to reduce the water consumption of plants. This would make the available water go further, if successful. Again, there exist grave problems both in application of the chemical and the evaluation, both physical and economic, of the effects.

But even if the use of monolayers in arid-zone reservoirs can be seen to be potentially beneficial, there exist many obstacles to be overcome in the course of establishing and maintaining such layers on reservoir surfaces. And the use of reservoirs for purposes of recreation—fishing, swimming, skiing, skin-diving, and boating—all of which will disrupt these films, conflicts with the attempt to save water. How these conflicts will be resolved, if at all, must await the passage of time.

From the standpoint of hydrology, however, no deleterious side effects are to be anticipated from experiments or projects that reduce evaporation. For of the total water content of the atmosphere only a minute fraction originates from land-locked bodies of surface water and only a very small fraction of this evaporation is likely to be impeded by monolayers. It is doubtful that the effect of all the attempts at evaporation reduction will be detectable in any of the meteorologic measurements now being made.

The modifications of the hydrologic cycle in the fields of precipitation and evaporation are still to be classified as "potential" when specific projects are under consideration. They are untried, although promising, and as procedures for achieving desired results in the field of water-resource development they are completely unproven.

In a totally different category are projects for modifying the distribution of surface water in time and space. It is unnecessary to discuss details of dam construction, river and lake intakes, hydropower installations, irrigation canals and drainage ditches, channel improvements, and flood-control projects. These devices and a multitude of lesser ones—farm ponds, land-forming, terracing, tile and ditch drainage, culvert and siphon construction, and pump and sprinkler installation—are all included as part of the ways and means of modifying the surface-water phase of the hydrologic cycle.

Probably the earliest activities in the United States that resulted in modifying the entire hydrology of a region were undertaken for a completely different purpose in the 1820s. These activities took the form of channel maintenance and improvement. There was no science of hydrology at that time, geology was just becoming comprehensible, and the practical men who had a continent to tame seized upon the only inexpensive avenue of transportation available to them—the rivers and streams that drained the midcontinent. The hydrologic effects attributable to channel improvement have been noted in the stage-discharge relationships at St. Louis and Vicksburg. Under these circumstances the energy of flowing water has been harnessed to cut river channels deeper and to enable the water to leave the drainage area more rapidly. The data relating stage with discharge thus early began to lose their hydrologic character. The concentration time of the alluvial valley presumably started to decrease.

As the years passed, the population increased and became urbanized. Cities found an increasing need for drinking water, especially in the present megalopolis area in the East. During the closing decades of the nineteenth century New York started to build the first of a long series of impoundments for water supply in the Catskill Mountains (the most recent of these is still under construction). Other cities followed suit. The success of these dams and reservoirs in the humid sections of the country inspired emulation in the West. The Reclamation Act of 1902 gave rise to similar construction for purposes of irrigation, Federally financed, in the arid regions of the United States. There were, however, a number of significant differences in the situations.

In the East, the rocks are relatively resistant to erosion, vegetation tends to armor the land against the energy of the raindrops, and the impounded streams are rather free of sediment. Moreover the impoundments in the East changed the hydrology of relatively small areas downstream, and the potential energy of the water was used to transport it through tunnels to distribution reservoirs and thence to the consumer. In the West the rocks are relatively young and friable, the land stands naked of vegetation due to the aridity of the climate, the reservoirs have had to carry over water from one year to the next (on the large projects, especially) and have slowly started to fill with solids, thus reducing their capacity to store water. More important, for an equal water yield the drainage areas of the West had to be far larger than those in the East. Thus, the hydrologic effects of the impoundments in the West have been far-reaching and well-nigh incalculable. There has been aggradation above the dams—that is, creation of deltas and alluvial deposits upstream with the consequent growth of useless, water-consuming vegetation. There has been degradation of the stream channels below the dams due to the release of turbulent, energy-laden water that has promptly begun to cut deeper the channels of the old river beds, to meander in the old flood plains, to "hunt" for a condition of near equilibrium. The net hydrologic effect of irrigation and other impoundments has been to degrade the quality of the river water, to reduce the flow from large drainage areas, and to render difficult, if not impossible, the rational design of structures that are based on hydrologic data in the several drainage areas.

These trends, which first manifested themselves at the turn of the twentieth century, picked up speed and momentum in the decade of the 1930s with the inauguration of the Tennessee Valley Authority. To the original reasons for building dams and reservoirs—water supply for municipal and agricultural use—were added the development of hydropower, the prevention of floods, the release of water for navigation and the dilution of wastes, and the establishment of facilities for aquatic recreation. Of these, as we have seen, technological improvements in the production of electricity for peaking purposes have cast doubt on Federal policy as it relates to hydropower. The expenditures for the prevention and abatement of floods have resulted, incredibly, in increased losses due to flooding. It has proved impossible to cure the pollution of streams by diluting wastes with stored water—you can't store enough. By contrast, the establishment of aquatic recreation facilities has been an outstanding success.

From the standpoint of hydrology, however, there has been a widespread destruction of the hydrologic character of the observed water data. The

U.S. Geological Survey has advertised this fact widely by requesting the establishment of hydrologic benchmarks throughout the country. A hydrologic benchmark is an area, untouched by man, in which the water data collected can be expected to depict reliably the effects of natural conditions on the flow of streams and fluctuations in ground-water levels. In short, as water data have been changed in character due to water-development projects, the Survey has found it increasingly difficult to act as an observer and interpreter of hydrologic fact and has been forced to devise and advocate heroic measures in order to maintain its identity as a scientific agency and perform the services required of it by law.

In practical terms, however, this change in the character of data has had the effect of making water projects less predictable—increasing the factor of ignorance—and thus making it necessary to provide for more acute extremes. The water crisis in St. Louis and the bridge failure at Sioux City, Iowa, can be considered to be the forerunners of an increasing number of construction failures due to lack of statistically valid design information. The very fact that such failures occur will cast additional doubt on the design criteria in use and increase costs over what they would have been if the data had not changed in character.

Inasmuch as the principal cause of the deterioration in the nature of the data is the construction of dams and impoundments, one of the principal tasks of modern hydrology is to find a practicable substitute—one that accomplishes the essential regulation of flow with a minimum of accompanying and deleterious side effects. There is every prospect that this may be achieved for those projects of water utilization that regard the water substance as a useful commodity. There is little prospect that this will be achieved for ends that regard water as a nuisance or a common enemy. In this latter category, the utilization of rivers for transportation must also be included. Although the long-range prospect of maintaining specified channel depths in alluvial rivers approaches zero, when open rivers are considered for use as highways for air-cushion or ground-effect vehicles, prospects are bright. We may conclude that the effects of the production of hydropower can be removed from the field of hydrology. In fact, if the production of power is used as the criterion, the need to construct dams on rivers is becoming less important. Thus, hydrologic complications due to dam construction for this purpose are being removed from the realms of hydrology at a rapid rate due to technical improvements in pumps and turbines.

The advances in the techniques of well construction and pump design and manufacture have interacted with increasing geologic knowledge to stimulate the use of ground water. The last decade of the nineteenth century saw the deep-well turbine pump developed simultaneously with inexpensive, small, sources of power. Aquifers have been found and brought into production with amazing speed. The history of ground-water in New York City, the

High Plains of Texas, Los Angeles, and Southwestern Louisiana, examined elsewhere in considerable detail, illustrates this statement.

The techniques of hydrogeology have kept pace with developments in the utilization of ground water. Field-testing procedures for determining hydrogeologic constants of water-bearing formations have been proposed and successfully applied. The evaluation of individual aquifers as filter plants, pipe lines, reservoirs, or mines can be reliably accomplished. This has had its impact in the fields of water supply, mine drainage, waste disposal, and the use of aquifers for the storage of foreign materials such as natural gas. The ground-water cycle from input to output, both natural and man made, has been thoroughly studied in many parts of the country, as attested by the available reports of the U.S. (and state) Geological Surveys, and the numerous, although largely unpublished, reports of companies and private consultants.

The unexpected side effects of ground-water development have been of purely local hydrologic significance: land subsidence, the encroachment of saline waters in certain areas, and the partial dewatering of aquifers are the most important. Of these, land subsidence is the most vexing. Although measures may be devised to reduce or halt subsidence, there is no reason to believe that the elevation of the land surface, once it has subsided, can be restored to its original level, regardless of what is done. The position with regard to the intrusion of sea water or saline water into an aquifer is much more favorable. A cure for the condition can at least be visualized, even though it may prove to be impracticable of achievement due to considerations of cost. The cure consists of replenishing the aquifer in certain critical areas with surface water of suitable quality and quantity. The same cure is available for partially dewatered aquifers.

THE NEW HYDROLOGY AND WATER DEVELOPMENT

General

Hydrology, an erstwhile scientific discipline, is being transformed into something else. This something else has been designated "modern hydrology" for want of a better term. Its data are not constant in character in the sense that hydraulic data are constant in character: A flow of 1 cubic ft per sec is just that whether measured now or then. But any particular measurement of flow in a given location may change in significance: An 8-ft stage now carries a different interpretation from what it did previously and from what it will mean if observed in the future. The field of hydrology is in a state of constant flux, like virology or bacteriology which must constantly deal with the new mutations that are appearing as a result of improved medical technology that has conquered existing strains of pathogens.

Modern hydrology is governed by the social, economic, and legal framework of the society whose engineering feats have altered the occurrence of water from its original, natural condition. The changes in the flow of water have been accomplished for the purposes of the society and within the rules that this society has established. Consequently it should be understood that modern hydrology will differ from country to country and from time to time. From one viewpoint modern hydrology can be considered a "temporary" aberration that will eventually be restored to its role as a scientific discipline by the forces of geomorphology. But this may be too long-range a viewpoint for a single generation of men to adopt, although it may exactly fit a viewpoint that considers five or six generations.

It is submitted that there have been two independent frameworks for the development of water resources in the United States, and that these may broadly be classified as political and economic. The political framework consists of harnessing, potentially, the entire wealth of the country to achieve some objective in the field of water resources as though this were important in itself, without regard to economic considerations. Some writers have termed this the pyramid-building attitude. Flood control, navigation, and the reclamation of arid lands in the West are examples of this type of resource development. The economic framework is based on local custom or common law and has manifested itself in the riparian and appropriation doctrines of water development. A third framework, the police power doctrine, has been suggested as an alternate to the economic framework of development. But although police power has been found suitable to maintain order and prevent damage, it has not proved successful in increasing the production of goods and services—the police state is neither a novel nor an untested method of organizing society. Possibly the police power may be effectively used in the prevention or abatement of pollution, but this is not certain. The writer believes that police power is an inappropriate doctrine for the development of water resources inasmuch as it is an essentially negative philosophy.

Political Doctrines

The political development of water resources is primarily a Federal matter, although certain states, notably California, have also entered the field. The powers of the Federal Government are theoretically limited to those delegated by the Constitution. As a practical matter, as the rivers to the interior of the continent became the highways for westward expansion, Federal political control was extended to rivers under the grant of power to regulate commerce among the states. Relying upon that power, the Federal Government took the responsibility not only to protect the flow of commerce on rivers from the political interference of local governmental units, but to physically improve and "protect" the navigability of waters. As we have seen, man-made impediments are far easier to remove permanently by Congressional action than are the impediments resulting from operation of the forces of geomorphology. Later, a similar responsibility for the control of floods on a national scale was assumed. The courts have sustained assertions of Federal authority in the nonnavigable upper reaches of rivers to protect the navigation potential of navigable waters and also to protect interstate commerce from flood damage.

In the West, the status of the Federal Government as the owner of public land has led to invocation of the proprietary power to enable Federal undertaking of irrigation responsibility. In addition Federal authority has been exercised to license non-Federal development of power on lands and in waters subject to the jurisdiction of Congress. It has also been increasingly employed to enable Federal development of hydropower as the financial underpinning of multipurpose projects to include navigation, flood control, irrigation, water supply, and recreation. Under existing legislation, many such projects also comprehend drainage, fish and wildlife preservation, pollution control and abatement, and salinity control.

From the standpoint of hydrology, existing Federal legislation concerning water resources can be summarized as being a complex array of regulations to govern human conduct that has been firmly based on the mistaken assumption that the law of gravity, as it refers to water, can be permanently repealed and its effects nullified. Essentially, the actual result of the impoundment of water and sediment is to keep soil and stones from moving downhill, and on a large scale this cannot be permanently accomplished by man's efforts. While the force of gravity can be temporarily overcome by the exertion of counterforce—exemplified by operation of airplanes and missiles—in the case of the nation's water we are dealing with the motion of at least 1 billion acre-ft of water (a trillion tons) a year falling through, possibly, an average of 400 ft on its way to the sea—and it *will* transport sediment. A small part of this energy may be temporarily and locally counteracted or harnessed, but it is folly to undertake to halt permanently the movement of sediment derived from a major fraction of the nation's drainage area. This is precisely what flood control, for instance, that is based on impoundments assumes can be done. Unfortunately for its Congressional sponsors, each reservoir will function as an efficient trap for silt and sediment until it fills. Long before it is filled, however, its value in the reduction of floods will have become small.

To consider such interference with the forces of geomorphology to be a rational goal for the entire social structure of the nation is incredible. One might just as profitably pass legislation making the value of π equal to 3, and setting up a bureau to enforce this, or outlawing the incidence of influenza and cancer and forcing violators to stand trial. Surely there must exist more rewarding goals, possibly attainable, upon which to lavish our resources.

In the chapter on water-resource development, detailed appraisals of the various programs have been presented. Some of the programs have been found to possess long-term hydrologic feasibility. However for many of the most expensive programs the long-term hydrologic feasibility has been shown to be vanishingly small, the damaging side effects large, and the real problem has been found to be akin to that faced by a man riding a tiger: how to get off in safety.

Economic Doctrines

Current doctrines concerning the capture and use of the water substance are clouded by an old myth: that water, of all natural resources, is so unique and essential that the rules of economic behavior that apply to land, food, transportation, housing, or clothing cannot be trusted to work. The ancient fear of monopoly was born in the era when the types of property and number of property owners were both severely limited. It still casts its long shadow into the machine age when new forms of property proliferate, owners are found everywhere, and where the only effective monopolies are those exercised by arms of the government or by private groups that have been granted the coercive power of the state to enable them to exert monopolistic control. It is difficult to conceive of natural monopolies of any consequence that are not buttressed by the governmental power. The ingenious substitutions of materials, the replacement of naturally occurring substances by artificial ones (for instance, rubber and silk by butyl rubber and nylon), the economic battles between steel and aluminum, aluminum and copper, coal and oil, nylon and rayon, cotton and synthetics, and so forth—all epitomize the antimonopoly trend of a free-market economy.

"Ah!" says the legislator, "But no one has come up with a good cheap substitute for water. We can't let anyone get control of it, or we die of thirst! Water is a special case".

Does anyone expect a hydrologist to believe this? With 1 billion acre-ft annually (more than 1000 billion tons!) appearing as stream flow, with 300 million acre-ft in surface impoundments, with some 13 billion acre-ft in storage in natural lakes, and with some 50 billion acre-ft accessible by the construction of wells and an installation of pumps (3)? Hydrologists may be ignorant of economics and politics, but they're not necessarily stupid! The myth of a limited, small water supply that could be easily monopolized by a tiny group which could then obtain undue payments from the rest of the population will not stand critical examination. The only possible exercise of monopoly power under a system of private and municipal property rights in water would be by the larger governmental units using the police power of the University of Michigan's Model Water Use Act!

Just as oranges are cheaper in Florida than in Minnesota, and fresh water is generally cheaper in Arkansas than it is in Arizona, the cost of producing and distributing water will vary from place to place and from time to time.

And should the local cost of water become too high, those who require large quantities of cheap water will have to establish themselves in areas that are hydrologically more favorable. Why should an industry that requires a river of water be subsidized so that it may be located in a desert? As to monopolies, there is already ample supervision of man-made monopolies to insure that the price of water is comparable to that of other materials and services. Thomas has pointed out that 90 percent of all water used by the public is non-consumptive, that industrial water use is 98 percent nonconsumptive, and that 94 percent of the water used by industry is for cooling (7). So, from the standpoint of technology, the cost of reclaiming and reusing water will serve as a readily available economic yardstick that will also automatically limit the cost of water production *de nova*. Whether the necessary economic and legal framework is available to make this yardstick effective must be considered separately.

If property rights in water are to be made comparable to the property rights of land ownership, then the mining of water must be differentiated from the right to capture, process, and use a given quantity of flowing water each year. Appropriation doctrine, modified in this manner, is probably the soundest base for the development of water resources. Riparian doctrine, since it serves only to insure the nonconsumptive use of water or, disguised as the doctrine of correlative rights, the mutual impoverishment of those who use it consumptively, is totally unsuited to the modern age.

Appropriation doctrine simply specifies that by putting water to beneficial use a property right in perpetuity to pump an annual quantity of water may be acquired. The first in time is the superior in right. As long as only the direct flow of a stream is involved, matters are relatively simple: as the senior appropriators utilize the flow, it diminishes and junior appropriators find less and less water available. There is a certain self-policing feature associated with the appropriation of stream flow.

The granting of a right to divert a perennial quantity of water is surrounded by limitations that may, or may not, be rational: the method and place of diversion may not be changed without bureaucratic approval, the capacity of the pumps used is sometimes specified, and the right to divert water may be lost by nonuse or by a change in use. Certain states have classified the use of water into more important and less important uses and prepared tables of use priorities. Transfer or sale of water rights is made difficult, if not impossible. Yet, despite all of the present restrictions, there is every reason to believe that the principle of prior appropriation can be successfully adapted for use throughout the country.

One important psychological obstacle to be overcome is the widespread belief that water is a special case that should, somehow, be immunized against changes in price to the consumer. The increasing difficulty encountered by run-of-river water plants in producing an acceptable water, the increasing cost of local impoundments and the long-distance transmission of water, and the tendency to overbuild water supply systems to "inexpensively" meet anticipated future water demands should constitute sufficient evidence that the actual cost of water production is rising just like that of any other manufactured product (9).

It must be recognized that new forms of organization will be needed in order to facilitate the integration of water into the system of private property. The conjunctive use of aquifers and streams is complex and will undoubtedly be expensive in many instances. Thus, arrangements will have to be made to enable the unitization of aquifers, or substantial portions of aquifers, if they are to be used as reservoirs for the storage of surplus surface water. In certain instances the rights of an individual property owner may have to be replaced by ownership of a share in the common pool. The replenishment of the aquifer might be assured by allowing the common-pool operator to obtain, by purchase or grant, a valid water right.

In the humid sections of the country the increased mineralization caused by water use might be evaluated on the basis of the net thermodynamic energy needed to remove the pollutant, and a charge might be levied on the user. In some instances, where the added minerals were particularly obnoxious (even in very small concentration), an added criterion might be needed.

The use of economic rather than political criteria in the development of legislation in the field of water resources would have a beneficial effect on hydrology. For one thing, it would tend to reduce or eliminate economically wasteful projects. This in itself would reduce the number of artificial earthquakes and earthquakes getting ready to occur (in the form of Congressional authorizations for dam construction). And if a project should prove to be uneconomic even when secondary benefits and direct negative side effects are excluded from the evaluation, everyone will be better off if it is not built.

Hirshleifer and his colleagues have suggested the proper role of governmental entities in a system of water law based on private property rights in water (2). Inasmuch as their statement clearly corroborates conclusions independently reached from considerations of hydrology (not to mention geomorphology), the writer has taken the liberty of adding to it as well as reorganizing and paraphrasing it:

The responsibility of government is to create rules under which the market system can operate in the field of water-resource development while protecting outside parties and the general public against harmful spillover or side effects. There is no need for the state to assume ownership of water already in use or to undertake its distribution among regions and among users. The functions of government, as they apply to other resources, may be listed as follows:

1. Establish a system of law that permits a clear definition of the extent of property rights in permanent water supply. This should be particularly

adapted to eliminate commonality problems that may pertain with particular force in the case of water: zoning, unitization, and similar procedures would be helpful.

2. Provide certainty of tenure for these rights and establish a clear basis for their transfer between individuals and private or public agencies under voluntary contractual agreements of purchase and sale.

3. Provide a procedure whereby rights to yet-unowned water (and permission to construct facilities for its transportation to points of use) may be secured by individuals, private or public agencies, or political entities. This might be accomplished by auction among competing claimants against a reservation price representing the value of the water for the state's own public uses.

4. Establish rules and procedures for the protection of outside parties against spillover effects caused by the actions of water-rights owners. These rules would protect against pollution, flooding, and the creation of drainage or sedimentation problems by water-right owners. Procedures might be established to facilitate the evaluation of, and compensation for, damages.

5. Conduct studies of the quality and quantity of water resources and research relating to improvements in practice and technology in the field of water production, utilization and waste disposal.

AREAS OF RESEARCH

Much work remains to be accomplished in hydrology and its associated disciplines. In a broad sense the goal of all of this work is to restore hydrology, as far as possible, to its original position as a discipline working with data of valid statistical character. For example, the U.S. Public Health Service has set the elimination or effective reduction of stream pollution as one of its objectives. As we have seen, the term "stream pollution" is popular recognition of the fact that the quality-of-water data obtained from a stream-sampling program are nonhydrologic in character. It follows that any program to remove or reduce pollution will tend to repair the nature of the quality-of-water data: to elevate them from historical to hydrologic.

The areas of research in hydrology are (1) basic, or concerned with the nature and laws of behavior of the water substance as it occurs, (2) applied, or concerned with formulating "laws" relative to the occurrence and discharge of water in nature, and (3) social, or concerned with the legal and economic framework within which water is brought into the productive process. Each subspeciality of hydrology has need of research in each of these areas.

Precipitation

Although the mechanism of precipitation is primarily a matter for meteorologists to discover, yet since raindrops fall on the land surface, it is partly the direct concern of the hydrologist. Basic research on the formation of water particles in the atmosphere might result in a better understanding of the occurrence and areal distribution of rain and thus would be of great importance to the hydrologist in his interpretation of the probable rainfall extremes. As a part of this program an increase in the number of rain gages and research leading to quantification of radar data would be most welcome. This work might make it possible to read the total precipitation, at any point at any time, directly from radar data obtained during storms.

Data obtained in this manner would improve the factual basis for statistical evaluations of such subjects as recurrence interval, the maximum rates and areal occurrences of rainfall, maximum point-rainfall values, and similar analyses on an area-by-area basis throughout the country. It would also facilitate the study of evaporation and other hydrologic phenomena.

There is also reason to anticipate that research on weather modification will continue and that eventually some results will be forthcoming that will be useful, at least to the air-transport industry and the military services. The scale of work underway is indicated by the fact that during the fiscal year of 1959, 69 projects involving a total expense of 3,711,450 dollars were in progress (10). These projects included the seeding of summer cumulus clouds, cloud-electrification studies, a precipitation-radar study, physical study of a hail-suppression program, a study of statistical evaluations of weather modification, freezing rain, and the dispersion or prevention of low clouds and fog at airfields.

One may be quite sure that the modifiers of weather, in their understandable enthusiasm for results, will begin operations at the earliest possible moment, regardless of the effects on hydrology. Probably the statement of Eberle, special consultant to the Kerr Committee, is representative of the approach of the workers in the field:

We have made great progress in the field of weather modification since 1946 when V. J. Schaefer first told the world of his laboratory experiments. Many of the skeptics at that time will admit that the seeding of the clouds under certain conditions will produce rain . . . .

The present (commercial) operators are qualified meteorologists and in the course of their operations have made a great contribution to the advancement of cloud physics and cloud modification. One cannot ignore the some 750,000 hours of seeding experience that they have had . . . .

Basic research is very important and it is only through it that we will be able to learn about the atmosphere and how we might be able to manage it for the betterment of mankind. I earnestly plead with our Congress, the National Science Foundation, the Federal agencies interested in this field and others interested, to step up basic research. At the same time I plead with these same groups that they publish their findings as soon as possible and that they give them to qualified cloud seeders, so they can put them to work.

People should not be asked to wait for years until the last facts of a particular study are known. Many areas of the country need to put to work the findings as they become available .... It doesn't take much additional rain at the right time to increase crop production in practically all States in the middle section of the United States (*10*, *44*).

It is not at all clear to the writer in what directions, if any, research into the political and economic framework of weather modification should be directed.

Evaporation

Effective control of evaporation must be preceded by an improvement in the methods of measuring it. This is a most complex problem, and the approaches now being followed are many and diverse. As we have noted, most projects for the control, storage, and use of surface water tend to increase evaporation, especially in the West.

Although the evaporation pan has been found to be a reasonably useful analog when the monthly or yearly evaporation is to be computed, it has certain deficiencies when used as a measure for shorter periods of time. Nonetheless it is doubtful that any synthetic system of combining other physical data to yield figures for evaporation will yield more reliable information.

We can expect that basic research into the two-phase, water-water vapor system will continue and be expanded. As part of this work the properties of numerous monomolecular layers will be tested in laboratories and sent out into the field for further proving.

Improvements in the field measurement of evaporation from free water surfaces will have to await more complete data on the distribution of rainfall upon them and better evaluation of the quantity of ground water entering them. There is much work to be done in this area of research. Engineering research into the reduction of evaporation must include the finding of ways to control phreatophytes and to cover free water surfaces with competent, long-lasting films and careful study of type localities in order to determine how best to reduce evaporation under a wide range of climatic, topographic, and geologic circumstances.

In the field of economics work still remains to be accomplished in evaluating the benefits to be derived from the reduction in evaporation. As we have seen, not only would more water be made available in arid regions, but the water quality would be improved by retaining the pure water that would otherwise be lost. Probably the greatest monetary return from evaporation suppression will be derived by the reduction of evaporation from stock ponds or small water supply reservoirs. At present, in many such instances in the West, as much as 90 percent of the water stored in the stock tank or pond may be evaporated. Even a 10 percent reduction in evaporation would, thus, double the useful water supply.

The only social research needed in connection with the suppression or reduction in evaporation is to determine how best to insure that a water-right holder who reduces evaporation will not be penalized by a reduction in his right to appropriate water.

Surface Water

It is not clear in what directions research into the hydrology of surface water should be oriented. For, as has been demonstrated, the foremost scientific agency in the field despairs of using most of the data that it now collects as the raw material for hydrologic evaluation.

True, research may refine the techniques of stream-flow measurement. And such improvements would be welcomed by the engineering profession. But this progress in hydraulics can hardly be classed as research in hydrology.

Nor can it be proposed that new forms of mathematical analysis are needed to convert the data obtained from measurements into useful design information. Such new techniques would be welcomed in the underdeveloped countries—but most of the basic data obtained in the United States are no longer readily amenable to such analysis.

It is possible that the course of hydrologic research, as it concerns the United States, must be channeled into the field of geomorphology. It must be directed into putting numerical values into the descriptive statements concerning morphologic phenomena. For instance, is there any possibility of predicting the position of the channel bottom of the Mississippi River under various assumptions of maintenance? Can the factors involved in erosion—rainfall, geology, topography, vegetative cover, and so forth—be analyzed so that the sediment yield of a water shed may be reliably evaluated without a long period of observation? Some progress has already been made in this field, but there is much still to be done (1). Is it possible to make a movable-bed analog of an existing river to depict conditions before and after reservoir construction and predetermine the upstream aggradation and downstream cutting of the channel? Can the bank and bed stabilization that will be needed downstream be predicted in advance of reservoir construction, so that the costs properly chargeable to the improvement can be taken into account? Is there some way whereby the effects of sedimentation on the operation of multipurpose projects can be predicted? What is the effect of losing X percent of the reservoir storage on the reduction in flood stages? Is the life of a reservoir that is filling with sediment properly expressed as the total time required until it is completely filled with solids? Or is the period that is required for it to lose one quarter of its capacity more meaningful? How do drainage projects reduce the concentration times of watersheds, and how may this be measured and taken into account in hydrologic evaluations? How should a reservoir be operated in order to minimize its effect on the geomorphology of the river channel and the entire upstream drainage basin? How can we best salvage long-term values from existing water-development projects?

Each of these questions can be used as the starting point in an entire research project—and the number of questions can be readily increased. So although research in hydrology will have to wait until the character of the data changes or will have to be confined to benchmark areas untouched by man's work, there is much that should be done in a closely associated scientific and engineering discipline.

As we have seen, growing demands for water are generating conflicts between water users. What changes in the law will best promote sound water development? At the moment Federal, and even state water-resources planning and development is dominated by agencies whose purpose it is to build projects. And while the structures have generally been sound, there is a strong likelihood that nonstructural solutions or less costly structural measures would have produced larger net benefits to the nation. There has also been little consistency between the water resources policies and other programs of the Federal Government. We have witnessed the reclamation of land at 1000 dollars per acre by one department in order to grow crops that are subject to the crop-reduction efforts by another department. What changes in administrative arrangements can be devised to minimize such expensive absurdities?

There is also the problem of writing water-legislation that will firmly establish the right of ownership in water, free for the most part of any restrictions not applicable to other commodities. The arrangements needed to bring closer the privileges and responsibilities in the field of water utilization are still to be worked out. How is the time lag between cause and effect to be handled? Pollution, sedimentation, or the reduction in stream flow due to the induced infiltration of water to wells can each serve as a good example of this problem. How is the responsibility for degradation of water quality to be attributed and evaluated so that matters will work out at the minimum cost to society?

The problems confronting the nation in the field of surface-water evaluation and utilization will require the best efforts of the most talented individuals among us in a wide range of fields from geomorphology to administration and legislation.

Ground Water

Basic research in ground water will undoubtedly concern itself with interaction between the slightly mineralized solutions of water and the various geological matrices in which it flows. There are base-exchange effects that are not precisely understood; there are changes in permeability of the rock matrix that may be due to certain impurities contained in the water. Some attention probably should be devoted to the slow migration of ions in ground water and the possible relationship of this to the concentration of minerals. There is still much work to be done in explaining the action of ground water, or the geological matrix, in the destruction of pathogenic microorganisms. It might also be worthwhile to study the movement of water under conditions of partial saturation, both when the directions of gravitational, molecular, and capillary forces coincide (as in recharge from precipitation) and when all of these forces do not act in concert.

In the field of applied or engineering research there are innumerable worthwhile projects. There is, for example, the better evaluation of ground-water movement in fractured and soluble rocks. Of course many of these must be accomplished while the finding and evaluating of specific ground-water supplies is underway. There is nation-wide mapping of aquifers still to be accomplished to a depth of, possibly 2000 or 3000 ft below land surface. Each aquifer constitutes a separate hydrogeological system that under appropriate circumstances should be evaluated. The quantity and quality of water to be obtained from each aquifer should probably be determined before development is started. The charting of formations to be used for the storage of wastes is another field of research.

There is in addition the preparation of mathematical or electrical analog models of aquifers, including their hydrogeological boundaries, based on the results of field testing. With properly constructed analogs useful predictions of offtake and drawdown for any spatial configuration of wells may be prepared. There is need for research in this field to discover proper electrical analogs that take into account changes in storage coefficient over a long period of time and changes in local transmissibility due to aquifer dewatering.

Yet it is to the deliberate utilization of aquifers for the storage of surface water that the principal efforts of ground-water hydrology and technology will probably be devoted in the future. For despite the lack of hydrologic permanence implicit in the construction of dams and impoundments, the continued use of the water substance by mankind makes the storage of water absolutely necessary.

It is fortunate that in the United States there are many aquifers favorably situated to supply centers of population with potable water. Such aquifers must be transformed from mines into reservoirs by means of systematic man-made replenishment, possibly by increasing the recharge opportunity in the outcrop areas of such aquifers, but more probably by recharge through structures such as injection wells of one type or another. Thomas has discussed the utilization of ground-water basins in the overall development of water resources, together with the engineering and legislative background, and has also set forth the opportunities and obstacles encountered in this effort (8).

The technical endeavors must include the evaluation of the reservoir potentials of individual aquifers, their geographic and geologic relationships to the source of water to be used for recharge, the compatibility of aquifer water to the water to be used for replenishment, and an economically attractive method of recharge. Inasmuch as this category of water project is, in the writer's considered opinion, the most important single area for future water-resource development, the detailed discussion of the actual circumstances surrounding such a project is warranted in order that the specific problems that confront the profession may be brought out.

Louisville will serve admirably as the model of a potential water-resource development project of the future. It is a medium-sized industrial city (1960 population 390,000) located on the Ohio River, drinking filtered and treated water from the river. Many of its industries and many private residences in surrounding areas operate wells that obtain water from an underlying shallow aquifer that consists of mixed sand and gravel.

Extensive studies by the U.S. Geological Survey showed that the shallow, sand and gravel aquifer on the Kentucky side of the Ohio River from Harrod's Creek (6 miles upstream from Louisville) to Kosmosdale (about 10 miles downstream) contains about 80 billion gal of water in storage (about 250,000 acre-ft) (4). The filter-plant capacity of the aquifer in the area north-east of Louisville (based on the induced infiltration of water from the Ohio River) was estimated to be a minimum of 280 million gal per day. The area southwest of Louisville was found to be capable of infiltrating a minimum of 50 million gal of water per day from the Ohio River. These figures are, if anything, on the low side because calculations were made on the basis of low river temperatures and pool stage of the river. The river is occasionally in flood, and the water temperature is usually higher than the assumed minimum, making the potential average yield considerably greater. However to achieve a larger average supply we must assume that storage will be available to be drawn upon during periods of minimum production. In addition to the potentially induced infiltration of river water, the annual accretion to the aquifer, which originates in precipitation, is in excess of 11 million gal per day.

Studies of the recharge potential show that if need be the present product of the municipal water-treatment plant can be utilized for purposes of recharge. During the winter and spring of 1944, a total of approximately 130 million gal of cold water was put into the aquifer through a single radial well at the Seagram plant so that water of low temperature would be available in large quantity for cooling purposes during the following summer (2a). Later experiments by companies with recharge pits, as a means of disposing of used cooling water to minimize the sewer tax, were at least partially successful. However the geologic overburden in many areas is relatively impervious, and in order to expose the surface of the aquifer to recharge through a pit, rather deep excavations must be made.

The principal use of water in the Louisville area is for the cooling of condensors of steam-electric generating plants (6). Of a total water pumpage of about 760 million gal per day (mgd) in 1952, 580 mgd were pumped by these plants from the river. An average of 65 mgd were pumped from the Ohio River by the municipally owned Louisville Water Company, treated and filtered, and then delivered to the consumers. In most part this water can be expected to have rejoined the river downstream. Of the remainder, 35 mgd were pumped from the principal water bearing formation, and the remaining 80 mgd were pumped from the river by chemical plants for cooling purposes.

Even this brief summary of the water situation indicates that, overall, there is no shortage of water for the Louisville area, nor will there be a shortage in the foreseeable future. The problems connected with water supply are those caused by stream pollution. This pollution tends to increase the cost and difficulty of producing safe, palatable water for municipal purposes. As pollution of the river caused by the residues of insecticides, weed killers, fertilizers, and other agricultural chemicals continues, production of safe, pure water will require great skill in water treatment. This will be accomplished only with an increase in the cost of materials and employment of ever more highly skilled personnel. On the plus side of the picture we should note that industrial-waste treatment and the treatment of municipal wastes upstream (under the interstate compact of the Ohio River Basin) have been increasingly effective in reducing the pollution of the Ohio River from these sources. Nevertheless, in the summertime and early fall, during periods of low flow, when the water impounded behind the navigation dams of the Ohio River becomes almost stagnant, it is becoming increasingly difficult to remove some of the deleterious substances found in the water.

If we turn to ground-water utilization under these circumstances, we are immediately confronted by the fact that the induced infiltration of surface water during periods of low flow is not particularly desirable. True, the pollutants will be diluted by admixture of previously infiltrated ground water, but the total weight of deleterious substances to be handled by the public supply would be the same even though it would be spread out over a longer period. If all use of river water could be stopped for, say, the 100-day critical period of low, contaminated flow, much trouble could be avoided.

The average annual production of a municipal supply is far less than the daily or monthly peaks. And the peak municipal water use at Louisville is in the summer, during periods of low flow in the river. Taking the average annual municipal water use as 65 mgd in 1952, then the offtake during the peak 100-day period might possibly have averaged as much as 100 mgd. Allowing for a 25 percent increase in demand since that time, the storage planned for the city supply should total at least 12.5 billion gal. Thus a total of 12.5 billion gal of aquifer storage would have been required in order to eliminate the problems to the Louisville municipal supply caused by pollution (assuming that these were severe enough). As we have seen, some 80 billion gal of water are available in storage in the area, so if proper recharge facilities were to be constructed and operated, there is no physical reason why a permanent solution to the problem should be difficult to achieve, even at a level of water use much higher than it was in 1952 or than it is today.

Neglecting, for the sake of simplification, any accretion to the aquifer from precipitation in the area, the total annual ground-water replenishment must be in the order of 12.5 billion gal to supply the municipal peak load during the summer. This total must be recharged during a 250-day period, when the surface source is not grossly polluted. This means that either the surface water treatment plant must provide water for recharge or the filter-plant capacity of the aquifer in Northeast Louisville, close to the municipal water plant, must be used to the extent of 50 mgd. Final selection would be made on the basis of cost.

According to a diagram prepared by Rorabaugh the quantity of ground water needed for recharge can be obtained by building six large-radius wells along the bank of the Ohio River near the present intake of the municipally owned Louisville Water Company (5). These would, of course, have to be matched by at least a similar number of units in the storage area of the aquifer to serve as the source of ground-water supply during the critical periods.

During the 250-day recharge period the induced infiltration of water from the Ohio River would supply the well field built along the river bank near the present municipal treatment plant. This water, untreated except possibly by protective chlorination, would be piped to the wells used for recharge purposes. During the 100-day period of offtake from storage, ground water would be pumped in a reverse direction through the same pipe line to supply the treatment plant with raw water. The river intake and the river-infiltration units would be shut down during this period.

This plan would be predicated upon engineering studies that had previously demonstrated its desirability and economic feasibility. The hydrologic studies of the river-infiltration portion of the system have been substantially accomplished by Rorabaugh. The hydrogeology of the area selected for use as a reservoir remains to be studied—in particular the operating characteristics, number of units, spacing, and so forth, of the dual-purpose input-offtake wells would have to be determined.

The most difficult problems pertain to the operation of the system: Who is to pay for the recharge that will also benefit nearby private wells? On what basis are charges to be assessed? Suppose that the present owners of wells in the area find that due to the recharge operation they can increase their offtake at no extra cost; should they be required to pay for the water that they use that has originated in the city's recharge operation? How is the water replenished by the city to be protected from new wells drilled by neighboring landowners after the project is built? Is the city obligated to pay the landowners of overlying lands for the use of the portion of aquifer underlying their properties? What new forms of corporate or municipal organization will be required to effectuate such a project? Does capture of the water from the Ohio River by the city give the city a property right in the river water as against upstream latecomers? An excellent discussion by Valantine of the problems of ground-water basin management in arid areas is in large part applicable to the humid eastern U.S. (*11*).

The preceding paragraphs have outlined the conjunctive use of surface-water and aquifer storage to produce a perennial water supply of large magnitude and good quality. In other humid areas, as in Illinois, the aquifer might be a deep sandstone that would be replenished by deep small-diameter input wells. But it should be noted that the physical problem of recharge by deep vertical wells has not yet received a really economical solution. Moreover, unless a surficial aquifer can be used as a natural filter plant for the water to be recharged, the cost of treating water so that it will be suitable for recharge will undoubtedly be high. Possibly the cost will be too high for all but a small fraction of agricultural uses, although we can expect that the cost will be within the capabilities of a municipal water system.

In areas of the West, where irrigation is the prime user of water, the problem of quality degradation of the surface source to be used for recharge, which is due to the return flow of irrigation systems, will merit serious consideration. Moreover the existing system of water rights and the established rates of offtake from surface and underground sources may serve to complicate matters.

Much work remains to be done in the realm of ground-water hydrology in the technical, organizational, and legislative fields. The establishment of a firm property right in a perennial ground-water supply has yet to be achieved in humid regions. Success in the efforts exerted in these directions might well result in the widespread availability of perennial water supplies at relatively low cost. It would appear that the deleterious effects of the forces of geomorphology might largely be avoided through the conjunctive utilization of our aquifers and streams.

NOTES

1. Ackermann, W. C., and Corinth, R. L., 1962, An empirical equation for reservoir sedimentation, *Int. Assoc. Hydrol, Comm. on Land Erosion, Pub. No.* 59, pp. 359–366, Ill. State Water Surv.
2. Hirshleifer, J., DeHaven, J. C., and Milliman, J. W., 1960, *Water Supply—Economics, Technology, and Policy*, Chicago, Univ. of Chicago Press, pp. 364–368.
2a. Guyton, W. F., 1946, Artificial recharge of glacial sand and gravel with cold filtered river water at Louisville, Kentucky, *Economic Geology*, v. 41, no. 6, pp. 644–658.
3. Koenig, L., January, 1963, Economics of ground-water utilization, *J. Am. Water Works Assoc.*, v. 55, no. 1, p. 61.

4. Rorabaugh, M. I., December, 1949, *Progress Report on the Ground-Water Resources of the Louisville Area, Kentucky, 1945–1949*. Report of the City of Louisville and the U.S. Geol. Surv., pp. 4, 5.
5. Rorabaugh, M. I., 1956, Ground water in Northeastern Louisville, Ky., *U.S. Geol. Surv. Water Supply Paper 1360 B*, Fig. 27.
6. Rorabaugh, M. I., Schrader, F. F., and Laird, L. B., 1953, Water resources of the Louisville area, Kentucky and Indiana, *U.S. Geol. Surv. Circ. 276*, p. 43.
7. Thomas, H. E., 1962, Water and the Southwest—What is the future?, *U.S. Geol. Surv. Circ. 469*, pp. 3, 4.
8. Thomas, R. O., 1961, Legal aspects of ground-water utilization, *Trans. Am. Soc. Civ. Eng.*, v. 126, pt. 3, pp. 645–654.
9. U.S. Senate, Select Committee on National Water Resources, January, 1960, *Future Water Requirements for Municipal Use*, Committee Print no. 7, pp. 21–24.
10. U.S. Senate, Select Committee on National Water Resources, January 1960, *Weather Modification*, Committee Print no. 22, p. 44.
11. Valantine, V. E., July, 1964, Ground-water management for the nation's future: effecting optimum ground-water basin management, *Proc. Am. Soc. Civ. Eng.*, v. 90, no. HY4, pp. 97–105.

Questions

INTRODUCTION

1. Describe in reasonable detail your present understanding of the hydrologic considerations involved in deciding the volume of a cistern and the requisite catchment area to supply each of a specified number of persons a fixed daily quantity of water.
2. What hydrologic factors are to be considered in selecting the proper size of a culvert? Is there any need to consider the season of the year as a critical factor in this study in your area? Justify your answer.
3. Describe the hydrologic cycle and the principle influences that prevent its phases from repeating themselves in an identical fashion from year to year.
4. Describe the geochemical cycle.
5. Compare the pharaonic system of basin irrigation with present-day irrigation practice in Egypt. In what essential way do they differ? Would you say that there has been a lessening of the incidence of disease in rural areas in modern times as compared to Roman times? What information supports your answer?
6. In what ways was the practice of hydrologic engineering in Mesopotamia more complicated than that practiced in Egypt?
7. Discuss the seeming coincidence that the earliest great civilizations were born in arid or semiarid zones in the valleys of great rivers. What effect did the need to record and understand river hydrology have on this process?
8. Comment on the interrelationship between the economic demand for drinking water and the development of wells and filtration plants. How did these developments foster the emergence of hydrology as a science?
9. Discuss the effect of the inauguration of the Bessemer process of steel making on the availability of ground water. Would you say that its impact was more important, relatively, on ground-water development than on the production of petroleum?
10. Discuss the effect of hydrologic engineering projects such as canals and water supplies on the development of hydrology as the science.

11. In what way has a knowledge of hydrology (or lack of it) influenced military tactics? In this regard how would you classify the German invasion of Russia in 1941, the Battle of Antietam Creek in the Civil War, or the British attack on the dams in the Roer River Valley of Germany in World War II?

EVAPORATION

1. Name five important factors that influence evaporation. Explain briefly how each affects the rate and time of occurrence of evaporation.
2. How would you measure the rate of evaporation in the laboratory?
3. On what factual data is the evaporation from a large water surface computed?
4. How does the mineralization of water affect the rate of evaporation?
5. Why are hydrologists interested in the annual rate of evaporation from free-water surfaces?
6. What are monolayers and how do they act to inhibit evaporation from water surfaces? Name the two compounds most frequently used as inhibitors of evaporation.
7. What are the principal problems facing experimenters who wish to demonstrate (a) a reduction in evaporation stemming from use of a monolayer and (b) the economic benefit of such reduction? Is the Meyers formula of any value in this connection?
8. Name four practical problems encountered in forming and maintaining a monolayer on the surface of a large reservoir.
9. In what way do you think that conflicts in the use of a reservoir surface as between recreation and water utilization can be resolved?
10. Do you think that in the long run the monolayer technique will be most useful by conserving water stored in lakes and reservoirs or by directly conserving soil water for agricultural purposes?

PRECIPITATION

1. Does the size of the catchment area of a rain gage have any significant effect on the depth of precipitation caught in it?
2. To what extent does the catch of a single gage represent the rainfall on the surrounding area? Present supporting information.
3. List five natural and man-made factors that may influence the distribution of rainfall in a given area.
4. What is an isohyetal map?
5. In what ways are the data concerning the occurrence and duration of periods of drought of importance to mankind?
6. Why is rain-gage data concerning snow and ice of less value to hydrologists than information concerning liquid water? What are snow courses?
7. What new methods of studying the occurrence and composition of rainfall are becoming important?
8. Discuss the military potentialities of weather control with particular emphasis on rain-making and rain-inhibiting techniques.
9. Name several substances used to initiate precipitation in cloud masses.
10. What are some of the potential advantages of weather modification?
11. List some reasons why artificial rain making or other forms of weather modification may be detrimental to society?
12. What is meant by inadvertent weather modification?

13. Can you suggest a procedure to differentiate precipitation data that are the result of inadvertent weather modification from data that are solely the result of natural events?

14. Summarize the present status of weather modification, with special emphasis on possible areas of research.

SURFACE WATER

Runoff Cycle

1. Describe the runoff cycle in nature.
2. How is the measurement of stream flow accomplished?
3. What is a Pitot tube and on what principle does it operate?
4. Explain how the unavoidable systematic error in the measurement of water velocity may lead to an overstatement of the rate of flow in an open channel.
5. What types of geological formations are the principal contributors to the mineralization of surface water? What mineral constituent in the water is usually associated with each type of rock?
6. Is the sediment flow from a drainage basin uniform throughout the year, or does it vary in a manner similar to the mineral characteristics of the river water from the same basin?
7. What sort of measurements are made in connection with streams and rivers? What is the practical significance of the information obtained from each type of measurement?
8. Describe several methods of arranging the hydraulic information obtained in a program of stream-flow measurements for later analysis.
9. Discuss the applicability of statistical methods to the analysis of hydrologic data and especially how they apply to stream measurement data. Is each daily measurement a random unit, or must a longer period of stage or discharge be used as a member of a statistical series? What evidence is there for or against use of the day as the proper unit of time? Do you think that the daily discharges of a river, constitute a truly normal or random series? If not, what period do you suggest for use, and how did you arrive at your answer?
10. What is a flood?
11. Explain the meaning of recurrence interval when used with reference to a flood discharge of given magnitude. Does the procedure used in the graphing of floods according to recurrence interval enable us to predict the magnitude and recurrence interval of floods that are greater than those already recorded? Should we place much confidence in the results of such extrapolation?
12. If your municipal water supply uses water from a surface stream, request the superintendent to furnish you with a copy of his record of periodic mineralogical analyses. Prepare graphs of the hardness, pH, chloride content, and (if it seems significant) the sulphate-carbonate ratio of the raw water. Prepare a frequency-distribution analysis of one of these data-sets and compare it with a normal-distribution curve. In what way can such an analysis be of value to a manager of a water plant in his planning?
13. Discuss the relationship between the geology of a river basin and the stream flow during a long rainless period. Include in your discussion the effect of water quality as well as the discharge rate.
14. Discuss the effect of the geology of a river basin on the duration of high discharges and quality of water, including the occurrence of sediment, during floods.

15. Discuss the concept of concentration time and show how the concentration time of a watershed may change seasonally due to natural forces or the works of man. In latitudes where freezing occurs would you expect the concentration time of a watershed to be constant throughout the year? State your reasons.

16. Inasmuch as the sun provides the motive power for the hydrologic cycle, what reasons can you suggest that cause you to expect that the annual quantity of solar energy arriving on earth should be connected in some fashion with the annual discharge of rivers?

17. Obtain a record of sunspot numbers and a long record of annual stream flow in your area and test the Williams hypothesis that some sort of correlation exists between them.

Control and Utilization of Runoff

1. How would you calculate the value of water when it is used for purposes of navigation as, for example, to replace the water used in canal lockage?

2. What is a run-of-river water supply, and in what ways do its operational problems, including expansion of the supply, differ from those of an impounded water supply?

3. If your city is not listed on Table 5.1, obtain the most recent data from the superintendent or manager of the city water supply and expand the table.

4. In what ways is water used by industry? Is the water substance diminished in volume after use—consumed—or is it merely changed in quality by being used? If your city has a sewage-treatment plant, obtain information to enable you to compare the quantity and quality of the effluent with the quantity and quality of raw water (prior to treatment) of the water supply.

5. The increasing use of irrigation in farming to supplement rainfall in the humid sections of the country has tended to reduce the flow of streams during dry periods. If the trend toward supplemental irrigation continues, what conflicts in the utilization of water resources can you foresee?

6. Describe the early uses of water power and identify the forerunners, if any, of our present hydroelectric generating systems.

7. Compare the effect of evaporation on the operation of multipurpose water-development projects in humid and arid regions. Do you think that the loss of water due to evaporation, and the resulting increase in mineralization of the remaining water, should be entered on the debit side of the ledger as an offset against benefits? How would you evaluate this?

8. Describe three methods of artificially providing a navigable waterway in bodies of water that would be otherwise unsuitable or inadequate. What are the effects of such construction on the hydrology of the affected area?

9. What is flood control and what are the principal methods of accomplishing it?

10. What is the effect of projects for the development of water resources on the statistical validity and comparability of hydraulic measurements?

11. List the principal uses of water for which multipurpose projects are being built.

12. Why does the theoretical operation of a multipurpose project based on an ex-post-facto analysis invariably yield more benefits than can be derived in the normal course of operation?

13. Explain how certain types of water utilization conflict with one another. Does the construction of a multipurpose project eliminate such conflicts? If so, how? If not, why not?

Side Effects and Feedbacks

1. Describe a hydrologic side effect that results solely from channel maintenance.
2. How would you classify the efforts at bank stabilization: as a side effect of channel maintenance, or as a feedback, the cost of which inhibits further channel improvement?
3. What do you consider to be the principal hydrologic side effect produced by reservoir construction?
4. Obtain a U.S. Geological Survey Water Supply paper that presents in tabular form information on surface runoff. Select a page containing hydrologic data and a page of historical data. Copy the explanatory material found on each page, and evaluate it in terms of planning a water supply or in terms of dilution of wastes.
5. Explain the U.S. Geological Survey's desire to establish hydrologic bench marks.
6. What widely publicized campaign testifies to the nonhydrologic character of data concerning the mineralization of rivers and lakes?
7. Present five examples that tend to show that the nonhydrologic character of data increases the cost of construction and operation of structures that depend for their design on hydrologic data.
8. Would adoption of the Leopold proposals for the establishment of hydrologic bench marks be of significant value in the design and operation of structures that normally would utilize hydrologic data. This type of structure would include public water supplies, reservoirs, culverts, levees, pumping equipment, and so forth. In what way would establishment of such bench marks be of practical value?
9. In what ways are natural fixed points or hinge points, similar to those established by dam construction?
10. In what manner does a natural fixed point, or hinge point, differ from an artificial one established by damming a river?
11. In terms of geomorphology how would you interpret the maintenance of a specified depth of channel in an alluvial stream? Is it the exact equivalent of a lowering of the virtual sea level? Explain your answer.
12. Considering the composition of the Coordinating Committee on the Missouri River, can you defend the stipulation that the majority vote of the committee shall decide the magnitude and incidence of water releases? Is there any reason to assume that this procedure will tend to produce optimum use of the available water? What other form of administration and organization can you suggest in its place? What operating principles might be more successful?
13. How has the construction of reservoirs in accord with the Pick-Sloan Plan affected the hydrologic extremes at St. Louis? Is there a method of extrapolating the presently available data on the flow of the Mississippi River at St. Louis to define the extremes of flood and low flow?
13. List and explain the principal forms of the doctrine of riparian rights.
15. What is meant by the doctrine of prior appropriation?
16. Is the doctrine of riparian rights considered to be well adapted to the needs of modern industrial civilization? Explain your answer giving specific examples to support your contention.
17. How might the thermal pollution of streams by owners of riparian lands be reconciled with the doctrine of riparian rights? What physical arrangements would have to be made?
18. What doctrine of water rights is dominant in your state? Has it fostered or

inhibited investments in projects that require a predictable supply of water? On what do you base your answer?

19. What is the Constitutional doctrine that has been interpreted as justifying the flood-control program of the Federal Government? The supplying of water to arid lands? The maintenance of navigation?

20. Why have the water-development doctrines of Constitutional origin been termed major diastrophic forces?

GROUND WATER

Occurrence and Measurements

1. Define the following terms: aquifer, vadose water, geohydrology, hydrogeology, zone of saturation, artesian, water table.

2. Why must a distinction be made between the microproperties of a waterbearing formation and its macroproperties? Explain why there is a difference between the porosity of a material and its specific yield—is this an example of the difference between micro- and macroproperties?

3. Differentiate between the coefficient of permeability as determined in the laboratory and the coefficient of permeability as determined by means of a field test. Which quantifies the aquifer properties most closely?

4. The workers in which fields of science and engineering besides hydrogeology are interested in the permeabilities of materials?

5. How are aquifers classified?

6. What are the principal functions of aquifers from the point of view of their usefulness to mankind?

7. What is the difference between an influent and an effluent stream?

8. Explain briefly the recharge of an aquifer by precipitation. Is there a fixed relationship between the depth of precipitation and the rise in water level?

9. Explain the recharge of an aquifer by the infiltration of water from a nearby stream. Are all changes in water level in the stream fully reflected by changes in piezometric surface in all parts of the aquifer?

10. What is a phreatophyte?

11. Why are phreatophytes important enough in the hydrology of the West to merit detailed study?

12. How does the annual quantity of water used by phreatophytes compare to the annual evaporation of water from all 50 of the largest man-made reservoirs or lakes in the United States?

13. Would the saving of water by the use of monolayers on the water surfaces in Question 12 be greater or less than the saving of water through the destruction of 50 percent of the phreatophytes in the 18 Western States?

14. What types of measurements are accomplished in the study of the occurrence and movement of ground water? Describe how such measurements are made.

15. What principle is employed in the measurement of water levels in a discharging well by means of an airline?

16. What methods are used to measure or estimate the discharges from aquifers?

Ground-Water Movement

1. What is laminar flow and how is it defined in hydraulic terms?

2. What is Darcy's law?

3. Obtain information on the grain size of a uniform sand and compute the

maximum velocity of water flow through it at which Darcy's law will probably hold good.

4. How is the permeability of an aquifer determined in the field?
5. What is an aquifer-performance test? How is an aquifer tested by the use of a tracer?
6. Name three materials commonly used as tracers. What are the advantages and disadvantages of each?
7. Discuss the possible application of tracer technique in elucidating the flow through a limestone or basalt aquifer.
8. What information is obtained from aquifer-tests that cannot be obtained in any other way?
9. Why must the temperature of ground water be determined as part of a geohydrologic study? What geohydrologic information can be deduced if the water temperature rises and falls cyclically?
10. Describe the three basic hydrogeologic boundary conditions used as a basis for the mathematical analysis of aquifer performance.

Development of Water Supplies

1. Discuss the concept of safe yield.
2. Can such a concept be justly included in law? State the reasons for your answer.
3. What are the principal functions of aquifers?
4. Under what particular separate set of conditions is each of these to be considered most important?
5. What independent, but determinable, factors govern the evaluation and utilization of an aquifer as a filter plant?
6. What geohydrologic constraints not to be determined by any direct or indirect physical measurements also govern the utilization of an aquifer as a filter plant? Give a specific example of each.
7. List the types of data obtained as part of the study of the Dubuque, Iowa, water supply. Were all of the data hydrologic in character?
8. How are high river temperatures related to high river stages, high concentrations of dissolved minerals, and high concentrations of suspended matter in the water? Draw generalized hydrographs and other graphs showing how the quality and quantity of water from a well field supplied by induced infiltration and operating at constant drawdown will change in response to changes in the river. Do all changes in ground-water composition or pressures reach their maxima or minima at the same time? How does our knowledge of field tests with tracer materials help us to understand the phenomenon of river infiltration. (HINT: consider a temporary high in mineral concentration as a slug of tracer material.)
9. What is the essential difference between a ground-water reservoir and a ground-water ore body or mine?
10. In the Wichita area does the yield of the well field depend on the wide spacing of wells, or could the same quantity of water be obtained from the same number of wells placed in a fraction of the area? If water spreading, or the induced infiltration of river water, were utilized in addition to the natural replenishment by rainfall, what factors would govern the ultimate steady-state magnitude of the ground-water supply?
11. Describe the functions of each aquifer in the Canton project.
12. What are the most important differences in hydrology, construction, and operation between the Wichita and Canton water-supply projects?
13. In what respects is the mining of ground water different from the mining of iron ore or coal, and similar to the extraction of petroleum.

14. What problems are sometimes caused by the mining of ground water and how may these, in principle, be solved?
15. Describe the problem caused by water mining in the Los Angeles area. What solutions were proposed?
16. Describe the relationship between fresh and salty ground water in the Chicot reservoir of southwestern Louisiana.
17. What is connate water, and why is it important in the evaluation of the water-supply possibilities of the Chicot reservoir?
18. What is coning, and how is an understanding of this phenomenon of great practical importance in southwestern Louisiana?
19. Describe an experiment that would prove that the salt water coming from a well was the result of coning and not due to the generally salty character of water in the aquifer.
20. What juxtaposition of observations caused investigators to conclude that the Vermilion River was replenishing the Chicot reservoir? What alternate interpretation of the data has been proposed? Why is it important from a practical standpoint to decide which of these interpretations is correct? What will be the result of an incorrect decision as far as (a) the farmers of the area are concerned and (b) the local and state governments are concerned?
21. Describe some of the most common side effects resulting from the withdrawal of ground water.
22. Prior to the construction of hydraulic structures such as canals, reservoirs, or river levees, is it usually desirable to include a ground-water investigation as part of the preliminary work? Explain your answer and illustrate it with examples, preferably drawn from material not included in text.
23. What are some of the principal problems caused by the subsidence of the land surface?
24. Describe the cycle of ground-water development in Brooklyn and the side effects that occurred.

Legal Considerations

1. Why must legal considerations be taken into account in planning ground-water withdrawals, in a manner similar to that used in evaluating a geohydrologic boundary?
2. What are the two basic doctrines controlling the withdrawals of water from the ground? Describe the origin of each doctrine as applied to underground water.
3. What is the difference between the English doctrine and the doctrine of reasonable use?
4. What assumption has been made with respect to the legal control of ground water that frequently does not coincide with the observed facts?
5. What is the doctrine of prior appropriation as it refers to ground water? Is this doctrine soundly applicable to areas of ground-water mining? What quasi-hydrologic concept is the basis for applying appropriation doctrine?
6. On what grounds is the classification of water uses into "higher" and "lower" categories to be criticized?
7. Would the diversion of ground water from its use in irrigation to use by a new industry located in the area invalidate an appropriative right if the principles advocated by the National Reclamation Association were enforced by law? In view of the different values of water for various purposes at different times would it be desirable to predetermine these forever by legislative decree?

8. Describe the differences between the priorities of the National Reclamation Association and those of Louis Koenig with regard to the development and utilization of ground water.

9. Would governmental control and allocation of all water resources result in eliminating conflicts and competition with regard to water? Illustrate your answer by specific examples.

10. What is police power, and what results may be expected if this doctrine be placed into operation, state by state? [HINT: How would it affect (a) individuals, (b) the relationship between states?]

WATER-RESOURCE DEVELOPMENT

1. In what ways do hydrologic factors determine the relative values of lands? Will availability of a reliable water supply increase land values? Will the construction of flood levees around property increase its value relative to similar, but unprotected, property?

2. Does the interest rate current at the time a project is evaluated affect its economic feasibility? Would you expect an increasingly higher rate to be used as the payout period, or period of amortization, increases? Why?

3. Would you expect to find a relationship between the economic life of a project and its period of amortization? What do you think that this relationship is? How can a knowledge of hydrology be used to determine the maximum period of amortization (or repayment of capital costs) of a project?

4. State the governmental principles used to evaluate projects involving hydrologic engineering. Discuss the significance of each principle and whether it can appropriately be used for this purpose.

5. What is the economic principle used in evaluating such water-development projects? When a multipurpose project is planned and there is a predictable conflict in water utilization, what procedure for decision can you suggest?

6. What is the reason for the statement that there is a pervading implication that the surface storage of water should be accomplished on a minimum basis and only where absolutely necessary?

7. What are some of the possible human adjustments to the flood hazard? Can one say, a priori, that one of these is invariably more desirable than any of the others?

8. Select a flood-control reservoir, obtain the data upon which it is predicated, and assume, in turn, rates of reservoir sedimation of 0.1, 0.25, and 0.50 percent a year. How does the probability of a damaging (200-year) flood increase as the time of reservoir operation increases?

9. Discuss the effect of dam construction on the regime of a river, upstream and downstream.

10. Can the costs of flood control be predicted merely by combining the costs and annual operating charges of the dams, reservoirs, and levees built as part of such a project? What additional costs must be included? Can these be accurately estimated for the entire life of the project?

11. Should the ultimate cost of a flood-control project also include the effects of the inevitable diminution in its effectiveness resulting from the forces of geomorphology, as they are manifested in the need to evacuate the flood plain? In what way do you think these costs can be estimated?

12. Summarize present trends in the field of flood control—their direct effects and side effects, together with the proposals made to overcome difficulties. What

forms of organization can you propose that might salvage temporary values from existing projects?

13. Describe three ways to make inland waterways navigable. Give an example of each method.

14. Describe the program for the improvement of the Arkansas River. What provisions have been made to reduce the deposition of sediment in the canalized river channel? How does the existence of the John Martin Reservoir affect the project? What is the estimated life of the John Martin Reservoir?

15. Discuss the effect of technological developments in the field of transportation on the need to maintain channels of specified width and depth in our inland waterways.

16. What is the basic hydrologic defect of a policy that causes a minimum channel to be maintained at all times in an alluvial river?

17. What is the story of King Canute, and what lessons of hydrology and geomorphology can be learned from his experience?

18. What technological developments achieved since passage of the Federal Water Power Act in 1920 have made it desirable to reexamine Federal policy in the field of hydropower?

19. Is there any reason to suppose that mere ownership of a hydropower site will confer upon the owner an unchallengeable monopoly on hydropower production? Explain your answer.

20. What is the difference between flood control and the reclamation of land?

21. What are the principal hydrologic effects of drainage projects?

22. Do you agree or disagree with the statement: "As a matter of public policy Federal Funds should not be used to establish and maintain drainage." Explain the reasons for your answer.

23. What two paths as regards water source and financial sponsorship have been followed in the reclamation of land through irrigation?

24. Since 1930, has the private development of irrigation been based primarily on surface water or ground water?

25. What are the two interrelated problems involved in combating stream pollution?

26. Into what two broad categories may the physical problem of water-quality reclamation be reasonably subdivided?

27. How may the problem of small quantities of nondegradable wastes, radioactive or chemical, be solved?

28. What do you consider to be the most serious obstacles preventing an effective solution to the problem of stream pollution? In what directions should research be directed in order to overcome such obstacles?

29. Comment on the advantages and disadvantages of a public water supply where the price to the consumer is so low that it is cheaper for him to waste water than to repair a leaky faucet or replace a worn washer. Do you have firsthand knowledge of such conditions? What are the reasons put forth to justify the construction of new facilities to expand the supply under such conditions of use?

30. Assemble some of the evidence presented in the newspapers and magazines of general interest as proof of a present or impending shortage of water and analyze its applicability and its statistical validity.

31. What is the hydrologic significance of the construction of small reservoirs sponsored by the Department of Agriculture under the Watershed Protection Act of 1954?

32. What is the principal hydrologic significance of the conversion of saline water in inland areas? How does the cost of water obtained in this fashion currently compare with the delivered price of water, to the home owner, in your city?

Appendix

Selected Conversion Values and Constants

1. Area:

   1 in.² = 6.452 cm²
   1 ft² = 929.03 cm²
   1 yd² = 0.8361 m²
   1 acre = 4.356 × 10⁴ ft² = 4.047 × 10³ m²
   1 mile² = 640 acres = 2.79 × 10⁷ ft² = 2.590 Km²
   1 hectare = 2.471 acres

2. Volume:

   1 million gal = 3.07 acre-ft
   1 billion (10⁹) gal = 3.07 × 10³ acre-ft
   1 million acre-ft = 3.259 × 10⁵ million gal
   1 cfs-day = 1.98 acre-ft
   1 acre-ft = 3.259 × 10⁵ gal
   1 acre-ft = 1.233 × 10³ m³
   1 m³ = 35.31 ft³ = 1.308 yd³ = 264.2 gal

3. Permeability: (K_s = laboratory coefficient of permeability):

   1 K_s = 1 meinzer = 1 gal per day per sq ft at 60°F
   1 meinzer = 1.34 × 10⁻¹ ft/day = 1.43 × 10⁻⁶ ft/sec = 4.07 cm/day
   1 darcy = 18.2 meinzers (for water at 68°F)
   1 millidarcy = 1.82 × 10⁻² meinzers (for water at 68°F)

   Note: The results of in-situ tests are expressed as meinzers at the observed water temperature, which is noted and recorded. Thus the laboratory coefficient must be corrected to the existing aquifer-water temperature before the values are used in the field. To correct the laboratory permeability to field permeability, divide Ks by the viscosity of water at the field temperature and multiply by the viscosity of water at 60°F.

4. Miscellaneous:

   1 Atmosphere = 1.013 × 10⁶ dynes/cm²
                 = 1.013 millibars
                 = 14.7 lbs/in²
                 = 33.9 ft water at 4°C
   1 ft water = 0.4335 lbs/in.²
   Density of Air at 1 atmosphere and 15°C = 1.256 × 10⁻³ gm/cm³
   To lift 1 gal water 1 ft requires 3.15 × 10⁻⁶ kwh
   Reciprocal of bulk modulus of elasticity of water = 3.3 × 10⁻⁶ in.²/lb
   One part per million (ppm) = 1 milligram/liter
   One grain per U.S. gal = 17.1 ppm
   Equivalent wt. of ion = atomic wt. of ion/valence of ion
   Milliequivalent per liter of ion (meg/l) = ppm of ion/eq. wt. of ion
   1 meg/l = 1 equivalent per million (epm)
   Viscosity of water at 68°F (20°C) = 1.005 centipoises
   Viscosity of water at 60°F (15.6°C) = 1.124 centipoises

Conversion Table for Volume

One is equal to	cu in.	gal	cf	cy	AF	Bbl.	cc	CM
Cubic inch, cu in.	1	4.33×10^{-3}	5.79×10^{-4}	2.14×10^{-5}	1.33×10^{-8}	1.03×10^{-4}	1.64×10^{1}	1.64×10^{-5}
US. gallon, gal	2.31×10^{2}	1	1.34×10^{-1}	4.95×10^{-3}	3.07×10^{-6}	2.38×10^{-2}	3.79×10^{3}	3.79×10^{-3}
Cubic foot, cf	1.73×10^{3}	7.48	1	3.70×10^{-2}	2.30×10^{-5}	1.78×10^{-1}	2.83×10^{4}	2.83×10^{-2}
Cubic yard, cy	4.67×10^{4}	2.02×10^{2}	2.7×10^{1}	1	6.20×10^{-4}	4.81	7.65×10^{5}	7.65×10^{-1}
Acre-foot, AF	7.53×10^{7}	3.26×10^{5}	4.36×10^{4}	1.61×10^{3}	1	7.76×10^{3}	1.23×10^{9}	1.23×10^{3}
Barrel (oil), Bbl.	9.70×10^{3}	4.2×10^{1}	5.62	2.08×10^{-1}	1.29×10^{-4}	1	1.59×10^{5}	1.59×10^{-1}
Cubic centimeter, cc	6.10×10^{-2}	2.64×10^{-4}	3.53×10^{-5}	1.31×10^{-6}	8.12×10^{-10}	6.29×10^{-6}	1	1.00×10^{-6}
Cubic meter, CM	6.10×10^{4}	2.64×10^{2}	3.53×10^{1}	1.31	8.12×10^{-4}	6.29	1.00×10^{6}	1

Conversion Table for Discharge

is equal to One	GPM	MGD	CFS	MBD	AF/D	LPS	CMH	CMD
U.S. gallon per minute, GPM	1	1.44×10^{-3}	2.23×10^{-3}	3.43×10^{-2}	4.42×10^{-3}	6.30×10^{-2}	2.26×10^{-1}	5.42
Million U.S. gallons per day, MGD	6.94×10^{2}	1	1.55	2.38×10^{1}	3.07	4.37×10^{1}	1.57×10^{2}	3.77×10^{3}
Cubic foot per second, CFS	4.49×10^{2}	6.46×10^{-1}	1	1.54×10^{1}	1.98	2.83×10^{1}	1.02×10^{2}	2.45×10^{3}
Thousand barrels (oil) per day, MBD[a]	2.92×10^{1}	4.20×10^{-2}	6.50×10^{-2}	1	1.29×10^{-1}	1.83	6.61	1.58×10^{2}
Acre-foot per day, AF/D	2.26×10^{2}	3.26×10^{-1}	5.05×10^{-1}	7.76	1	1.42×10^{1}	5.11×10^{1}	1.23×10^{3}
Liter per second, LPS	1.59×10^{1}	2.28×10^{-2}	3.53×10^{-2}	5.45×10^{-1}	7.03×10^{-2}	1	3.60	8.64×10^{1}
Cubic meter per hour, CMH	4.40	6.34×10^{-3}	9.81×10^{-3}	1.51×10^{-1}	1.95×10^{-2}	2.78×10^{-1}	1	2.40×10^{1}
Cubic meter per day, CMD	1.83×10^{-1}	2.64×10^{-4}	4.09×10^{-4}	6.29×10^{-3}	8.13×10^{-4}	1.16×10^{-2}	4.17×10^{-2}	1

[a] In the water industry, M is an abbreviation for "million"; MGD is million gallons a day. In the petroleum industry, where the barrel is the unit of volume, M is the notation for "thousand", and MM (a thousand thousand) is used for million. Thus, 8 MBD is 8,000 Bbls/D, and 8 MMBD is 8 million Bbls/D. People in the petroleum industry tend to use oil terminology when discussing water.

Inverse Table of the Well Function W(u)
[Mathematical Identification $-Ei(-u)$]

The Theis formula is

$$s = \frac{114.6\,Q}{T}\,W(u)$$

where

$$u = \frac{1.87\,r^2 S}{Tt}$$

and the quantities are defined as follows:

s = drawdown, in feet, of piezometric surface in the vicinity of the well.
Q = discharge of the well in gallons per minute.
T = transmissibility of aquifer, gpd/ft.
r = distance from discharging well, in feet, to point where drawdown is measured.
S = storativity, or coefficient of storage, of aquifer.
t = time well has been discharging, in days.

The following table enables the selection of the value of $W(u)$ to an accuracy of one in the second decimal place, without interpolation. For example, if the result of a computation yields a value, $u = 1.342 \times 10^{-5}$, then the table should be entered in the right hand column, where the exponent is listed, in this instance 5. Then the value closest to 1.342 should be found (in this instance 1.344) and the value of $W(u)$ is read directly to be 10.64.

W(u)	0	1	2	3	4	5	6	7	8	9	×10⁻
0.0	∞	3.211	2.668	2.360	2.146	1.984	1.853	1.745	1.652	1.571	0
0.1	1.500	1.436	1.379	1.327	1.279	1.235	1.194	1.156	1.120	1.087	0
0.2	1.056	1.026	$\bar{9}$.983	$\bar{9}$.719	$\bar{9}$.469	$\bar{9}$.231	$\bar{9}$.004	$\bar{8}$.788	$\bar{8}$.581	$\bar{8}$.383	0
0.3	8.193	8.011	7.836	7.667	7.505	7.349	7.199	7.053	6.913	6.777	1
0.4	6.646	6.519	6.396	6.276	6.161	6.048	5.939	5.833	5.730	5.630	1
0.5	5.532	5.437	5.345	5.255	5.167	5.082	4.998	4.917	4.837	4.760	1
0.6	4.684	4.610	4.538	4.467	4.398	4.331	4.265	4.200	4.137	4.075	1
0.7	4.014	3.955	3.897	3.840	3.784	3.729	3.676	3.623	3.572	3.521	1
0.8	3.471	3.423	3.375	3.328	3.282	3.237	3.193	3.149	3.106	3.064	1
0.9	3.023	2.983	2.943	2.904	2.865	2.827	2.790	2.753	2.718	2.682	1
1.0	2.647	2.613	2.579	2.546	2.514	2.482	2.450	2.419	2.389	2.358	1
1.1	2.329	2.300	2.271	2.243	2.215	2.187	2.160	2.134	2.108	2.082	1
1.2	2.056	2.031	2.006	1.982	1.958	1.935	1.911	1.888	1.866	1.843	1
1.3	1.821	1.800	1.778	1.757	1.736	1.716	1.696	1.676	1.656	1.637	1
1.4	1.617	1.598	1.580	1.561	1.543	1.525	1.508	1.490	1.473	1.456	1
1.5	1.440	1.423	1.407	1.391	1.375	1.359	1.344	1.328	1.313	1.298	1
1.6	1.284	1.269	1.255	1.241	1.227	1.213	1.199	1.186	1.173	1.160	1
1.7	1.147	1.134	1.121	1.109	1.096	1.084	1.072	1.060	1.049	1.037	1
1.8	1.026	1.014	1.003	$\bar{9}$.922	$\bar{9}$.813	$\bar{9}$.706	$\bar{9}$.599	$\bar{9}$.494	$\bar{9}$.391	$\bar{9}$.288	1
1.9	9.187	9.087	8.988	8.889	8.793	8.698	8.604	8.510	8.418	8.327	2

Inverse Table of the Well Function $W(u)$ (Continued)
[Mathematical Identification $-Ei(-u)$]

$W(u)$	0	1	2	3	4	5	6	7	8	9	$\times 10^-$
2.0	8.237	8.148	8.060	7.974	7.888	7.803	7.719	7.636	7.554	7.473	2
2.1	7.393	7.314	7.236	7.158	7.082	7.006	6.932	6.858	6.785	6.712	2
2.2	6.641	6.571	6.501	6.432	6.364	6.296	6.230	6.164	6.098	6.034	2
2.3	5.970	5.907	5.844	5.783	5.722	5.662	5.602	5.543	5.485	5.428	2
2.4	5.371	5.314	5.259	5.203	5.149	5.095	5.042	4.989	4.937	4.885	2
2.5	4.834	4.784	4.734	4.685	4.636	4.587	4.540	4.492	4.446	4.400	2
2.6	4.354	4.308	4.264	4.219	4.176	4.132	4.090	4.047	4.005	3.964	2
2.7	3.923	3.882	3.842	3.802	3.763	3.724	3.686	3.648	3.610	3.573	2
2.8	3.536	3.500	3.464	3.428	3.393	3.358	3.323	3.289	3.255	3.222	2
2.9	3.189	3.156	3.123	3.091	3.060	3.028	2.997	2.967	2.936	2.906	2
3.0	2.876	2.847	2.818	2.789	2.760	2.732	2.704	2.677	2.649	2.622	2
3.1	2.595	2.569	2.543	2.517	2.491	2.466	2.440	2.416	2.391	2.367	2
3.2	2.343	2.319	2.295	2.272	2.249	2.226	2.203	2.181	2.159	2.137	2
3.3	2.115	2.093	2.072	2.051	2.030	2.010	1.989	1.969	1.949	1.929	2
3.4	1.910	1.890	1.871	1.852	1.833	1.814	1.796	1.778	1.760	1.742	2
3.5	1.724	1.707	1.690	1.673	1.656	1.639	1.623	1.606	1.590	1.574	2
3.6	1.558	1.542	1.527	1.511	1.496	1.481	1.466	1.451	1.437	1.422	2
3.7	1.408	1.394	1.380	1.366	1.352	1.338	1.325	1.311	1.298	1.285	2
3.8	1.272	1.259	1.247	1.234	1.222	1.209	1.197	1.185	1.173	1.161	2
3.9	1.150	1.138	1.127	1.115	1.104	1.093	1.082	1.071	1.060	1.050	2
4.0	1.039	1.029	1.018	1.008	$\bar{9}.979$	$\bar{9}.879$	$\bar{9}.780$	$\bar{9}.681$	$\bar{9}.584$	$\bar{9}.488$	2
4.1	9.392	9.298	9.205	9.112	9.021	8.930	8.841	8.752	8.664	8.577	3
4.2	8.491	8.406	8.322	8.238	8.156	8.074	7.993	7.913	7.833	7.755	3
4.3	7.677	7.600	7.524	7.449	7.374	7.300	7.227	7.154	7.082	7.011	3
4.4	6.941	6.872	6.803	6.735	6.667	6.600	6.534	6.469	6.404	6.340	3
4.5	6.277	6.214	6.152	6.090	6.029	5.969	5.909	5.850	5.791	5.733	3
4.6	5.676	5.619	5.563	5.507	5.452	5.397	5.344	5.290	5.237	5.185	3
4.7	5.133	5.082	5.031	4.980	4.931	4.881	4.833	4.784	4.737	4.689	3
4.8	4.642	4.596	4.550	4.504	4.460	4.415	4.371	4.327	4.284	4.241	3
4.9	4.199	4.157	4.115	4.074	4.033	3.993	3.953	3.914	3.875	3.836	3
5.0	3.797	3.760	3.722	3.685	3.648	3.612	3.575	3.540	3.505	3.470	3
5.1	3.435	3.401	3.367	3.333	3.300	3.267	3.234	3.202	3.170	3.139	3
5.2	3.107	3.076	3.046	3.015	2.985	2.955	2.926	2.896	2.868	2.839	3
5.3	2.811	2.783	2.755	2.728	2.700	2.673	2.647	2.620	2.594	2.568	3
5.4	2.543	2.517	2.492	2.467	2.443	2.418	2.394	2.370	2.347	2.323	3
5.5	2.300	2.277	2.255	2.232	2.210	2.188	2.166	2.145	2.123	2.102	3
5.6	2.081	2.060	2.040	2.019	1.999	1.979	1.960	1.940	1.921	1.901	3
5.7	1.883	1.864	1.845	1.827	1.808	1.790	1.773	1.755	1.738	1.720	3
5.8	1.703	1.686	1.670	1.653	1.637	1.620	1.604	1.588	1.572	1.557	3
5.9	1.541	1.526	1.510	1.495	1.480	1.465	1.451	1.436	1.422	1.408	3

$W(u)$	0	1	2	3	4	5	6	7	8	9	$\times 10^-$
6.0	1.394	1.380	1.366	1.353	1.339	1.326	1.313	1.300	1.287	1.274	3
6.1	1.261	1.249	1.236	1.224	1.212	1.200	1.888	1.176	1.164	1.153	3
6.2	1.141	1.130	1.119	1.108	1.097	1.086	1.075	1.064	1.054	1.043	3
6.3	1.032	1.022	1.011	1.002	$\overline{9}$.916	$\overline{9}$.817	$\overline{9}$.720	$\overline{9}$.623	$\overline{9}$.527	$\overline{9}$.432	3
6.4	9.336	9.243	9.151	9.061	8.971	8.882	8.792	8.705	8.619	8.533	4
6.5	8.448	8.364	8.281	8.199	8.117	8.036	7.956	7.877	7.798	7.721	4
6.6	7.644	7.568	7.493	7.419	7.345	7.272	7.200	7.128	7.056	6.986	4
6.7	6.917	6.848	6.780	6.712	6.646	6.579	6.513	6.448	6.382	6.319	4
6.8	6.257	6.194	6.133	6.072	6.012	5.952	5.892	5.833	5.775	5.718	4
6.9	5.661	5.604	5.549	5.494	5.439	5.385	5.331	5.278	5.226	5.174	4
7.0	5.122	5.071	5.021	4.971	4.922	4.872	4.823	4.775	4.728	4.681	4
7.1	4.635	4.588	4.542	4.497	4.452	4.408	4.364	4.321	4.278	4.235	4
7.2	4.193	4.152	4.110	4.069	4.029	3.988	3.949	3.910	3.871	3.832	4
7.3	3.794	3.756	3.719	3.682	3.645	3.609	3.573	3.538	3.503	3.468	4
7.4	3.433	3.398	3.364	3.331	3.298	3.265	3.232	3.200	3.168	3.137	4
7.5	3.106	3.075	3.044	3.014	2.984	2.954	2.925	2.896	2.867	2.838	4
7.6	2.810	2.782	2.754	2.727	2.700	2.673	2.646	2.620	2.594	2.568	4
7.7	2.543	2.517	2.492	2.468	2.443	2.419	2.395	2.371	2.347	2.324	4
7.8	2.301	2.278	2.255	2.233	2.211	2.189	2.167	2.145	2.124	2.103	4
7.9	2.082	2.061	2.041	2.020	2.000	1.980	1.961	1.941	1.922	1.903	4
8.0	1.884	1.865	1.846	1.828	1.810	1.792	1.774	1.756	1.739	1.722	4
8.1	1.704	1.687	1.671	1.654	1.638	1.621	1.605	1.589	1.573	1.558	4
8.2	1.542	1.527	1.512	1.497	1.482	1.467	1.452	1.438	1.424	1.409	4
8.3	1.395	1.382	1.368	1.354	1.341	1.327	1.314	1.301	1.288	1.275	4
8.4	1.263	1.250	1.238	1.225	1.213	1.201	1.189	1.177	1.166	1.154	4
8.5	1.143	1.131	1.120	1.109	1.098	1.087	1.076	1.065	1.055	1.044	4
8.6	1.034	1.024	1.013	1.003	$\overline{9}$.931	$\overline{9}$.833	$\overline{9}$.735	$\overline{9}$.638	$\overline{9}$.542	$\overline{9}$.447	4
8.7	9.353	9.260	9.168	9.077	8.986	8.897	8.808	8.721	8.634	8.548	5
8.8	8.463	8.379	8.295	8.213	8.131	8.050	7.970	7.891	7.812	7.735	5
8.9	7.658	7.582	7.506	7.431	7.357	7.284	7.212	7.140	7.069	6.999	5
9.0	6.929	6.860	6.792	6.724	6.657	6.591	6.525	6.461	6.396	6.332	5
9.1	6.270	6.207	6.145	6.084	6.024	5.964	5.904	5.846	5.788	5.730	5
9.2	5.673	5.617	5.561	5.505	5.451	5.396	5.343	5.289	5.237	5.185	5
9.3	5.133	5.082	5.031	4.981	4.932	4.883	4.834	4.786	4.739	4.691	5
9.4	4.645	4.598	4.553	4.507	4.462	4.418	4.374	4.331	4.288	4.245	5
9.5	4.203	4.161	4.119	4.078	4.038	3.998	3.958	3.919	3.880	3.841	5
9.6	3.803	3.765	3.727	3.690	3.654	3.617	3.581	3.546	3.510	3.475	5
9.7	3.441	3.407	3.373	3.339	3.306	3.273	3.240	3.208	3.176	3.145	5
9.8	3.113	3.082	3.051	3.021	2.991	2.962	2.932	2.903	2.874	2.845	5
9.9	2.817	2.789	2.761	2.734	2.707	2.680	2.653	2.627	2.601	2.575	5

Inverse Table of the Well Function $W(u)$ (Continued)
[Mathematical Identification $-Ei(-u)$]

$W(u)$	0	1	2	3	4	5	6	7	8	9	$\times 10^-$
10.0	2.549	2.524	2.499	2.474	2.449	2.425	2.401	2.377	2.353	2.330	5
10.1	2.306	2.284	2.261	2.238	2.216	2.194	1.172	2.151	2.129	2.108	5
10.2	2.087	2.066	2.046	2.025	2.005	1.985	1.965	1.946	1.927	1.907	5
10.3	1.888	1.870	1.851	1.833	1.814	1.796	1.778	1.761	1.743	1.726	5
10.4	1.709	1.692	1.675	1.658	1.642	1.625	1.609	1.593	1.577	1.562	5
10.5	1.546	1.531	1.515	1.500	1.485	1.471	1.456	1.442	1.427	1.413	5
10.6	1.399	1.385	1.371	1.358	1.344	1.331	1.317	1.304	1.291	1.279	5
10.7	1.267	1.253	1.241	1.228	1.216	1.204	1.192	1.180	1.168	1.157	5
10.8	1.145	1.134	1.123	1.111	1.100	1.089	1.079	1.068	1.057	1.047	5
10.9	1.036	1.027	1.016	1.006	$\bar{9}.957$	$\bar{9}.858$	$\bar{9}.760$	$\bar{9}.663$	$\bar{9}.567$	$\bar{9}.472$	5
11.0	9.377	9.284	9.192	9.100	9.010	8.920	8.831	8.743	8.656	8.570	6
11.1	8.485	8.401	8.317	8.234	8.152	8.071	7.991	7.911	7.833	7.755	6
11.2	7.678	7.601	7.525	7.451	7.376	7.303	7.230	7.158	7.087	7.017	6
11.3	6.947	6.878	6.809	6.742	6.675	6.608	6.542	6.477	6.413	6.349	6
11.4	6.286	6.223	6.161	6.100	6.039	5.979	5.920	5.861	5.803	5.745	6
11.5	5.688	5.631	5.575	5.520	5.465	5.410	5.356	5.303	5.250	5.198	6
11.6	5.146	5.095	5.044	4.994	4.945	4.895	4.847	4.798	4.751	4.703	6
11.7	4.657	4.610	4.564	4.519	4.474	4.430	4.385	4.342	4.299	4.256	6
11.8	4.213	4.171	4.130	4.089	4.048	4.008	3.968	3.929	3.890	3.851	6
11.9	3.813	3.775	3.736	3.700	3.663	3.627	3.591	3.555	3.519	3.484	6
12.0	3.450	3.415	3.381	3.348	3.314	3.281	3.249	3.217	3.184	3.153	6
12.1	3.121	3.090	3.060	3.029	2.999	2.969	2.940	2.910	2.881	2.853	6
12.2	2.824	2.796	2.768	2.741	2.714	2.687	2.660	2.633	2.607	2.581	6
12.3	2.556	2.530	2.505	2.480	2.455	2.431	2.407	2.383	2.359	2.336	6
12.4	2.312	2.289	2.267	2.244	2.222	2.200	2.178	2.156	2.135	2.113	6
12.5	2.092	2.072	2.051	2.031	2.010	1.990	1.971	1.951	1.931	1.912	6
12.6	1.893	1.874	1.856	1.837	1.819	1.801	1.783	1.765	1.748	1.730	6
12.7	1.713	1.696	1.679	1.662	1.646	1.630	1.613	1.597	1.581	1.566	6
12.8	1.550	1.535	1.519	1.504	1.489	1.474	1.460	1.445	1.431	1.417	6
12.9	1.403	1.389	1.375	1.361	1.348	1.334	1.321	1.308	1.295	1.282	6
13.0	1.269	1.256	1.244	1.232	1.219	1.207	1.195	1.183	1.172	1.160	6
13.1	1.148	1.137	1.126	1.114	1.103	1.092	1.081	1.071	1.060	1.049	6
13.2	1.039	1.029	1.018	1.008	$\bar{9}.983$	$\bar{9}.884$	$\bar{9}.785$	$\bar{9}.688$	$\bar{9}.592$	$\bar{9}.496$	6
13.3	9.402	9.308	9.215	9.124	9.033	8.943	8.854	8.766	8.679	8.592	7
13.4	8.507	8.422	8.338	8.255	8.173	8.092	8.012	7.932	7.853	7.775	7
13.5	7.697	7.621	7.545	7.470	7.396	7.322	7.249	7.177	7.106	7.035	7
13.6	6.965	6.896	6.827	6.759	6.692	6.625	6.559	6.494	6.429	6.365	7
13.7	6.302	6.239	6.177	6.116	6.055	5.995	5.935	5.876	5.818	5.760	7
13.8	5.702	5.646	5.589	5.534	5.479	5.424	5.370	5.317	5.264	5.212	7
13.9	5.160	5.108	5.058	5.007	4.957	4.908	4.859	4.811	4.763	4.716	7

Inverse Table of the Well Function $W(u)$ (Continued)
[Mathematical Identification $-Ei(-u)$]

$W(u)$	0	1	2	3	4	5	6	7	8	9	$\times 10^-$
14.0	4.669	4.622	4.576	4.531	4.486	4.441	4.397	4.353	4.310	4.267	7
14.1	4.224	4.182	4.141	4.100	4.059	4.018	3.978	3.939	3.900	3.861	7
14.2	3.822	3.784	3.747	3.709	3.673	3.636	3.600	3.564	3.529	3.493	7
14.3	3.459	3.424	3.390	3.356	3.323	3.290	3.257	3.225	3.193	3.161	7
14.4	3.130	3.098	3.068	3.037	3.007	2.977	2.947	2.918	2.889	2.860	7
14.5	2.832	2.804	2.776	2.748	2.721	2.694	2.667	2.640	2.614	2.588	7
14.6	2.562	2.537	2.511	2.487	2.462	2.437	2.413	2.389	2.365	2.342	7
14.7	2.318	2.295	2.273	2.250	2.228	2.205	2.283	2.162	2.140	2.119	7
14.8	2.098	2.077	2.056	2.036	2.016	1.995	1.976	1.956	1.936	1.917	7
14.9	1.898	1.879	1.861	1.842	1.824	1.806	1.788	1.770	1.752	1.735	7
15.0	1.718	1.700	1.684	1.667	1.650	1.634	1.617	1.601	1.585	1.570	7

Note: The indicated value of u is to be multiplied by the power of 10 shown in the last column to the right. All values of this exponent are negative.

Source: Abridged from U.S. Geological Survey, Ground Water Division of the Water Resources Branch, December, 1941.

Index